## Date Due

# CANADA IN VIEW

John Molyneux
Vice Principal
Bloor Collegiate
Toronto, Ontario


Marilyn Olsen
Head of Geography
Harbord Collegiate
Toronto, Ontario

McGRAW-HILL RYERSON LIMITED
Toronto   Montreal   New York   St. Louis
San Francisco   Auckland   Bogotá   Düsseldorf
Johannesburg   London   Madrid   Mexico
New Delhi   Panama   Paris   São Paulo
Singapore   Sydney   Tokyo

# CANADA IN VIEW

ISBN 0-07-082557-2

1  2  3  4  5  6  7  8  9  10  JD  7  6  5  4  3  2  1  0  9  8

Printed and bound in Canada

Maps and illustrations by Frank Zsigo

Canadian Cataloguing in Publication Data

Molyneux, John, 1932-
    Canada in view

Includes index.
ISBN 0-07-082557-2

1. Canada - Description and travel - 1950-          *
I. Olsen, Marilyn.   II. Title.

FC75.M64          917.1          C77-001573-5
F1016.M64

## Acknowledgements

Pages 5, 88, 203: The Public Archives of Canada. Pages 6, 32, 33, 57, 76, 77, 80, 89, 90, 96, 97, 98, 99, 113, 115, 136, 137, 138, 145, 156, 157, 165, 196, 212, 216, 232, 242: John Molyneux. Page 9: Northern Transportation Co. Ltd. Page 14: Reproduced with the permission of The Minister of Supply and Services, Canada. Page 21 (bottom): Parks Canada. Page 40: Atmospheric Environment Service, Fisheries and Environment Canada. Pages 41, 59, 116, 120, 174, 176, 177, 185, 187, 204, 207, 244, 258, 269, 278, 281, 294, 296, 308, 326: Gulf Oil Canada Ltd. Pages 53, 61, 64, 68, 73, 81: Surveys and Mapping Branch, Department of Energy, Mines and Resources, Ottawa. Pages 54, 57: Information Canada. Pages 69, 164, 190, 207, 279, 318: Canadian National. Pages 69, 75, 80, 82, 83, 337: National Film Board of Canada. Pages 77, 164, 342: Canadian Pacific. Page 93: Central Mortgage and Housing Corporation. Pages 96, 165, 289: Marilyn Olsen. Pages 119, 187, 201: Agriculture Canada. Page 120 (top): International Harvester. Pages 129, 131, 186: International Nickel. Page 144: The permission of the Government of Ontario and University of Toronto Press to make use of plate 8 in Economic Atlas of Ontario/ Atlas Economique de l'Ontario is gratefully acknowledged. Page 146: Ford of Canada. Page 148: Panda Associates. Page 149 (top): National Air Photographic Library, Department of Mines and Technical Surveys. Page 149 (bottom): Stelco. Page 150: Northway Survey Corporation Limited. Pages 153, 323: St. Lawrence Seaway Authority. Pages 171, 183: Reprinted by permission of Copp Clark Publishing. Pages 176, 177: Courtesy, Canadian Petroleum Association. Page 195: MacMillan Bloedel. Page 198: British Columbia Government. Page 227: New Brunswick Travel Bureau. Page 235: Original photo supplied by the Department of Energy, Mines and Resources. Pages 239, 244: Department of Public Relations, Montreal. Pages 253, 264: Michael Jones. Page 292: Toronto Area Transit. Page 303: Imperial Oil Limited. Page 315: Quebec Tourist Branch. Pages 316, 322: Nova Scotia Communications and Information Centre. Page 331: D.R.E.E. photo.

# CONTENTS

# PREFACE

In **Canada in View** the authors are trying to present an image of Canada that truthfully displays the variety and dynamism of the country as well as reflecting the pride and hope that people have in it. They expect that the reading level and the nature of the questions and exercises will make the book ideal for use in the beginning grades of Secondary School. It is in these grades that most students come to a clearer awareness of the world around them. The authors accordingly hope to extend and deepen that awareness so that students using this book become more thoughtful about Canada, more understanding of its problems, more proud of its achievements, and more realistic about its future.

As an organizational change from regional and thematic frameworks, the authors employ the concepts approach in the handling of material. The advantages of this approach are not only that a logical blend of regional and thematic topics is possible but also that great internal variety is permitted. For example, ways of life in the Arctic could be examined from the viewpoint of *life support*, but in such a specially dynamic area as the Arctic this relatively static view would probably be inadequate; the authors prefer to use the viewpoint of *change*. This means defining the Arctic as a region and analyzing the changing and growing nature of the interactions between the Arctic and the rest of Canada. In this manner, some of the factors causing change are investigated, and some of the problems are raised. It should be noted that while these details of change may be particular to the Arctic, the general nature of the causes and the consequent problems may be of much wider application. Some students could undoubtedly be encouraged to apply the general principles to other areas or to themes, such as Canada's energy production.

It is also possible to examine any single topic, whether region or theme, from the viewpoint of several different concepts. This should always be borne in mind, for a fuller picture can always be gained when different angles are noted. Teachers may therefore wish to expand the treatment of any topic under study so as to include consideration of other concepts. Limitations of space prevent us from doing so here.

We wish to thank our editors, Rosina Daillie and Loralee Case, for their help in the preparation of this book.

The Authors

Toronto, 1978

# CHAPTER 1

# ORIENTATION

## GRAPHICACY

Have you ever played the sport of orienteering? If you have you will know that the chief objective is to follow a set of instructions and directions — using a map — and so find your way from the starting point to the finishing point in as fast a time as possible. You therefore need to know maps: what they tell you; how they can be used; how they relate to words. These are the skills of *graphicacy*.

In order to train these skills, what must you do? One of the first things — as with all other activities — is to practise. If you practise well, then eventually you get the feel of things. This is what this first chapter is about: practising the skills of graphicacy. And practising until you get the feel of what Canada is like in maps.

One of the first things that will help you practise is the pride you might feel in the subject you are studying. You are studying Canada. As a starting point in this "orienteering" lesson, read the following extracts from a speech made by the Prime Minister of Canada.

*Orientation* means finding your bearings, or getting to know your way about. In any geography study, it is one of the most important things you can do. For your own country, it is essential.

1

# Our Common Destiny To Perpetuate Character

*Excerpts from a speech by Prime Minister Pierre Trudeau at the National Newspaper Awards dinner in Toronto, April 9, 1972.*

If Canadians ever lose their consciousness of the vastness and the natural beauty of this country, they will have been deprived of the essentials for understanding both Canada and themselves. . . .

We should be grateful that our country is of heroic size. How commonplace it would be to live in a small one . . . If we were deprived of our vast spaces we should be without much of our challenge. Even more we should have lost that essential quality which is part of us all and which makes us different from others. Rupert Brooke wrote that he was most impressed with the "fresh loneliness" of Canada. He wrote that "the soul — or the personality — seems to have indefinite room to expand". Blair Fraser understood the wilderness which is Canada when he wrote of "the vast empty land in which for more than three centuries a certain type of man has found himself uniquely at home" . . .

Only occasionally, as on centennial celebrations, are we given reason to reflect on Blair Fraser's "certain type of man". We should think much more often about some of them, for example of the voyageurs whose courage and endurance is almost unbelievable when judged by modern standards. The great transcontinental canoe system of two centuries ago was a phenomenal institution, quite unmatched anywhere else in the world. For the 50 and more years of its peak, furs were carried the 3000 miles[1] from the Athabasca basin in northern Alberta to Montreal, and trade goods back, in the course of each 5 month summer season.

In other countries, that epic accomplishment would be the subject of folk-tales and songs. . . . It was an endeavour which opened the north-west, which created a working partnership between white man and Indian and between English and French speaking. . . .

Newspapers, universities, governments, could all do more to inform Canadians of their own unique accomplishments. In the result we are denied knowledge of a good deal of excitement; we are denied as well a good deal of ourselves. We need to be reminded regularly of the miracles wrought by Canadians.

Schefferville is one. In order to construct the rail line from that remote iron mine in Labrador to Sept Iles on the St. Lawrence, much of the equipment and supplies, and many of the men, had to be flown in. . . . That operation may well be the largest single civilian airlift in the entire world. . . .

One of the world's botanical miracles was wrought in Canada by a young man named Charles Saunders, a person of many talents. He developed a rust-resistant, fast-maturing wheat suitable for the harsh climate of the western plains. He called his new

[1] 48 000 km

strain Marquis. In 1907 only 23 pounds[2] of his seed existed. Ten years later over 300 million bushels[3] of Marquis wheat were harvested in Canada and the United States.

Fort Macleod is a small city in southwest Alberta . . . it was to Fort Macleod that the original troop of Northwest Mounted Police proceeded 100 years ago. The Mounties represented law and order, and they rode into the west in advance of the settler. That fact has influenced all of Canada. The Mounted Police ensured that the relationship between the settler and the Indian did not involve the excesses which occurred south of the border.

These are Canadian episodes and we need to be reminded of them. These incidents are . . . part of the distinctiveness which is Canada. . . .

Canada continues to be regarded by outsiders as a wondrous place. And so it is . . .

In the waters off Canada's three coasts oceanographic research work is proceeding at a pace which is widening from day to day the world lead which Canadian scientists enjoy in this future-oriented field. In the spaces above our

atmosphere complex communications signals are flashing back and forth at blinding speed employing Canadian - designed and manufactured equipment. Canadian snow and all-terrain vehicles dominate the world market from the wastes of Siberia to the marshes of Borneo. Canadian STOL aircraft are the standard of the industry. In these and dozens of other fields ranging from new surgical techniques to agricultural innovation to urban social accomplishments Canadians are adjusting to change and proving their abilities in the process . . .

Canada is as deep from north to south as it is wide from east to west. This fact alone is descriptive of the immensity of the challenge. . . . When bitterness of climate and the formidable nature of the terrain are added to that factor of distance, the explanation becomes even more acceptable. Yet it is unthinkable that Canada can continue to regard the Arctic as an exciting but isolated appendage. All our efforts to protect the ecology and assist the welfare of the native peoples will be limited unless we are in a position to ensure the rational impact of northern development. A transportation system is the key.

A transportation system

of the scope which is evolving is evidence that imagination, confidence and forward planning are not absent from Canada . . . that we have in this country a combination of space, resources and a certain kind of men and women that permits us to accomplish much. . . . We have few senseless internal divisions to sap our strength. We have a land so large and a climate so difficult that only extraordinary efforts will suffice. Our history is the narrative of that kind of effort. And our reward is an opportunity for fulfilment, of happiness, of absence of fear, in a landscape of breathtaking beauty; a style of life which permits us to be more individual and less subject to uniformity than any peoples in the world.

Of all the changes which will come to Canada in the next generation, therefore, we must prevent, surely, any of a sort which will diminish the essential beauty and lonely nature of this country. For if that beauty is lost, or if that wilderness escapes, the very nature and character of this land will have passed beyond our grasp. Denied an opportunity to breathe the brisk freshness of an Atlantic gale, to view the unbelievable glory of a Prairie sunset, to feel the

[2] 10.35 kg

[3] 76 000 000 mt

overwhelming silence of a northern lake, we would no longer be Canadians...

We are a particular breed, we Canadians. We hail from many sources but we have a common destiny: it is to perpetuate the character of this land and to share the benefits that result. Canada is not a country for the cold of heart or for the cold of feet. For those who qualify, the rewards exceed those of any other country.

So now you want to know more about the "bones" of Canada. We shall therefore proceed in this chapter to look at the skeleton of Canada — in maps, of course. However, before we start, let us try some questions:

1. Where do you think Canada ranks in size among the countries of the world?
2. Is Canada really crowded, as many people say? Or is it relatively empty?
3. How many provinces are there? What are they called?
4. Where are Canada's boundaries? Can we see them?
5. Why were rivers and lakes important to early explorers? Why are they important now?
6. Do most Canadians live in the city or the country? Where do you live?

Let us take a closer look.

## A: EXPLORING CANADA

Archaeological diggings in the southern parts of Canada, especially in Alberta and southern Ontario, show that the earliest remains of original Indian occupancy can be dated back to about 10 000 years ago. There may have been some Indians in Canada even before this time, but we cannot be sure. What is certain is that Canada would have been very cold 10 000 years ago, because the great Ice Age was nearing its end.

The Indians were the first people to live in Canada. Thousands of years later the Eskimos also came; but neither group did much exploring, nor did they publish much about their occupancy. Canada's existence was unknown to outsiders. Not until Leif Ericson sailed here from Greenland about the year 1000 did outsiders learn of the existence of Canada. Unfortunately, Leif did not keep good records, so no one else got a chance to learn of his discoveries.

During the 1400s there was considerable interest among Europeans in the matter of opening up trade with China and India. Some sailed east around Africa, trying to reach the Orient; others sailed west across the Atlantic. Among those sailing west was John Cabot, who set out from England in 1497. He found a new land, which he logically called New Found Land. If you go to Cape Bonavista on the Atlantic shore of Newfoundland, you can see a statue in memory of John Cabot. Perhaps you have already seen it.

**Figure 1-1**   Cabot sighting the New Found Land.

The Eskimos probably came into Canada 3000 years ago. It is likely that they migrated into Canada from Asia, via Alaska.

In the 800s, 900s, and 1000s there were many voyages of exploration and discovery by Norse sailors. The people of the Scandinavian fiords, often called Vikings, sailed far and wide in their search for trade and adventure. They reached well into the Mediterranean Sea; they penetrated Europe as far as Kiev; and they voyaged across the Atlantic via Greenland. Remains of their foothold in North America have been found in northern Newfoundland, and there is even a map, called the Vinland Map, which purports to show the northeast coasts of Canada as explored by the Scandinavians. The map may be genuine, but it may also be an elaborate forgery; no one is quite sure.

Columbus was one of the most important of these westward adventurers. He was the first to reach land and return to inform the rest of Europe. The land he first reached in 1492 was most likely somewhere in the Bahamas, but he visited many places after that.

John Cabot kept good records. Other people therefore rapidly learned about Canada's existence: the rush for discovery and exploration was on. The reasons for the rush were twofold:

*Reason No. 1.* Navigators and traders were trying to find a way through to Asia. They now knew that there was land in the way, so they tried to find a passage *either through it* (by rivers and lakes) *or around it* (by sea). The sea passage that they tried to find became known as the *Northwest Passage*. It was not easy to find; hundreds of people died in the many searches for it.

**Figure 1-2**  Statue of John Cabot at Bonavista, Newfoundland.

Reason No. 2. Traders learned of the wealth in furs and fish in and around Canada. They found these items of wealth as they were looking for a passage through. Many decided that Canada's wealth was adequate for them, so gradually the search for a passage was abandoned.

The names of many of the early navigators and traders are still visible today in the land of Canada. In particular they can be seen as the place names of rivers and bays. One of the best known of the early navigators was Jacques Cartier, who explored most of the coast of the Gulf of St. Lawrence. He even sailed up the St. Lawrence River itself, getting as far as the present location of Montreal. Today in Montreal one of the big bridges over the St. Lawrence River is named after Jacques Cartier.

Another famous navigator was Henry Hudson, who explored the northern areas, such as Hudson Strait and Hudson Bay. Unfortunately for Hudson, his crew did not like the cold weather, so they mutinied, and left him stranded on the southern shore of Hudson Bay while they set sail back to England. He was never seen again.

Champlain was another busy navigator. He explored most of the eastern coast of Quebec, as well as many of the larger rivers

> The St. Lawrence gets its name from the fact that Jacques Cartier anchored near its estuary on August 10th, which was the feast of St. Lawrence.

and lakes in what is now Ontario. Look at Figures 1-3 and 1-5. You can see that Cartier mapped mainly the east coast, while Champlain mapped the rivers and lakes of the interior. Naturally, neither of these early maps is as accurate as the ones we have today. However, by comparing them with their accompanying maps (which show the shapes as we presently know them) you should be able to see fairly easily how well the St. Lawrence and Great Lakes area was known in Canada's early years.

It was natural for the first explorer to sail around the coasts, and for later explorers to be the ones who travelled further inland. As far as the curious Europeans were concerned, Canada was a land to be approached and explored from the sea. The process of learning about the interior and then the west was a slow one, only to be attempted after the eastern coasts and rivers had been explored.

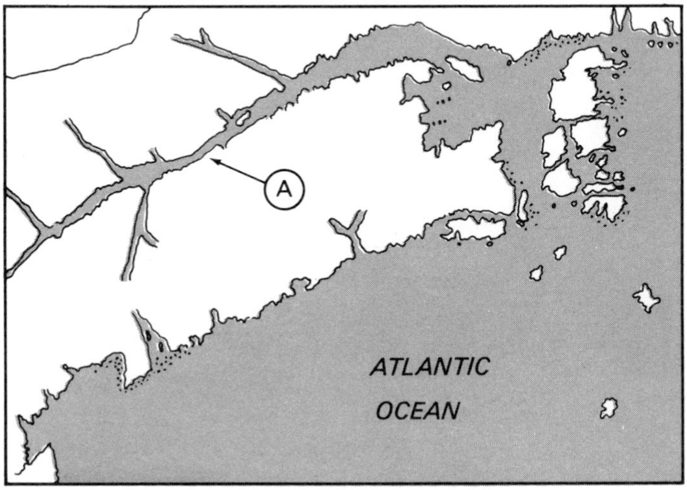

Figure 1-3   Cartier's Own Map of his Explored Area

Figure 1-4   Present Day Map Showing Cartier's Voyages

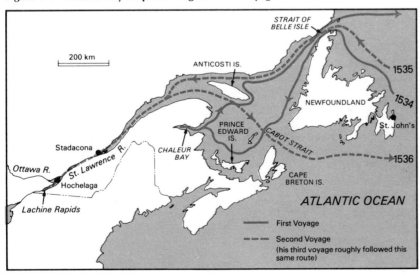

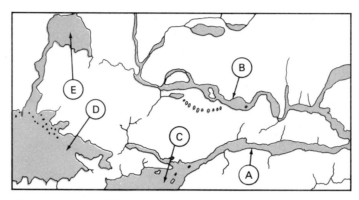

**Figure 1-5    Champlain's Own Map**

**Figure 1-6    Present Day Map of Champlain's Explorations**

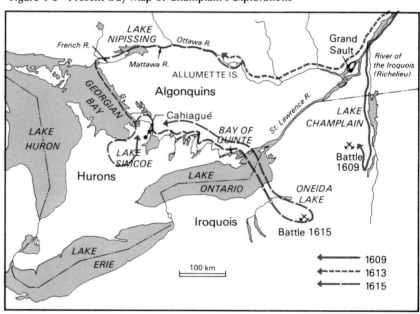

The word *portage* derives from the French word *porter,* to carry. It was applied by the voyageurs to all areas where they had to take their canoes out of the water and carry them around obstacles such as waterfalls and rapids. The most common type of portage was, however, that across a divide between one river and the next.

If we now look for a moment towards the interior and at the traders in search of furs, we find a whole new set of people: the *voyageurs.* They sailed in canoes, which they carried across portages, which often led around rapids and waterfalls. They explored the interior, and even across to the Pacific Ocean. One of the most famous voyageurs was Pierre Radisson. When he was a young man he was captured by the Iroquois Indians, but he escaped and became a fur trader. He travelled widely through Ontario and Manitoba, bringing back to Quebec as many beaver pelts as he could carry. But later, because of disagreements with the local governor, Radisson sailed for England to try to make a new trade agreement there. The English were very receptive, and supplied ships and money for a new expedition. The expedition was so successful and the English were so delighted with the valuable cargo of beaver pelts that Radisson was readily helped to form a new trading company called the *Hudson's Bay Company*. The year was 1670.

Men from the Hudson's Bay Company explored the rivers of the Prairies, especially the Nelson, the Churchill, the North Saskatchewan, and the South Saskatchewan. You will find all these rivers shown in Figure 1-8. However, as the years went by, other men began to see the profits from furs. Eventually they set up a competing company called the *North West Company*. More than 100 years had passed since "The Bay" started; it was 1787.

The North West Company sent men such as Alexander Mackenzie, David Thompson, and Simon Fraser to explore the far west. As you can tell from Figure 1-8, Mackenzie explored the northwestern parts, reaching the Beaufort Sea in 1789. He sailed from Lake Athabasca down to Great Slave Lake, where he was lost for three weeks. He could not find a way out of the lake. At last he succeeded, however, and so continued down to Great Bear Lake, where an Indian told him that the sea was only ten days' journey away. Figure 1-7 shows you the Mackenzie River; it's a huge river, isn't it?

The French voyageurs of the early fur trade allied themselves with the Huron Indians, who generally lived and trapped the lands north of the St. Lawrence River. The Iroquois Indians lived south of the St. Lawrence, and they were much more friendly with the English and Dutch. Accordingly the Iroquois would feel quite happy at catching Pierre Radisson, who was not only a friend of the Hurons, the lifelong enemies of the Iroquois, but who was also French, the traditional rivals of the English.

The original Hudson's Bay Company ship was a little wooden vessel called the *Nonsuch*. A replica of it was made in 1970 for the tercentenary celebrations of the Company; it is now in Winnipeg, where The Bay is currently headquartered.

**Figure 1-7**   Mackenzie River near its delta

Mackenzie was the first European to reach the Arctic Ocean across northwestern Canada; he was also the first European to reach the Pacific by travelling across Canada.

Unfortunately for Mackenzie it was the Beaufort Sea that he reached in 1789. He had really been hoping to reach the Pacific; so he initially called his river the River of Disappointment. He tried again to find the Pacific, this time using the Peace River (see Figure 1-8) and cutting across the mountains. He eventually achieved his goal of reaching the Pacific in 1793.

Simon Fraser and David Thompson operated farther south. Thompson actually canoed all the way out of Canada altogether, along the Columbia River. When he tried claiming the land for Canada he found that the Americans had beaten him to it by two months. Fraser meanwhile travelled the Fraser River, but could not actually reach the sea because Indians blocked his path.

As you can imagine there are many more stories that could be told; the stories do not even end with the reaching of the Pacific. The Northwest Passage still had not been found, and many more attempts were made before it was eventually travelled in 1906. The first person to sail through was a Norwegian, Roald Amundsen, who later became the first person to reach the South Pole!

**Figure 1-8**
**Rivers and Lakes of Canada**

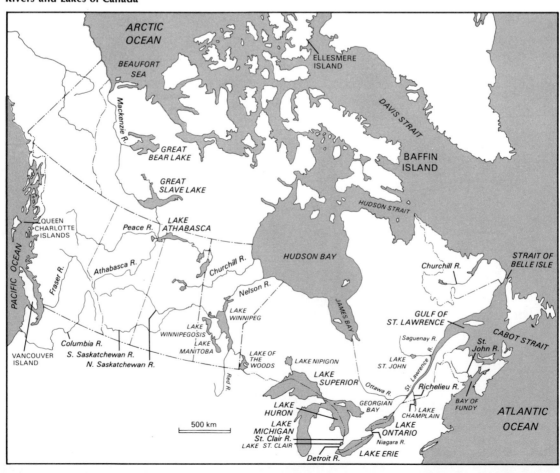

# Inland Surveys

The first accurate surveys of the Canadian prairies and the forests to their north were made by the "inland surveyors" hired by the Hudson's Bay Company to map the various canoe routes into central Canada. This exploratory surveying work had a calculated commercial value; it was done to make the movement of supplies inland more efficient, and thus increase the number of furs returned to the coast of Hudson Bay. Philip Turnor was the first of these inland surveyors. He was recommended to the Hudson's Bay Company by William Wales, who, because of his work at Fort Prince of Wales, knew something of the conditions which would be met in northwestern Canada.

In 1776, Turnor commenced the gigantic task of surveying the Hudson Bay territories. During the early stages of his assignments he also trained two assistants, David Thompson and Peter Fidler. In his famous *Narrative*, Thompson gives the following concise description of the work he and his colleagues were doing:

"My instruments for practical astronomy, were a brass sextant of ten inches[1] radius, an achromatic telescope of [1] 25 cm high power for observing the Satellites of Jupiter and other phenomena, one of the same construction for common use, parallel glasses and quicksilver horizon for double Altitudes; Compass. Thermometer, and other requisite instruments which I was in the constant practice of using in clear weather for observations on the Sun, Moon, planets and Stars; to determine the positions of the Rivers, Lakes, Mountains and other parts of the country I surveyed from Hudson Bay to the Pacific Ocean."

Reprinted from *Canadian Geographical Journal*, March 1972, by L. M. Sebert

# The St. Roch

The search for a sea passage north of the continent of America to Asia goes back at least to Sir Martin Frobisher's voyages in 1576–1578. Amundsen, 1903–1906, sailed through the North-West Passage from Davis Strait to the Bering Sea.

In 1940 the R.C.M.P. schooner *St. Roch,* used on patrol duties in northern waters and to carry supplies to isolated police posts, became the first ship to navigate the hazardous passage from west to east. Then it sailed back through the passage, traversing waters never before sailed by any vessel. On another occasion *St. Roch* sailed from Vancouver to Halifax by way of the Panama Canal, becoming the first ship to circumnavigate the continent of North America.

Royal Bank of Canada *Monthly Letter*, May 1973

● 1. Examine the maps made by Jacques Cartier and Samuel de Champlain. Compare them with the present day maps of the same areas. Identify the features marked with the letters A, B, C, D and E.

● 2. On a blank outline map of Canada draw in as *neatly and as accurately as you can* all the rivers and lakes which were noted in this chapter as being used by the voyageurs and other explorers. *Name* all the rivers and lakes that you draw.

● 3. Using the information in the clipping *Inland Surveys* answer the following questions:
   (a) Why were accurate surveys required by the Hudson's Bay Company?
   (b) Why do you think David Thompson has been described as "a great geographer"?

● 4. The R.C.M.P. ship, the *St. Roch,* sailed twice through the Northwest Passage. It did not set out to carry supplies to isolated police posts on these two voyages. Can you think of one reason why the *St. Roch* was ordered by the Canadian Government to make these voyages?

Notice that none of the maps of Canada has a north arrow. The reason is that Canada is so broad from west to east that a single north arrow would not be enough. All North arrows point to the North Pole, of course, but the North Pole is a point. A north arrow in Newfoundland would run next to the 50°W longitude line, whereas a north arrow in the Yukon would run next to the 141°W line. Both arrows would point to a spot some distance north of Ellesmere Island, which is where the North Pole is.

## B: THE ADMINISTRATIVE FRAMEWORK

Canada was born as a nation in 1867. At that time it contained only the areas shown in the 1867 map in Figure 1-10. You can see that it was quite small. Since then, however, Canada has grown greatly; you can see its growth in the other maps in Figure 1-10, showing that it reached its present size with the acquisition of Newfoundland in 1949.

As a result of this growth, Canada now stretches from near 50°W next to Newfoundland to 141°W at the Alaska U.S.A. border, and from 42°N in Lake Erie to over 83°N in Ellesmere Island. You can see the details in Figure 1-9.

You can also see that many of the borders of Canada follow lines of latitude and longitude. The most famous of these borders is the *49th Parallel,* which follows the 49°N latitude line all the way from the southern end of the Ontario-Manitoba border across to the coast of British Columbia. However, the Canada-U.S. border that most people live close to lies much farther south than the 49th Parallel. It lies along the 45th Parallel and the St. Lawrence

River in southern Quebec, and along Lakes Ontario and Erie in southern Ontario. The farthest south it reaches is 42°N at Midway Island in Lake Erie.

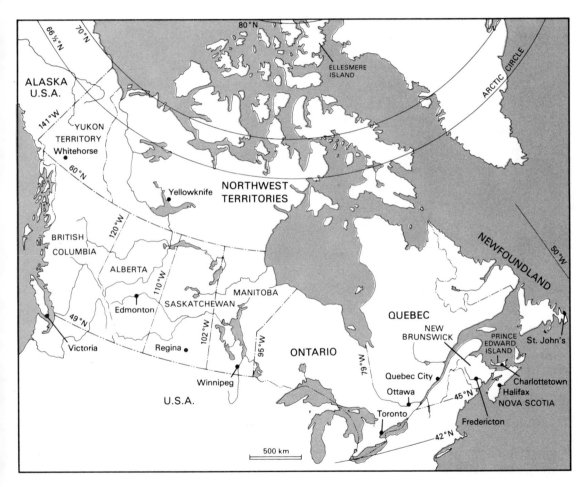

Figure 1-9  Boundaries, Provinces, and Capitals

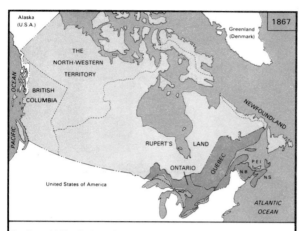

New Brunswick, Nova Scotia, and Canada are united in a federal state, the Dominion of Canada, by the British North America Act (July 1, 1867). The province of Canada is divided into Ontario and Quebec. The United States of America proclaims the purchase of Alaska from Russia (June 20).

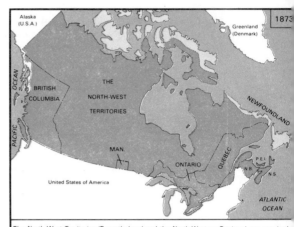

The North-West Territories (Rupert's Land and the North-Western Territory) are acquired Canada from the Hudson's Bay Company (1870). From part of them Manitoba is created as th fifth province (1870). British Columbia joins the Dominion of Canada as the sixth province (187 followed by Prince Edward Island as the seventh province (1873).

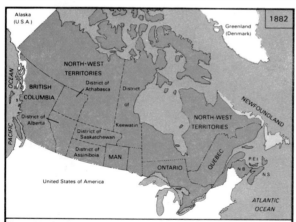

New provisional northern and western boundaries of Ontario are described (1874). The District of Keewatin is created (1876). British rights to the arctic islands pass to Canada (1880). The boundaries of Manitoba are extended (1881), but the extension to the east is contested by Ontario. The provisional Districts of Assiniboia, Saskatchewan, Athabasca, and Alberta are created (1882).

The Ontario-Manitoba boundary dispute is settled by the Ontario Boundary Act (1889). Th District of Yukon becomes a Territory separate from the North-West Territories (1898). Albert and Saskatchewan are created as provinces to make a total of nine provinces in the Dominion Canada (1905). The District of Keewatin is transferred back to the Northwest Territories. Due changes in adjoining areas the boundaries of the Northwest Territories are redefined (1906)

Ontario and Manitoba attain their present boundaries. Quebec is extended northward to Hudson Bay and Hudson Strait, thereby absorbing mainland Ungava. Quebec-Labrador boundary remains unsettled.

The Imperial Privy Council provides a settlement of the Quebec-Labrador boundary questio (1927). At its own request, after a plebiscite, Newfoundland enters the Confederation (1949

**Figure 1-10   Territorial Evolution of Canada**

# Decline in Fish Landings Helps Support Demand for 320 km Limit in Atlantic

News reports through the late 1960s and early 1970s persistently underlined the diminishing catch of fish off the Atlantic coasts of Canada. For example, the first 6 months of 1975 showed fish landings which were 34 per cent lower than those in the first 6 months of 1974. Not only were fewer fish being reported caught, but the fish were also reported to be much smaller. Fish were being brought home in 1975–76 which a few years previously would have been thrown back into the sea. For example, Newfoundland fishermen were keeping cod which were only about 40 cm long compared with a minimum retained size of about 60 cm a few years previously. In response to these diminished catches and smaller sizes, the Atlantic fishermen were reportedly very vociferous in their demands to have the federal government extend Canada's territorial limits from 19 km to 320 km in order to control the presumed overfishing of the fishing grounds by vessels registered to foreign fleets.

# How Canada Showed It Can't *Control* The Arctic

Canada lays claim to the Arctic islands as far north as the North Pole. However, if that claim is to be recognized by other countries then Canada needs to show the rest of the world that it is serious about holding the claimed territories. To this end Canada has tried to resettle Eskimo groups in the islands, so that the islands are at least occupied by a few Canadians. Canada has also tried sending round various ships and aircraft to patrol the Arctic islands. The *St. Roch* is a good example.

There have been challenges to Canada's claims. In 1969 the Americans sailed a giant oil tanker called the *Manhattan* right through the Arctic from Newfoundland to Alaska. Fortunately for Canada the tanker became stuck in the ice and had to be rescued by a Canadian icebreaker; Canada's claims thus made more sense to the Americans. In 1974 a Polish ship sailed into the Canadian Arctic without anyone in Canada knowing about it until it reached Baffin Island. The Canadians then asked it to leave. The next thing anyone in Canada knew was that the ship was sailing past Labrador, headed for Newfoundland, where it eventually docked. The incident of the Polish ship alarmed many people in Canada, because they realized that other countries could get into the Arctic without Canada knowing about it. Canada's claims therefore didn't seem to mean very much. There has therefore been an outcry for increased surveillance and patrolling of the Arctic, if Canada's claims are to be recognized seriously by other countries.

● 5. (a) List the provinces in the correct order in which they joined Canada, together with their dates.

(b) How many "Territories" does Canada possess?

(c) How many provinces are there?

(d) Name the provinces that are landlocked, with no direct access to the sea.

(e) Name all the provinces that have a coastline giving direct access to the Atlantic Ocean.

● 6. (a) What do you think happens at Customs?

(b) Write not more than three or four sentences suggesting why countries have Customs Houses along their frontiers or boundaries.

● 7. Most people in Canada live close to the U.S. border. Write about five sentences describing what things might affect your life if you lived very close to the U.S. border. Remember that some things may be advantageous to you, while others may be disadvantageous.

## C: POPULATION AND CITIES

How large is Canada? How many people live here? Where do most people live in Canada? How does Canada rank in size with the other large countries of the world? Would you call Canada densely or sparsely populated? Where are most of the towns and cities located? Why do most people live close to the U.S. border?

These are possibly some of the questions that you might at various times have asked, or have been asked. The answers to some of them are straightforward, though none of them is capable of an exact answer. For example, no one really knows *exactly* how large Canada is. Other countries do not even agree with the Canadian government as to the exact location of its borders, especially in the extreme north. We do not know *exactly* how many people live in Canada either; for example there are many people living here illegally, and we do not know how many there are. Even apparently simple questions are therefore not always possible to answer simply. Other questions may be more difficult to answer still: how do you answer the call to say whether Canada is densely or sparsely populated? What are your units of measurement? What do they mean?

Nevertheless, we should try to arrive at answers. There are some clues in the maps and photographs following.

Even if we knew of every person living in Canada, such a figure would be out of date in no time. People die, others are born; some emigrate, others immigrate: the population is never fixed and stable.

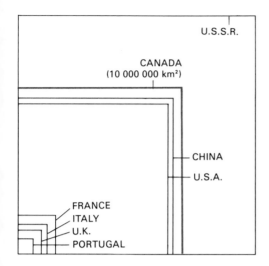

Figure 1-11   **Areas of Some Selected Countries Compared**

**Figure 1-12   Populations of Some Selected Countries Compared (Simplified)**

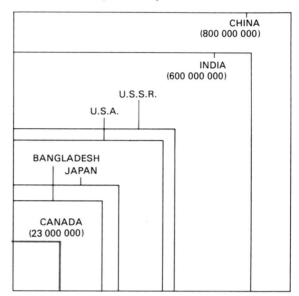

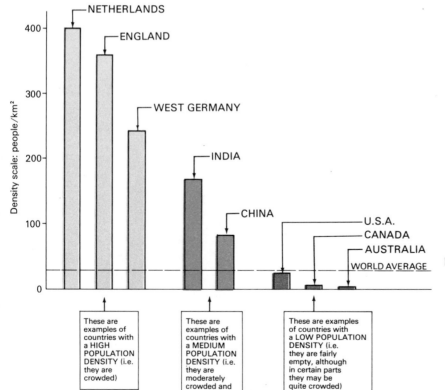

**Figure 1-13   Some Population Densities for Comparison with Canada**

WORLD AVERAGE

These are examples of countries with a HIGH POPULATION DENSITY (i.e. they are crowded)

These are examples of countries with a MEDIUM POPULATION DENSITY (i.e. they are moderately crowded and may be very crowded in certain parts)

These are examples of countries with a LOW POPULATION DENSITY (i.e. they are fairly empty, although in certain parts they may be quite crowded)

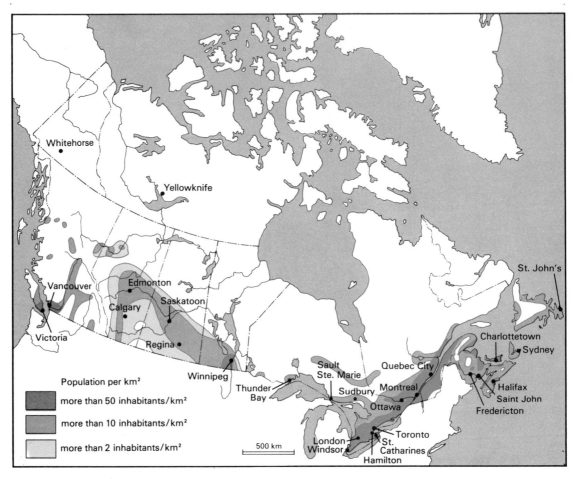

Population per km²

more than 50 inhabitants/km²

more than 10 inhabitants/km²

more than 2 inhabitants/km²

500 km

**Figure 1-14 Population Density and the Main Towns of Canada**

**Figure 1-15** Part of the Anyuittuq National Park in the Arctic.

**Figure 1-16** Southern farmland.

**Figure 1-17   Farmed Areas of Canada**

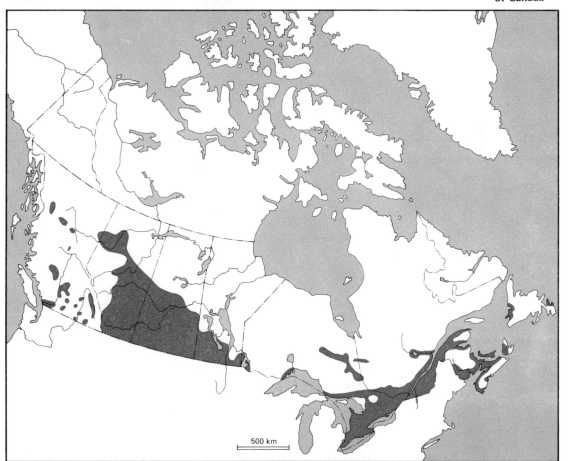

500 km

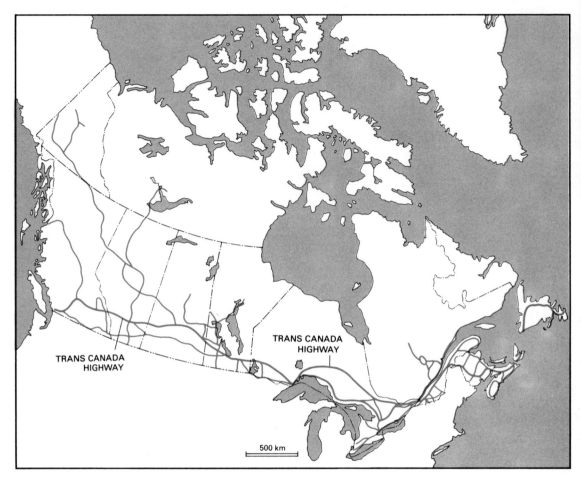

TRANS CANADA
HIGHWAY

TRANS CANADA
HIGHWAY

500 km

**Figure 1-18    Major Roads of Canada**

Certain aspects of Canada's population and cities stand out. Can you see in Figure 1-11 that Canada ranks as the second largest country in the world, after the U.S.S.R.? Approximately how large is Canada?

In Figure 1-12 you can see that Canada ranks a long way down in population. Even more than it seems, really: about 20 countries with larger populations have not been drawn in, because the diagram would then be too crowded.

So it seems obvious that the population density will be quite low, as Figure 1-13 tells you. You can see where most people live and you can see where most of the larger towns and cities are (Figure 1-14). The other maps and photographs tell you . . . what?

Let us see.

- 8. In not more than about ten lines say what you think the map of *The Farmed Areas of Canada* has to do with the distribution of population shown in Figure 1-14.

- 9. In not more than about ten lines say how Figures 1-14 and 1-17 show why most Canadians live in the south, near the U.S. border. Indicate also why the farmed areas of Canada are in the south.

**Figure 1-19   Main Railway Lines of Canada**

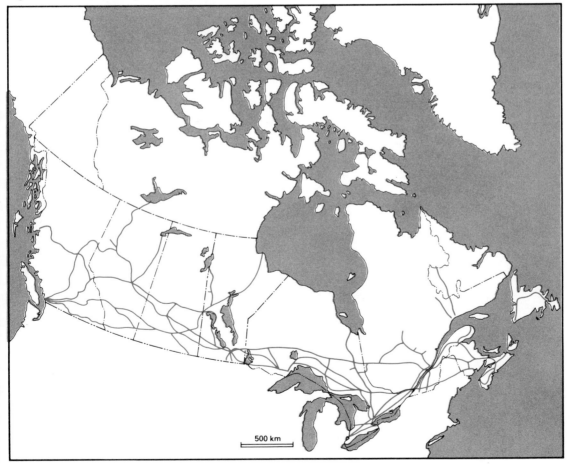

500 km

**Figure 1-20** Part of the Trans Canada Highway across the Prairies.

● 10. Figures 1-18 and 1-20 show roads. Figure 1-7 shows Mac-kenzie Valley barges. Figure 1-19 shows rail lines. You can see from them all that there are some things worth noting, such as:

   (a) Most major roads are in the south.

   (b) Most major rail lines are in the south.

   (c) The North uses few road and rail links.

   Write at least *one sentence on each* of these points, explaining them. Use what you have learned or deduced from the other maps and material in this chapter.

## CONCLUSION

Now try these wrap-up questions.

● 11· Write five sentences, mentioning any five things about Canada that we are urged to take pride in. Refer to the extracts from Prime Minister Trudeau's speech at the beginning of this lesson.

● 12. Using the extracts from Trudeau's speech, say — in not more than about five sentences — what some of the challenges are in Canada's geography that Canadians have had to deal with.

# CHAPTER 2

# THE CLIMATES, VEGETATION, AND SOILS

## AREAL DIFFERENTIATION

Have you ever wondered why Montreal gets longer, colder winters than Toronto? Or why Vancouver gets mostly rain in winter rather than snow? Perhaps the occasional droughts in the Prairies have made you curious, or maybe the frequency of the storms of the Great Lakes-St. Lawrence corridor has puzzled you. Possibly you have asked questions on a larger scale, such as *why is the Arctic so cold?* and *why is British Columbia so wet?* Probably the most common question to be asked is *why are Canadian winters so severe?*

The most famous droughts of the Prairies were those of the early 1930s, when the black topsoil was simply blown about by the wind in great "black blizzards".

Climate and weather are certainly very popular subjects of conversation. Many people even think that some of their actions are influenced by the weather, as you can see from the following articles.

# The Weather

When researchers at Queen's University Faculty of Medicine, Kingston, reviewed car accidents that had occurred in Frontenac County between June and September, 1968, they discovered that 80 per cent of the fatal mishaps and 73 per cent of the non-fatal accidents had occurred when the barometric pressure was falling. A check on the three previous years revealed similar percentages under the same conditions.

excerpted from "The Weather" by Sidney Katz
in the *Home Maker's Magazine*, June 1973

# The Weather

Meteorpsychiatrists are specific when describing how we are affected by dropping barometric pressure which is characteristic of the period before a storm. "People feel low and depressed and they complain more about aches and pains," says Dr. Henry Durost, a Toronto psychiatrist and hospital director. When the barometric pressure is falling, a motorist is more apt to be uncomfortable, listless and distracted, hence the high number of serious car accidents as revealed in the Queen's University study in Frontenac County.

One survey showed that there are more suicides during low pressure periods; another, that cats display marked restlessness and aggressiveness during these periods. There's a logical explanation for these changes.

Lowered atmospheric pressure means that a person will have a decreased amount of oxygen in his bloodstream. Lowered oxygenation of the blood adversely affects mood. Reduced atmospheric pressure also forces the heart to work harder, and it's also likely to alter the functioning of the endocrine glands. All of these changes can lead to physical and/or mental malaise.

from "The Weather" by Sidney Katz
in the *Home Maker's Magazine*, June 1973

● 1 (a) Consider both articles. Write at least five sentences to explain in what ways people feel that low atmospheric (barometric) pressure can cause them problems.

OR

(b) What is the evidence mentioned that weather influences the behaviour of people?

● 2. What is the worst sort of weather for car travel, according to the research evidence presented in the articles?

## A: TEMPERATURE AND PRECIPITATION DIFFERENCES ACROSS CANADA

Where does Canada stand in relation to the climatic extremes for the world?

| Continent | highest temperature °C | | lowest temperature °C | |
| --- | --- | --- | --- | --- |
| Africa | Azizia, Libya | 58 | Ifrane, Morocco | −24 |
| Antarctica | Palmer Peninsula | 14 | Vostok | −88 |
| Asia | Tirat Tsvi, Israel | 54 | Omykon, U.S.S.R. | −68 |
| Australia | Cloncurry, Queensland | 53 | Charlotte, N.S.W. | −22 |
| Europe | Seville, Spain | 50 | Ust-Shchugor, U.S.S.R. | −55 |
| North America | Death Valley, California | 57 | Snag, Yukon | −63 |
| South America | Rivadavia, Argentina | 49 | Sarmiento, Argentina | −33 |

Antarctica is the only polar land mass; the Arctic region is mostly ocean. Within Antarctica the warmest, or least cold, areas, are around its edges, and the coldest parts are towards the interior. Vostok, the coldest place so far known, is a Russian research base in the interior.

You can see that while Canada is not listed amongst the warmest places in each continent, it *is* listed amongst the coldest. Indeed, the coldest place in North America is Snag in the Yukon.

# Would You Rather Be In Snag?

It's saddening to learn that weather reports will no longer be sent out from White River in northern Ontario. The service there is a victim of inflation.

For generations, White River, north of Lake Superior, was famed as Canada's coldest spot. The temperature fell to −72°F[1] Jan. 23, 1935.

That may not be much compared to the −126.9°F[2] that has been recorded in Antarctica, but it was impressive for Canada. And while White River never again equalled its 1935 record, it tried hard almost every winter.

For people in other parts of Canada on cold winter mornings, there was a certain perverse pleasure in hearing the bad news from White River.

It might be snowing and blowing and freezing in Toronto or Montreal or Winnipeg, but it was always somehow consoling to learn that out there in the Lake Superior forests it was 30 or 40 degrees worse. On the rare occasions when White River warmed up, it was always possible to start a conversation by remarking that Toronto this morning was actually colder than White River.

A substitute is obviously needed to maintain Canada's winter morale. We have to know that somewhere else the weather is definitely more miserable than it is here. We would suggest Snag, in the Yukon. The temperature

[1] −58°C
[2] −88°C

there dropped to –81°F³ Feb. 3, 1947 — the lowest ever recorded in this country — and its ordinary tem-
³ –63°C

peratures seem as vicious as White River's.

It has besides, the advantage of a name as disagreeable as its climate.

"Would you rather be in Snag?" should be the perfect putdown for anyone who complains about the cold.

from the Toronto *Star*, February 20, 1976

*Mean* is another word for *average*. Mean daily temperatures are calculated by adding the recorded maximum and minimum for a 24 hour period and dividing by two. In order to obtain the mean daily temperature for a *month*, the individual daily means are added for the month and then divided by the number of days in the month. Because a particular month in one year is not necessarily the same as that month in another year, it is normal to add together the mean temperatures for a particular month over a period of many years and then divide by the number of years. In this way a *true mean* is reached, and it may then be used to represent the average for a particular place.

At most times of the year it is impossible to tell whether you are on an island or on part of the frozen ocean. Some of the northernmost islands are quite mountainous, so you can tell there, but elsewhere it can be very difficult.

• 3. (a) Why do you think people need to talk about a place that is worse off than they are?

(b) Do you think you can really love winter? Why do you say that?

Coldness — as talked about in the last article — is indeed one of the dominant characteristics of Canada's climate. Let us examine it briefly.

### Coldness

The map of mean daily temperatures for January (Figure 2-1) shows the extent of the coldness during one of the winter months. You can see that the coldest parts are generally in the north, as you would expect. Here temperatures regularly fall below –35°C in at least two areas: (i) the extreme northern islands, and (ii) the districts just west of Hudson Bay. The warmest parts of Canada in winter are also where you probably expect them to be: in the south, ranging from a positive 5°C in western Vancouver Island to a –5°C in both southwestern Ontario and the eastern coastal strip of the Atlantic Provinces.

The Arctic areas are the coldest parts of Canada in summer as well as in winter. In summer mean temperatures usually fail to rise above 10°C. Most months are indeed below the freezing point, and the summers are correspondingly quite short as well as quite cold. The climatic data for Cambridge Bay illustrate the extent of coldness in the Arctic. How many months are below freezing? What is the average annual temperature?

| Cambridge Bay | J | F | M | A | M | J | J | A | S | O | N | D |
|---|---|---|---|---|---|---|---|---|---|---|---|---|
| temperature °C average –15°C | –33 | –34 | –28 | –23 | –10 | 2 | 8 | 7 | –1 | –12 | –23 | –29 |
| precipitation mm total 143 mm | | 8 | 5 | 6 | 4 | 7 | 11 | 28 | 24 | 16 | 14 | 13 | 7 |

Not all of Canada is in the Arctic, of course. Nevertheless, even places much farther south than Cambridge Bay still experience long, cold winters. The data for Kapuskasing show what the winters are like in a fairly "typical" Canadian location. Notice again that many months (how many is that?) are below freezing, and that the average temperature for the year is quite low (how low is it in fact?).

| Kapuskasing | J | F | M | A | M | J | J | A | S | O | N | D |
|---|---|---|---|---|---|---|---|---|---|---|---|---|
| temperature °C | −18 | −17 | −10 | −1 | 8 | 14 | 17 | 16 | 11 | 4 | −5 | −14 |
| average 0°C | | | | | | | | | | | | |
| precipitation mm | | 50 | 35 | 42 | 42 | 58 | 71 | 84 | 81 | 82 | 54 | 60 | 52 |
| total 711 mm | | | | | | | | | | | | |

It is only when you get out to the Vancouver area that winters cease to have months regularly below freezing point. The data for Vancouver show that the lowest mean monthly temperature there is 3°C in January. Nevertheless, the average over the year in Vancouver is not strikingly high — it is about the same as the Arctic summer maximum.

| Vancouver | J | F | M | A | M | J | J | A | S | O | N | D |
|---|---|---|---|---|---|---|---|---|---|---|---|---|
| temperature °C | 3 | 4 | 7 | 10 | 13 | 16 | 18 | 18 | 15 | 11 | 7 | 4 |
| average 10.5°C | | | | | | | | | | | | |
| precipitation mm | 201 | 153 | 133 | 92 | 69 | 54 | 35 | 41 | 80 | 167 | 175 | 243 |
| total 1443 mm | | | | | | | | | | | | |

So it's with some justification that we can describe Canada overall as having a generally cold set of climates, even though the amount of cold varies from place to place.

## Heat

Canadian winters are world famous. Canadian summers, however, are known only locally. Even people visiting from the U.S.A. are jokingly reputed to bring skis with them in July.

But Canadian summers are quite hot. The highest temperature ever recorded in Canada is 46°C in Alberta in 1903. But although summer temperatures usually do not even come close to that, it is still hot in most parts of Canada. The warmest parts of the Arctic (Figure 2-2) range up to about a mean daily temperature of 10°C in July. Farther south, however, the mean daily July temperatures reach over 20°C. This is relatively warm, for a mean of 20°C could mean a daytime temperature of 30°C averaged with a dawn temperature of 10°C, and 30°C is quite hot. Which are two chief areas where this happens?

Have you ever wondered how we obtain climatic data for places? We do it by having meteorologists or other technical staff take measurements day after day, month after month, year after year. In most places this is not a hardship, because there are many people, but in others it is quite a difficult task.

Coldness is the normal state of the universe. Heat is a positive phenomenon that pushes back the cold, but when the source of heat is remote or turned away from, then the heat rapidly disappears, and the coldness reasserts itself. The earth's source of heat is the sun, but when the earth's axis is so arranged that Canada is tilted away from the sun then the natural universal coldness begins to reestablish itself over the country. It is only when the earth's axis is brought around to tilt Canada once more towards the sun that Canada's coldness is pushed back for a while. This is during Canada's summer time.

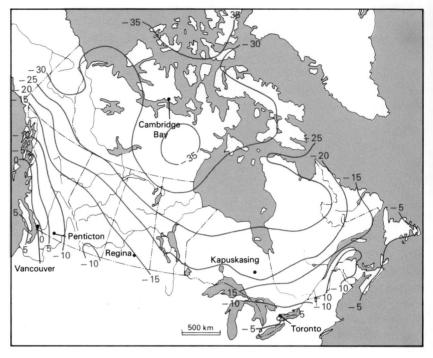

The coldest time during a 24 hour period is usually a little after dawn. The reason is that the earth generally loses heat all through the night, becoming colder and colder towards dawn. At dawn the sun starts to put back some heat, but for a little while the amount being lost exceeds the amount being gained, and so it is generally coldest a little while after dawn.

**Figure 2-1  Mean Daily Temperatures, January (°Celsius)**

**Figure 2-2  Mean Daily Temperatures, July (°Celsius)**

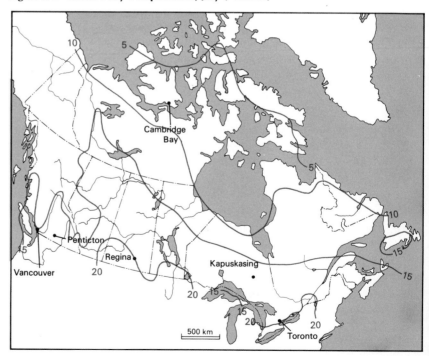

## Precipitation

In addition to being a generally cold country, Canada is also a generally dry one. There are some places which certainly have a lot of rain and snow, but there are even more which receive very little. Some parts of Canada are indeed as dry as deserts, while many others parts do not receive enough moisture for all their needs. The amount of precipitation varies across the country. The precipitation pattern is shown in Figure 2-3. Generally if a place receives over 1000 mm/year we can consider it to be "fairly wet". Which parts of Canada receive over 1000 mm/year? Will you shade them in on *your* map? In deep blue, if you have it! That's not much of the country, is it?

Places which receive between 500 mm/ year and 1000 mm/year are fairly dry. They have enough moisture most of the time, but if

Precipitation means any form of condensed water vapour which eventually collects on the ground. Rain is the most common type of precipitation, but there is also snow. Hail is classified as rain (fozen water droplets), while sleet is classified as partly melted snow.

**Figure 2-3    Total Precipitation (in mm)**

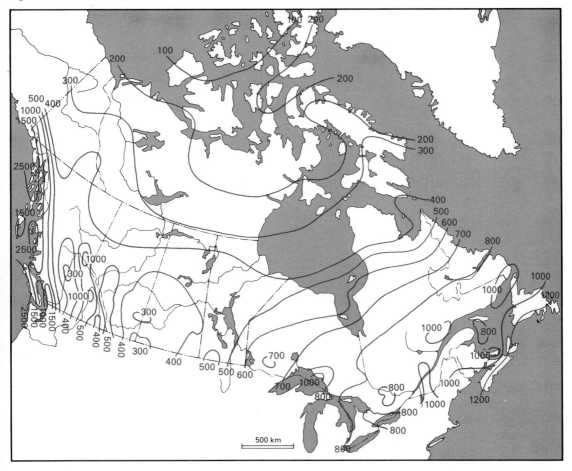

Why should a large population make a difference as to whether there is enough precipitation or not?

Are the "water shortage areas" ever likely to support large populations? What could be done to obtain more water?

It is easy to measure how much rain falls. A *rain gauge* is used; it collects the rainfall in a particular spot into a calibrated glass jar, so that the amount can be read off very quickly. Snow is less easy to measure. Usually a core sample is taken and melted. The amount of water produced is then measured in the same way as rain. Generally it is found that ten millimetres of snow converts into one millimetre of *rainfall equivalent*. All precipitation figures are given for rainfall and/or rainfall equivalent.

many people live there then it is possible that there will be water shortages at times during the year. You can shade these areas on your map too if you wish. Use a regular blue colour, and label it "possible water shortage areas".

Those areas of the country that you still have left to shade are those which receive under 500 mm/year. They are dry areas. If you want to finish shading your map, use a really pale blue for these areas, and label them "water shortage areas".

- 4. Draw a vertical bar graph to illustrate these figures:

| City | annual total precipitation (mm) |
|---|---|
| Cambridge Bay | 143 |
| Regina | 383 |
| Kapuskasing | 711 |
| Toronto | 785 |
| Montreal | 1061 |
| Vancouver | 1443 |

Which places are "fairly wet"? Which are areas of "possible water shortage"? And which ones are dry enough to be in areas of "water shortage"?

- 5. Much of the slight precipitation in the Arctic falls as snow. Can you tell from the data for Cambridge Bay just how many months snow can be expected to fall?

- 6. (a) Kapuskasing is warmer than Cambridge Bay in both summer and winter. Add the monthly temperature figures for each place separately for April through September. How much is Kapuskasing's total *extra* warmth in the summer?
  (b) Add the monthly figures for each place separately for October through March. How much is Kapuskasing's total *extra* warmth in winter?
  (c) During which season (summer or winter) do you think the northern areas suffer most *by comparison with the southern areas?*

## B: THE MAJOR CLIMATE REGIONS OF CANADA

From what you have studied already you can see that the climate of Canada differs considerably from one area of the country to another. It is possible to group the differences into five main areas, so that we could talk of the "Arctic region", for instance, and know generally what it is like. The five main climate regions are shown in Figure 2-4. Can you name them?

Let's have a quick look at them all, one by one.

## The Arctic Climate Region

This is *very cold* and *very dry,* as we have seen in the data for Cambridge Bay (can you find Cambridge Bay on the map in Figure 2-4?). Nine months out of the year have average temperatures below the freezing point, and that is *very cold.* The average for the year is only –15°C; that is *very cold* too. The climate data also show that total precipitation (rain + snow) is only 143 mm; that is *very dry.* Looking back at your shaded precipitation map, can you see which zone Cambridge Bay would be in? And if you bear in mind that throughout the world any place with under 250 mm/year is classified as a desert, you will again realize that Cambridge Bay is *very dry.* The Arctic is in fact *very cold* and *very dry.*

**Figure 2-4**   Climate Regions of Canada

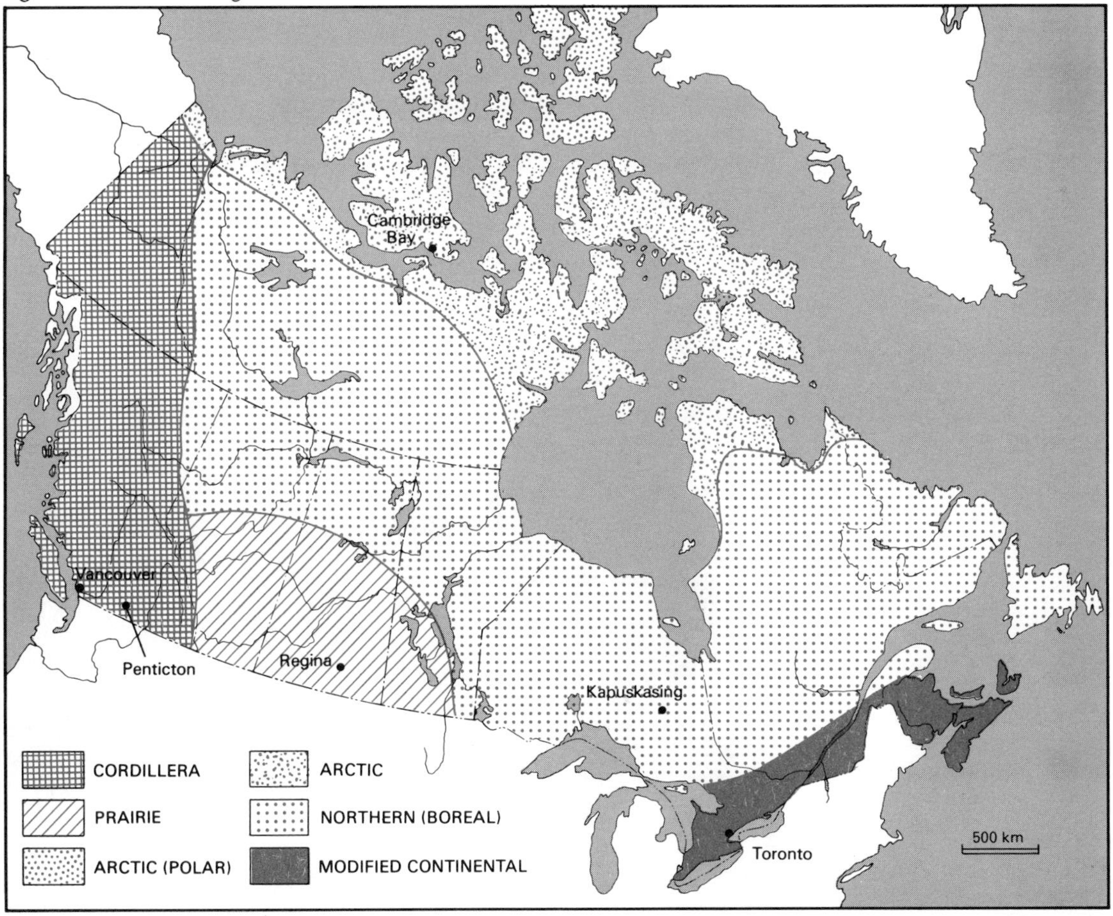

Isn't "typical" the word we used to describe Kapuskasing in section A?

*Boreas* was, in Greek mythology, the god of the *north* wind; he was cold and heartless.

What is Kapuskasing's total precipitation compared with Cambridge Bay's?

### The Northern (Boreal) Climate Region

This is the largest climate region in Canada. You *could* call it the "typical" Canadian climate. However, because of its great size it is clearly not the same all over. For example, it is generally colder and drier in the northern areas, near the Arctic, and milder and wetter in the southern parts. Kapuskasing, as you can see from Figure 2-4, is in the milder and wetter southern parts.

The average temperature for the year in the Boreal climate region is about 15°C warmer than in the Arctic, and this is generally enough for trees to be able to grow throughout the Boreal zone. There are almost no trees in the Arctic, but the Boreal zone is one of the major forest areas in the world.

Trees are also encouraged to grow by the greater precipitation of the Boreal region. Because the Boreal zone is farther south, a larger proportion of the precipitation also falls as rain rather than as snow: at Cambridge Bay over 50% of the precipitation falls as snow, but the proportion is down to about 30% at Kapuskasing.

### The Prairie Climate Region

One of the chief characteristics of this zone is the great difference between the summer and winter temperatures. This difference is called the *annual range of temperature*. In the Prairies it is very large. Do you remember that the highest temperature ever recorded in Canada occurred in Alberta, one of the Prairie provinces? In fact summers are usually warm and at times they can be very hot. Winters on the other hand are always cold. Indeed they

**Figure 2-5** Part of the Boreal forest in northern Ontario.

**Figure 2-6** Winter in Toronto: not too wet, not too cold.

are often very cold, with blizzards. As for precipitation, it is usually slight, not much above the limits for a desert (which are 250 mm/year). The data for Regina are fairly typical of the Prairie climate:

A blizzard may be a snow storm of great severity, or it may be violently blowing snow from a previous snow fall.

| **Regina** | **J** | **F** | **M** | **A** | **M** | **J** | **J** | **A** | **S** | **O** | **N** | **D** |
|---|---|---|---|---|---|---|---|---|---|---|---|---|
| temperature °C average 2.3°C | −17 | −15 | −7 | 4 | 11 | 16 | 19 | 18 | 12 | 5 | −6 | −13 |
| precpitation mm total 383 mm | 16 | 15 | 20 | 21 | 41 | 82 | 54 | 44 | 31 | 22 | 22 | 15 |

**Figure 2-7** Cooler and wetter towards the Atlantic. This is the Gaspé coast of Quebec.

Large bodies of water (seas, oceans, lakes) are slower to warm up in summer than land areas. The reasons are that the sun's rays penetrate to a greater depth in water and consequently have more water to warm up. The results are that the large bodies of water exert a cooling effect on neighbouring lands in summer. In winter, however, the land loses its heat very quickly, because the heat was only in the very top layer. The land thus rapidly becomes colder than the water bodies, which thereby exert a slight warming effect on the land next to them. This cooling in summer and warming in winter is called the *moderating effect* of water bodies.

*Cordillera* is derived from a Spanish word meaning little cord or rope. It refers to a range of mountains, or a chain of mountains.

Sagebrush is a plant with grey-green leaves and a minty odour. It grows only in near-desert conditions; indeed, it is the state flower of Nevada.

## The Modified Continental Climate Region

A *continental* climate is one which has a large annual range of temperature, such as that of the Boreal or Prairie zones. A *modified continental* climate is one in which the annual range of temperature is quite large, but not so large as it would be without the *modifiers*. The modifiers are usually large lakes or branches of the sea, which have a cooling effect in summer and a warming effect in winter. Thus the effects of continentality are lessened, or *modified*. In Canada the modifiers are the Great Lakes and the Gulf and Estuary of the St. Lawrence. As well as modifying the temperatures these bodies of water also provide plenty of moisture for precipitation; so the modified continental areas usually have enough water for their needs (but not in all places: look at the map in Figure 2-3).

| **Toronto** | **J** | **F** | **M** | **A** | **M** | **J** | **J** | **A** | **S** | **O** | **N** | **D** |
|---|---|---|---|---|---|---|---|---|---|---|---|---|
| temperature °C average 7.7°C | −4 | −4 | −1 | 6 | 12 | 18 | 22 | 19 | 16 | 9 | 3 | −3 |
| precipitation mm total 786 mm | 70 | 60 | 59 | 57 | 70 | 68 | 70 | 70 | 67 | 65 | 65 | 65 |

Toronto is fairly typical of the inland sectors, but as you go down the St. Lawrence towards the Atlantic the climate changes slightly. The temperature is cooler and there is more precipitation, particularly snow.

## The Cordillera Climate Region

The Cordillera in western Canada consists of mountains and gorges, plateaus and trenches, islands and submerged valleys. The climate is equally varied, according to where you are within the Cordillera. In some of the interior valleys it is almost desert: sagebrush and cactus grow, and irrigation is needed for crops. But in the mountains, especially the Coast Mountains, precipitation is very heavy indeed. The North American record is held by a station at Henderson Lake on the west side of Vancouver Island, where precipitation averages 6655 mm/year, and actually reached as much as 8222 mm in 1931. In some of the interior valleys, on the other hand, precipitation may be as low as 200–250 mm/year. So British Columbia is by no means all wet. Nor even *always* wet in those areas where precipitation is heavy, for the rainfall is usually very slight in summer. It is during the winter that most precipitation falls. Using the Vancouver data in section A of this chapter, calculate what percentage of the annual precipitation falls in the period April through September. Is it more or less than 50%? What percentage is it in fact? In view of this figure would you call the Vancouver summers fairly dry or not?

As an example of the variations in the Cordillera climate region, examine the data for Penticton, which is located in one of the interior valleys.

| Penticton | J | F | M | A | M | J | J | A | S | O | N | D |
|---|---|---|---|---|---|---|---|---|---|---|---|---|
| temperature °C | −3 | 0 | 4 | 10 | 14 | 18 | 21 | 19 | 15 | 9 | 3 | 0 |

average 9.2°C

| precipitation mm | 25 | 20 | 19 | 21 | 25 | 25 | 20 | 21 | 23 | 25 | 26 | 31 |
|---|---|---|---|---|---|---|---|---|---|---|---|---|

total 292 mm

Can you see any differences between the data for Vancouver and those for Penticton? What are they?

- 7. Most photos of the Arctic show *lots of snow,* yet — as you know — it is a *very dry* region. Can you explain this apparent contradiction?

- 8. Find the difference in temperature between Kapuskasing and Cambridge Bay for each month of the year. For example, in January (J) Kapuskasing's temperature is −18° whereas Cambridge Bay's temperature is −33°C. The difference is therefore 15°C (−18 subtracted from −33 = 15).
  (a) In which month is the difference greatest?
  (b) In which month is the difference least?
  (c) Is the Arctic spring unusually mild or unusually cold in relation to the Boreal spring?

- 9. Calculate the annual temperature ranges for the following places:

| | maximum in °C | minimum in °C |
|---|---|---|
| Kapuskasing | 17 | −18 |
| Regina | 19 | −17 |
| Toronto | 22 | −4 |

In which place is the range largest?

- 10. By comparing the climate statistics for Regina and Kapuskasing you can see that Regina is slightly warmer in all months. However, the extra warmth is not equally distributed through summer and winter.
  (a) *Add* the temperature figures for each place separately for October through March. Regina's total is −53°C (try it: Oct +5, Nov −6, Dec −13, Jan −17, Feb −15, March −7 = −53). What is Kapuskasing's total? What is the difference between the totals; in other words, what is the amount of Regina's *extra* warmth?

For comparison, 51% of Toronto's precipitation falls during the six month period April-September, giving it the very slightest of summer maximums. In effect, Toronto has precipitation equally through summer and winter.

(b) *Add* the temperature figures for each place separately for April through September. Kapuskasing's total is 65°C (– 1 + 8 + 14 + 17 + 16 + 11 = 65). What is Regina's total? What is the amount of Regina's total extra warmth?

(c) In which season (summer or winter) does Regina have *most* of its extra warmth?

● 11. Using the information in this assignment, copy and complete the graph (Figure 2-8) and answer the questions below:

| City | winter minimum | summer maximum | total precipitation | snow in rainfall equivalent |
|---|---|---|---|---|
| | °C | °C | mm | mm |
| Toronto | –4 | 22 | 785 | 139 |
| Ottawa | –11 | 21 | 886 | 205 |
| Montreal | –9 | 21 | 1061 | 256 |
| Quebec City | –11 | 20 | 1137 | 314 |
| Halifax | –5 | 18 | 1378 | 163 |

(a) What do you notice about the *summer maximum* line from west to east?

(b) What do you notice about the *total precipitation* line from west to east?

(c) Can you explain the drop in the *winter minimum* line in the St. Lawrence Lowlands region (Ottawa, Montreal, Quebec City)?

(d) Which part receives the snowiest winters?

● 12. Construct hythergraphs for Vancouver and Penticton. Draw both of them on the same graph paper, and then answer the questions below:

(a) Which place, Penticton or Vancouver, do you think has the more *continental* climate?

(b) Which place, Penticton or Vancouver, receives more precipitation?

(c) During which season of the year, summer or winter, are the two places most alike?

(d) Write *warm and dry* in an appropriate place on your graph.

(e) Write *cool and wet* in an appropriate place on your graph.

(f) Write *cold and dry* in an appropriate place on your graph.

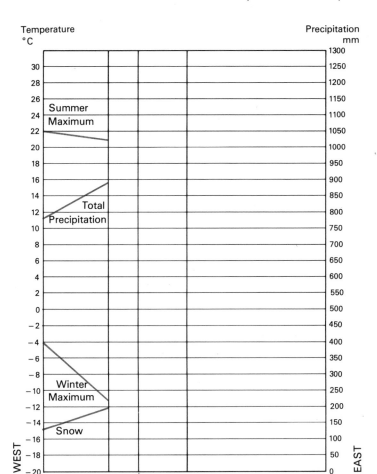

Temperature
°C

Precipitation
mm

**Figure 2-8   Graph for Use in
Assignment 11**

● 13. In not more than about ten lines or so suggest a *definition*
for a climate region. Which single one of the regions we
have noted in Canada *least* fits into your definition? Why is
that, do you think?

## C: SOME REASONS FOR THE VARIETY OF CLIMATES

### Latitude

Canada is a large country. It extends over many latitudes. The most
southerly latitude is 42°N in Lake Erie, and the most northerly is
the North Pole itself. This means that the southernmost parts of
Canada are actually closer to the Equator than they are to the

Canada claims all the
islands as far north as
the North Pole; other
countries do not
necessarily agree. At
least no one else
claims them.

You can calculate the angle at which the sun's rays reach the earth's surface by subtracting from 90° the difference between the point where the sun is actually directly overhead and the point you want to calculate the angle for. For example, on December 21st, the sun is directly overhead at the Tropic of Capricorn at 23.5°S. Toronto lies at a latitude of about 43.5°N, so the difference between it and the Tropic of Capricorn is 67°. Subtract 67° from 90° and the answer is 23°. This is then the angle at which the sun's rays reach Toronto on December 21st. What is the angle on June 21st, when the sun is directly overhead at the Tropic of Cancer? Cambridge Bay has a latitude of almost 70°N. What is the angle of the sun's rays there on June 21st? And on December 21st? What do you think this last answer means?

North Pole, the halfway mark being 45° N (Figure 2-9). However, *most* of Canada lies between 45°N and the North Pole (90°N); so it is fair to describe Canada as a northern country. This is one reason why it is generally a cold country. Another reason involves the tilt of the earth's axis, and the location of Canada in relation to the sun's rays at different times of the year. Figure 2-10 shows Canada's position in December and June. It is obvious that in December the sun's rays do not even shine at all in northern Canada; it is dark and very cold. Even in southern Canada the sun's rays in winter have very little warming effect.

In summer things are a little different. All parts receive sunshine, and in the south the rays provide quite a lot of warmth.

### Air Masses

Air masses are simply masses of air. They have certain characteristics which they take with them when they move. For example, an air mass which starts in the polar regions (a *Polar air mass*) will likely be cold, while a *Tropical air mass* will be warm. An air mass which starts over the sea (a *maritime air mass*) will usually contain much moisture, while a *continental air mass* will more likely be dry. Thus it is possible to have moist, warm air masses (maritime Tropical air masses), dry cold ones (continental Polar), and so on. What would a dry warm air mass be called? And a moist cold one?

Canada usually experiences weather brought by three major air masses:

a. the *continental Polar air mass,* which exists in the Arctic and spreads southwards over the rest of Canada at various times during the year. It covers most of Canada for much of the winter, and it can even bring cool spells in summer.

b. the *maritime Tropical air mass,* located over the Gulf of Mexico and the Caribbean. It is warm and damp. It usually pushes into

**Figure 2-9   The Latitudinal Position of Canada**

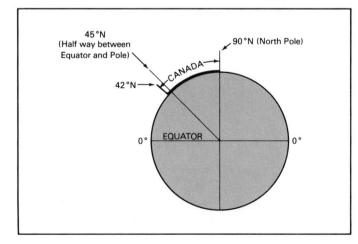

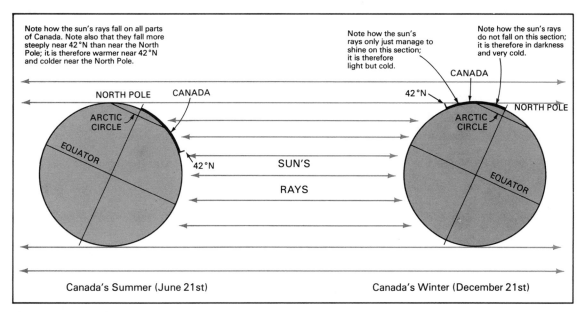

**Figure 2-10 Canada's Summer, Canada's Winter**

southern Canada during the summer, and also occasionally in the winter (when it brings mild spells).

c. the *maritime Polar air mass,* which lies over the North Atlantic Ocean. It brings cold wet weather to the Atlantic Provinces in winter, and cool wet weather in summer.

Figure 2-1 illustrates one of the effects of the continental Polar air mass in January. The isotherms are pushed southwards over the centre of Canada. Look, for example, at the −20°C isotherm: it enters Canada from Alaska, but instead of going straight across to northern Quebec it is pushed well south instead. This is caused by the huge quantities of cold Polar air blowing southwards in winter. Look at the weather chart for April 7, 1976, in Figure 2-11. You can see quite clearly how the cold Polar air mass reaches southward not only into Canada but also into the United States.

Figure 2-2 shows one of the effects of the maritime Tropical air mass. Warm air pushes northwards into Canada in summer, and its front edges can be imagined from the shape of the 20°C isotherm. The edge is a little bit ragged because Canada is so far north. Even so, the 15° isotherm is still pushed considerably northward, especially in the Mackenzie Valley.

One other feature of air masses before we leave them: where they meet each other there is usually unsettled weather. The line they meet along is called a *front,* and it is usually characterized by cloud and rain and possibly by a few storms. Because the continental Polar air mass meets the maritime Tropical air mass so

*Isotherms* is a term used to mean lines on a map joining places which have the same temperature. For example, the 10°C isotherm joins places which all have temperatures of 10°C. On either side of the line the temperatures are either above or below 10°C, depending upon which side of the line you are.

There are different types of fronts. A cold *front* occurs wherever the cold air is pushing in behind it, while a *warm front* has warm air moving in behind it.

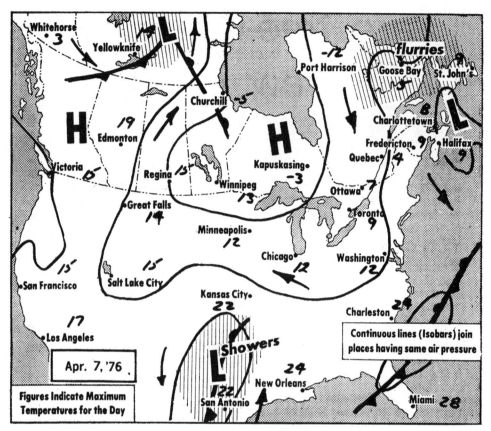

Figure 2-11   Weather Chart for April 7, 1976

There is usually a great deal of precipitation associated with a front because the warmer air is lifted up by the colder air, which digs in underneath it. As the warmer air is tossed upwards, the water vapour in it condenses, forming clouds and possibly giving rain or snow.

frequently over Canada there are usually many storms passing over the country. Generally they start in the Prairies (either of Canada or the United States) and travel eastwards towards the Atlantic Ocean. Because of the shape of the landscape most of the storms are funnelled along the line of the Great Lakes-St. Lawrence valley, in between the Canadian Shield to the north and the Appalachian Mountains to the south (Figure 2-13).

When the storms reach the Atlantic they often interact with the maritime Polar air mass, thereby causing even more precipitation. Look back at the data in Figure 2-8 and see how much more precipitation there is in Halifax than there is in either Toronto or Montreal.

### Landscape

As well as funnelling storms along the St. Lawrence Valley, the landscape of Canada also has other effects on climate. For

**Figure 2-12** Note the manner in which the Rockies cause clouds to form, keeping the moisture out of the dry interior in the foreground.

example, the general flatness of the Prairies allows continental Polar air to spread south *very easily*. So easily in fact that the cold air can even get to Florida on occasion. The most noticeable effect of the landscape, however, is in the west, where the Cordillera virtually blocks out any influence from the Pacific Ocean. The moist air over the Pacific is kept out. Only the coast and the mountains receive much precipitation. Notice in Figure 2-3 how the west coastal areas all receive over 1000 mm/year, but that once you come inland a little way the amount of precipitation greatly decreases (Figure 2-14). Across the Interior Plateaus of British Columbia the precipitation is very low — less than 50 mm/year. The Rocky Mountains push the precipitation up again to over 1000 mm/year, but only in a few places. It is not really until the Atlantic Provinces are reached that the annual precipitation goes over 1000 mm/year again. Most of Canada is in fact fairly dry.

In the great storm of January 1977, cold air pressed all the way to southern Florida. Snow fell on the orange groves; indeed, snow even fell in the Bahamas for the first time ever, as far as anyone knows. In the meantime, Toronto schools were closed for half a day, and Buffalo was declared a disaster area.

- 14. By examining Figure 2-10 can you say what the origin of the Arctic Circle is?

- 15. Can you suggest at least one way in which the information shown in Figure 2-10 explains the differences which occur between summer and winter?

**Figure 2-13 —The Great Lakes - St. Lawrence Storm Funnel**

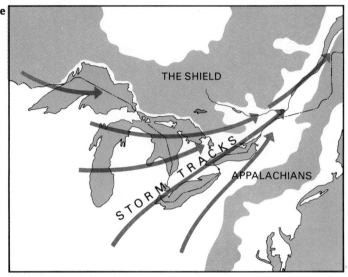

**Figure 2-14 Precipitation in British Columbia**

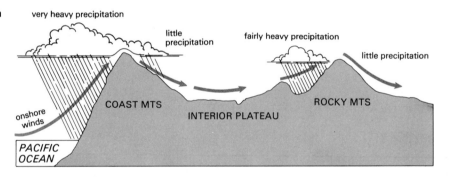

● 16. What sort of air mass is represented in Figure 2-11? If you were required to prepare a weather forecast for April 7, 1976, what would your forecast be for (a) southern Ontario, and (b) northern Ontario? If you think they would be the same, explain why; if you think they would be different, explain why also.

● 17. For *each* of the five major climate regions of Canada write a few lines saying what you think are the advantages and disadvantages of that particular type of climate to the people who live there. It would be a good idea to write five paragraphs, one for each climate region.

● 18. Do you have any questions of your own about the climates of Canada? If so, ask your teacher—or perhaps research them.

# D: VEGETATION AND SOILS

Just as climate differs from area to area within Canada, so do vegetation and soils. The type of climate that an area has exerts a profound influence upon the type of vegetation that grows there, and both have an effect upon the type of soil that develops.

There are essentially three types of vegetation across Canada: tundra, grassland, and forest.

**Tundra** vegetation consists of dwarf bushes, heather, mosses, and lichens. It is found in the regions of Arctic climate, as a comparison of Figure 2-15 with Figure 2-4 shows. Limitations on plant growth are imposed both by the prolonged coldness of the Arctic and by its dominant dryness. Plants that survive in the Arctic have adapted to the persistent cold and dryness of the area by their small size, extremely slow growth, lack of foliage, and water storing texture. In the northern islands of the High Arctic the characteristic dryness and cold become severe, and there is almost no plant growth at all. The ground consists instead of bare rock, shattered rock fragments, and ice; in winter all is covered by a light mantle of snow. Farther south, in the mainland parts of the Arctic, tundra vegetation provides a much more complete cover for the land. In response to the greater permanence of this mainland vegetation, the surface rocks of the Low Arctic have rotted and fractured, and mixed with the remains of decayed vegetation. This has happened to only a very small extent, but it nevertheless has produced the basis of a simple and skeletal soil cover for the Low Arctic. Further soil development is hindered by the occurrence of *permafrost* in all parts of the Arctic (Figure 2-16). Permafrost is a condition of the ground where the lower layers of the surface soils and gravels are permanently frozen. This occurs because the warmth of Arctic summers is not sufficient to penetrate the soils and gravels deeply enough to thaw their lower horizons, which thus remain permanently frozen. Summers are warm enough, however, to thaw the upper horizons. The water released by the thawing of the upper horizons cannot soak down into the ground, as it might do elsewhere, because the lower layers are permanently frozen, and therefore impermeable. The surface consequently becomes waterlogged in summer, and pools form in available hollows. As temperatures drop in the fall, the water becomes locked in as it freezes, to be released to waterlog the surface again the following summer.

**Grassland** forms the natural vegetation of the Prairie climate region. Figure 2-3 confirms that this region is an area of water shortage almost as much as the Arctic is, and when the additional

Stunted bushes are mostly birches and willows. The tundra is so scantily covered with vegetation that its nickname is *The Barrens*.

The extremely slow growth is illustrated by the fact that some lichens grow only one to two centimetres per *century*.

The High Arctic is an imprecise area. It generally exists north of about 70°N, and it certainly includes all the islands north of Melville and Lancaster Sounds.

Decayed vegetation is called *humus*. When humus mixes naturally with finely shattered rock fragments, soil is produced. The speed at which vegetation grows and decays is determined by climate; in the Arctic it is very slow. The skeletal nature of the soils of the Arctic can be further explained by the fact that it is only about 10 000 years since the last traces of the ice sheets melted away.

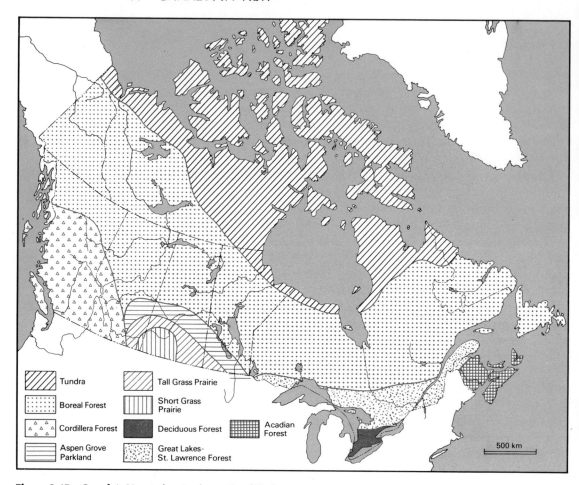

**Figure 2-15 Canada's Vegetation Regions, Simplified**

Legend:
- Tundra
- Boreal Forest
- Cordillera Forest
- Aspen Grove Parkland
- Tall Grass Prairie
- Short Grass Prairie
- Deciduous Forest
- Great Lakes-St. Lawrence Forest
- Acadian Forest

500 km

In descriptions of soils, **the** word *horizon* refers to a layer within the soil. Upper horizons are upper layers, and lower horizons are lower layers.

*Impermeable* means that water cannot pass through. The lower horizons are impermeable because they are frozen solid.

summer warmth of the Prairie region is taken into account it becomes clear that the grassland is a direct response to small precipitation totals coupled with high summer evaporation losses. The control exerted by this water supply balance is further demonstrated by a comparison of the prairie section of Figure 2-15 with that of Figure 2-3. The driest parts of the prairies have less than 300 mm precipitation per year, and they support only very short grass along with some cactus and sagebrush. In contrast, the more humid edges of the prairies, with precipitation totals rising to 400 mm/year and even in places to 500 mm/year, support much richer and taller grasses. Even farther from the dry heart of the Prairie region lies the Parkland Belt. This is often called the *Aspen Grove* vegetation zone, and it marks the gradual transition between the moisture deficient grassland of the Prairie region and the water adequate forest zones which surround the prairie.

The soils of the Prairie region reflect the control of climate and vegetation. Generally the deficiency of precipitation means that soil moisture is drawn upwards, either to be used by plants or to be evaporated. Soils which experience persistent upward percolation of water are called *pedocals*. As their name implies, they tend to be rich in lime, which is produced in the remains of decayed vegetation. They are fertile. However, where there is not enough precipitation and soil moisture to support more than short grass and sagebrush, there is generally a restricted supply of decaying vegetation, and therefore also of lime. The soils of the dry prairie heart do not therefore take on the black appearance of soils rich in humus; they are merely *brown*. They are also correspondingly less fertile; but not infertile. As the amount of moisture increases away from the dry heart, there is accordingly more vegetation —

Pedocals: ped = soil; cal = calcium (lime).

**Figure 2-16   Canada's Soil Regions, Simplified**

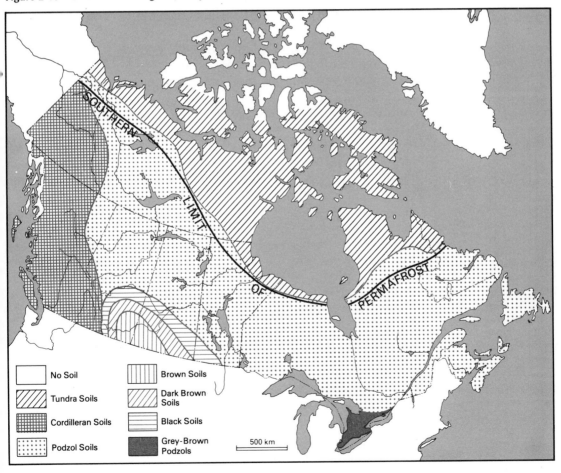

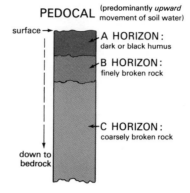

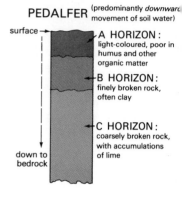

**Figure 2-17   Typical Soil Profiles, Greatly Simplified**

Even during Arctic summers the air is rarely warm enough to evaporate much of the water which lies on or near the surface. The ground therefore is, and looks, very wet; which seems strange in a region which has the precipitation of a desert. One of the side effects of all the surface moisture is that conditions are made favourable for the breeding of billions of mosquitoes and black-flies. Another side effect is that ground transportation is made hazardous: vehicles become trapped in the mud. Buildings may even sink into the mud; so people build them either on solid rock or on piles.

*Chernozem* is the name given to the most famous type of pedocal soil; it is black, rich in lime, and very fertile.

that is, tall grass rather than short grass. Soils still experience upward water percolation; they are still pedocals, rich in fertile humus; but because they contain more humus than the soils of the short grass prairie they take on a *dark brown* colour. In the Parkland Belt the greater quantities of vegetation produce sufficient humus for the soils to become truly *black* (Figure 2-16). They are sometimes called *chernozems,* which is the Russian word for *black earth.* Outside the Parkland Belt the movement of soil moisture begins to be downward rather than upwards, and conditions favour forest rather than grassland.

**Forests** naturally cover most of Canada outside the tundra and grassland areas. By far the largest tract of forest occurs throughout the Boreal climatic region. Within the boreal forest the dominant trees are conifers, especially spruce, although fir and pine are also important. The characteristics of the Boreal forest undergo modification around the edges of the Boreal region. Towards the Arctic, for example, trees are smaller in size and more scattered in distribution, eventually surviving only in sheltered river valleys, and finally ceasing to exist altogether in the true tundra. Towards the western mountains of the Cordillera region the dominant conifers become modified by localized climatic variations caused by differences in the landscape. For instance, in the highest parts of the mountains the clothing of conifers is replaced by tundra-like vegetation, while in the very dry valleys of the sheltered interior sagebrush is common. On the other hand, in the very mild and humid Coast Mountains, conifers grow to a giant size.

To the southeast, the Boreal forest merges into the forests of the modified continental climate region. In the Great Lakes region the coniferous Boreal forest gradually passes through a transition of mixed forest to the only area of deciduous forest in Canada

(Figure 2-15). The long warm summers of southern Ontario are responsible for this change in the nature of the natural forest cover, and they help to support the growth of such trees as oak, hickory, elm, sugar maple, and walnut. Farther down the St. Lawrence valley deciduous trees become gradually less common, and the forest takes on more characteristics of the Boreal forest proper, with only a few stands of deciduous woodland, especially sugar maple. This transitional forest continues into the Atlantic Provinces, where it is called the Acadian forest.

The soils of the forest zones, despite some variety, are characterized by an overall downward percolation of soil water. The effect of this is to carry the fertile humus deep into the soil leaving the topsoil to consist largely of aluminum and iron compounds. Such soils are generally called *pedalfers,* and the chief type is called *podzol* (Figure 2-17). The best podzols for agriculture are those where the humus is not washed completely out of the soil. Such *grey-brown podzols* occur throughout the moderate precipitation but high evaporation areas of southern Ontario's deciduous forest regions. In all areas of mixed forest, the cooler conditions (reflected in the smaller number of deciduous trees) favour less evaporation and therefore greater downward percolation of soil water. Soils therefore develop a *leached* quality, and fertility declines. Throughout the purely coniferous areas of the Boreal forest, soils are heavily leached. They are correspondingly infertile for crops.

- 19. Define and explain the following terms: **pedocal, pedalfer, chenozem, podzol, percolation, leaching.**

- 20. On the basis of *first principles,* suggest what different soils might be expected to exist in the Cordillera region, and explain how they would relate to variations in climate and vegetation.

Water gets into the soil from precipitation, either by rain or by melted snow. Left to itself it will soak down under gravity, but if the climate is dry and hot the water will be drawn upwards out of the soil to the surface, where it will be evaporated.

Pedalfers: ped = soil; al = aluminum; fer = iron.

*Leached* refers to soils that have had the fertile humus and lime washed out of them by strongly and persistently downward percolating water.

*First principles* is a term used to describe an approach to a problem which relies solely upon a knowledge of what *ought* to happen when certain conditions exist.

# CHAPTER 3

# THE PHYSICAL LANDSCAPE OF CANADA, Part I

## GLOBAL VIEW

The physical landscape is the sort of landscape that would exist if *all* traces of living matter were removed, or had never existed. Thus it takes no account of plants or animals any more than it does of the works of humans.

For instance, you are probably thinking of several examples of river valleys that have been put to crop or grazing use, such as the St. Lawrence Valley, the Grand River Valley, the Fraser Valley, the Red River Valley, and so on. Can you think of any examples of marshes that have been drained and farmed? And how about mountains with tunnels through them?

The physical landscape is the sort of landscape that would exist if the results of people's activities were completely removed — or had never even existed. It consists of the mountains and plains, the marshes and the river valleys, the coastal cliffs and the bays, the icy snowfields and the rocky wastes.

In many parts of the world the physical landscape has been heavily used by the people who live there. River valleys have been ploughed up or used as grazing land; many have had towns or villages built in them. Marshes have been drained and farmed; mountains have been riddled with transportation tunnels and mine shafts; even icy snowfields have become the centres of varied tourist attractions.

All these things have happened in Canada too, but not to the same extent as in many other parts of the world. You can probably think of many parts of Canada that have hardly been worked by people at all, or at least where there is no sign of human activity. On the other hand, of course, there are some parts of Canada that show signs of human activity as great as in any other place in the world.

● 1. In not more than one page describe some of the parts of Canada that you would expect had received very little attention from people, and are therefore still largely in their natural state. Include an explanation of why you think people have left these areas in their natural state.

● 2. The landscape that people have created — the towns, villages, fields, factories, etc. — is called the *cultural landscape,* to distinguish it from the natural physical landscape. In not more than one page describe the cultural landscape of the area in which you live. Note in your answer whether any of

48

the natural physical landscape is very visible. It is there, of course: underneath things made by people. But how much of it shows through? Have people and their works completely covered it?

Examine Figure 3-1. It shows the chief divisions of Canada's physical landscape. How many divisions are there? Can you see if there is any sort of order or pattern to the divisions?

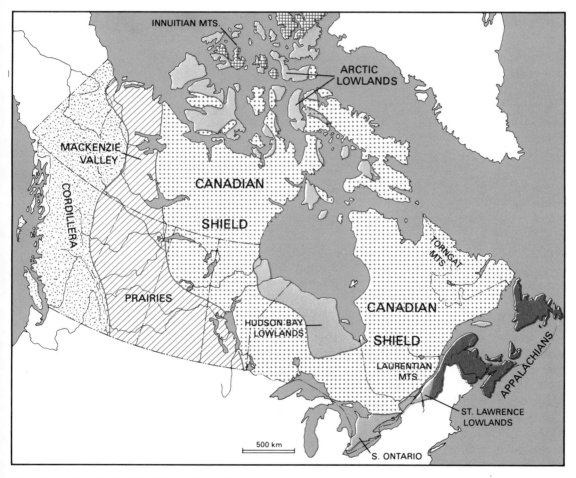

**Figure 3-1   The Physical Divisions of Canada**

The order arises from the pattern, as follows. The Canadian Shield comes *first,* because it is the oldest. Then comes a series of lowlands, namely

> the Prairies
> the Mackenzie Valley
> the Arctic Lowlands
> the Ontario Lowlands, and
> the St. Lawrence Lowlands

These all come *second* because they are the second oldest in formation after the Shield. *Finally,* come the outer mountain regions which almost surround Canada, namely

> the Appalachians
> the Innuitians, and
> the Cordillera systems.

If you have followed the order on the map in Figure 3-1 you will have realized that the landscape divisions of Canada fall into a very simple, though incomplete, pattern. It is something like an onion with three different layers. In the centre lies the Canadian Shield; around it lie several lowlands; then around the outside edge lie mountains (except in the south, near the U.S. border).

## A: THE CANADIAN SHIELD

This region contains some of the oldest rocks in the world. They are about 3.3 billion years old. Not all the rocks in the Shield are that old however. Some of the rock is only about one billion years old, especially in the eastern parts of Quebec. Even just one billion years is *old,* however, because most of the rocks in the world are much younger than that.

Because it is so old the Shield is often said to be composed of *Precambrian* rocks (Figure 3-2). Precambrian is a word indicating the age of the rocks: you can see from Figure 3-2 that the ages indicated by Precambrian are from approximately 600 million years ago to about 3800 million years ago. This last age (3.8 billion years ago) represents the earth's oldest rocks, which may be found in parts of Greenland. Canada's oldest rocks — in the Shield — are about 3.3 billion years old, as we have already seen.

The rocks are mainly different types of *granite* and *gneiss.* These are examples of *igneous* and *metamorphic* rocks. Igneous means rocks that were formed by cooling from a molten state, while metamorphic means rocks that have been changed from one type to another by means of either great pressure or great heat. Igneous and metamorphic both fit in with the great age of the Shield: igneous because the very first rocks would be formed as the earth's

There are several ways to spell Mackenzie: sometimes it has a capital *K,* as in Mac-Kenzie, and at other times it has no *a,* as in McKenzie. However, the *only correct* way to spell Mackenzie Valley is with a small *k* and an included *a.*

We have already seen how the names of many of Canada's landform features have been taken from actual people; the Mackenzie Valley is an example, and so is Hudson Bay. The name *Innuitians* comes from the name given to themselves by the Eskimos. They call themselves the *Inuit,* which means *people.* The mountains in the High Arctic are named after the *people.*

A great length of time, such as 3.8 billion years, is very difficult to comprehend. It may be just a little easier to think of if you can imagine each second in a single day lasting for 120 years; then all the seconds in a day would be worth 3.8 billion years. What proportion of the final second of the day would your life be worth?

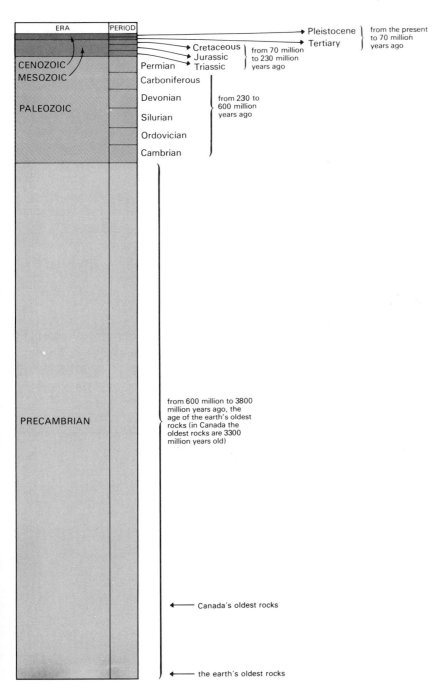

**Figure 3-2   Geological Time**

There are hundreds of different sorts of rocks, but broadly they fall into three major classes: igneous, sedimentary, and metamorphic.

crust cooled and became solid rock, and metamorphic because during the great age that has passed since the oldest rocks were formed there has clearly been plenty of opportunity for earth movements to produce pressures which would change the already existing rock.

The surface appearance of the Shield shows certain characteristics. Foremost among these is the uneven rocky nature of the land (Figure 3-5). The Shield may be quite low lying, as in its southern parts; or it may be quite mountainous, as in the east (Torngat Mountains) and southeast (Laurentian Mountains). But in all parts it is rocky and uneven. This surface irregularity is a major feature of the Shield, and it causes another common characteristic, namely many lakes and swamps (Figure 3-6).

For the location of the Torngats and Laurentians see Figure 3-1.

The chief features (uneven surface plus many lakes and swamps) can be seen on Topographic Map #1 (Figure 3-4). The writing on the map points out the chief features.

### Contour Glossary

Contours are lines on topographic maps which represent height and indicate the shape of the land surface. The numbers on the lines indicate the elevation in metres above sea level. The difference in elevation between one contour and the next is always the same for a given map. It is usually 7.5 or 15 m.

Some of the more common shapes are illustrated below.

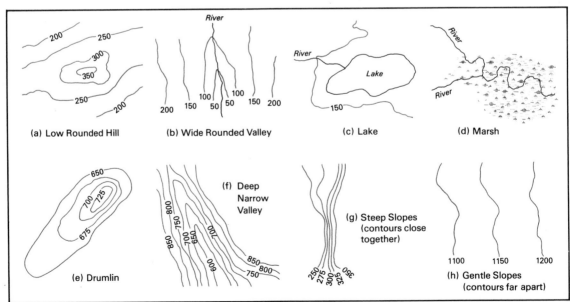

(a) Low Rounded Hill     (b) Wide Rounded Valley     (c) Lake     (d) Marsh

(e) Drumlin     (f) Deep Narrow Valley     (g) Steep Slopes (contours close together)     (h) Gentle Slopes (contours far apart)

**Figure 3-3   Contour Glossary**

**Figure 3-4   Topographic Map #1**

For legend for Topographic Maps, see Appendix A, p. 344.

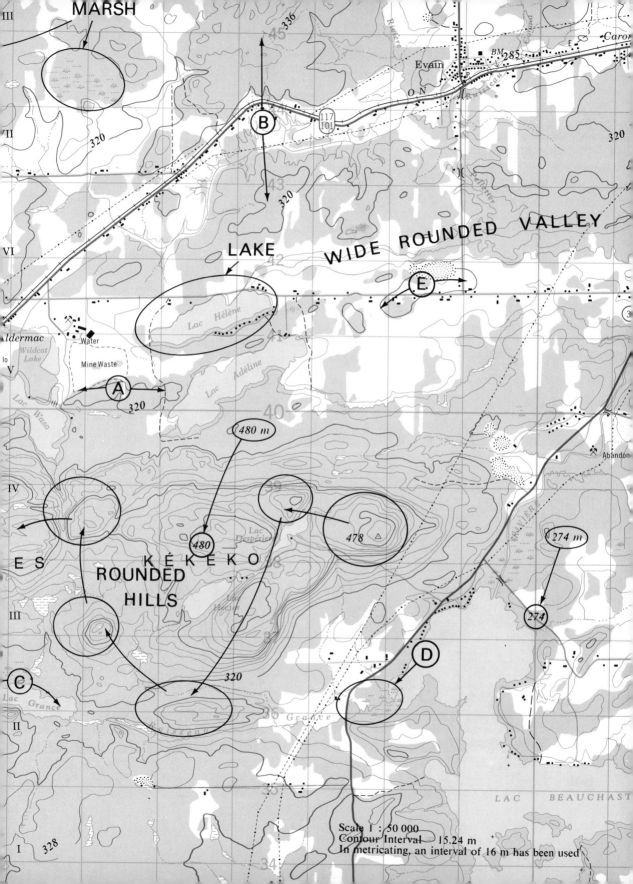

MARSH

III

45
336

III

River

Caron

Evain

BM 285

ON

E

Caron

II

320

B

117
101

320

320

Water

VI

LAKE

WIDE ROUNDED VALLEY

42

320

ldermac

lo

Wildcat
Lake

V

Mine Waste

Lac Hélène

E

Lac Adéline

A

320

40

480 m

IV

480

Lac Despérie

478

274 m

ES

KÉKEKO

ROUNDED

III

HILLS

274

Lac
Hector

Riviere

Abandon

C

Lac
Grance

320

D

II

Boisseau

Grance

I

328

34

LAC BEAUCHAST

Scale 1 : 50 000
Contour Interval 15.24 m
In metricating, an interval of 16 m has been used

All lakes in the world are in the process of being filled in. They are being filled in by sediments brought into them by rivers, or washed in by rainwater; they may also be being filled in by vegetation which grows in them; or they may be evaporating in a hot dry region. In Canada, most lakes are being filled in by sediments brought by rivers. In time, as a lake becomes filled with sediment, it turns into marsh, and then eventually into dry land.

Examine the topographic map very carefully, using the Contour Glossary to help you. Notice that the map shows part of a low lying area of the Shield rather than a mountainous part; you should realize that this is about as flat as the Shield can be. But as you can see, it is not very flat at all. Instead there are low rounded hills every few kilometres, and several small lakes and marshes where lakes have been filled in. You cannot see that it is very rocky; but then a topographic map would not often show you that. Figure 3-5 does, though.

- 3. Look back in this section, and answer the following questions:
  - (a) What is the name of the region under study?
  - (b) What is the geological age of the region?
  - (c) What are the chief types of rock in the region?

- 4. Using the Contour Glossary to help you, name the types of landforms which exist at letters A, B, C, D, and E on Topographic Map #1 on page 53.

- 5. Using *both* Figures 3-5 and 3-6 together *with* Topographic Map #1 write a description of the general appearance of the Shield. Give explanations and examples wherever possible. Do not write more than one page.

**Figure 3-5**   Uneven and rocky land near Mica Bay, Ontario.

**Figure 3-6**   Canadian Shield north of Sioux Lookout, Ontario.

## B: WESTERN AND NORTHERN LOWLANDS

Refer to the map of landscape regions in Figure 3-1 and notice that where the Shield's surface edges are located on land there are always lowlands next to the Shield — never any mountains, always lowlands. The Torngats and Laurentians do not count of course: they are part of the Shield, *in it* rather than outside it.

To the west you have the Prairies, to the northwest the Mackenzie Valley, and to the north the Arctic Lowlands. To the south you have Southern Ontario, towards Hudson Bay you have the Hudson Bay Lowlands, and to the southeast you have the St. Lawrence Valley. All that adds up to six separate lowland areas around the edges of the Shield, and not a single region of mountains. Indeed the mountains are all farther out from the Shield. In order to get to the mountains from the Shield you would always have to cross an area of lowland.

Surrounding the Shield then are several lowland areas. These were all formed *after* the Shield, and are mostly of *Paleozoic* age (see Figure 3-2 again). They are composed of layers (*strata*) of rock which were deposited as sediments in the seas which once surrounded the Shield. During the times when the Shield was all of Canada, namely, in Precambrian times, the surface of the Shield was constantly being worn away (*eroded*) by rivers and winds, and the eroded rock was being carried out to sea and deposited as layers of sediment (Figure 3-7).

*Paleozoic is a word describing the age of rocks which means ancient life: the paleo part means ancient, and zoic refers to life (as in zoo). The very earliest rocks in the world contained no life at all, in other words there are no fossils. An examination of Figure 3-2 shows that there was no life on earth for most of earth's history. Can you tell when the very first signs of life began to appear on earth?*

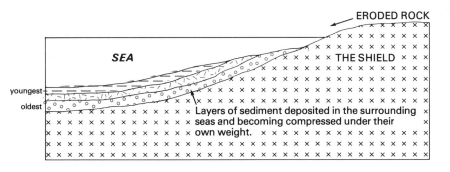

**Figure 3-7   Formation of Sedimentary Rocks**

In time the surrounding seas disappeared, leaving the compressed sediments exposed as *sedimentary rock*. Fossils may be found in these rocks. They tell us that the strata belong mostly to the Paleozoic age. Special examples of fossils in these rocks are the so-called *fossil fuels* (namely coal, oil and natural gas), which exist in all the surrounding lowlands except the St. Lawrence Valley.

*Fossils are the remains of any previously living matter which might now be buried in the rocks. Coal, for example, is the compressed remains of former forests and swamps.*

Coral is a fossil rock: it is composed of the remains of former animal life. Indeed, some coral, in some parts of the world today, may still be living. Coral is formed from the shells of tiny organisms called *polyps*. In order to survive, coral polyps require salt water which is both shallow and free of sediment, as well as a temperature of at least 20°C. These conditions are met today in tropical waters such as the Caribbean and the South Pacific. The existence of coral reefs buried many metres below the surface of the Prairies indicates that at one time this part of Canada must have had a climate very similar to that of the Caribbean or South Pacific.

The term *Prairie Mountains* is used to describe any of the rather low hills that stick up above the otherwise fairly level prairie plains. None of the Prairie Mountains would be called mountains anywhere else than a very flat region.

Don't forget that *all* lakes are in the process of disappearing for one reason or another.

## The Prairies

The Paleozoic rocks of the Prairies slope down gently towards the west. The strata are only very gently folded, and in amongst them are the remains of old coral reefs that existed there when warm seas used to cover the area in Devonian times (Figures 3-2 and 3-10). On top of the Paleozoic rocks in Alberta and Saskatchewan there are additional strata of much younger and more recent rocks. These extra layers are of *Cretaceous* age. (See Figures 3-2 and 3-10 again).

The very gentle slope of the strata favours the development on the surface of large areas of fairly level ground. This gives the Prairies their special character of a very open region, and it also favours the growth of farming and of transportation systems. Because some of the strata are much harder than others, the surface is not completely flat. The harder and more resistant strata stick out on the surface, forming ridges of hills, such as the Manitoba Escarpment. The Missouri Coteau forms another set of "Prairie Mountains" across Saskatchewan and Alberta (Figure 3-10). The steep sides of these ridges of hills all face eastwards towards the Shield. Towards the west, behind the hills, the land rises up towards the Rockies in Alberta, so that whereas the Manitoba Lowland is only 250 m above sea level the High Plains of Alberta are as much as 1000 m above sea level. The land rises in three great steps: the lowest is the Manitoba Lowland in the east, the next up is the Saskatchewan Plain, and the top level is the High Plains of Alberta (Figure 3-11).

The buried coral reefs are important because they are the location of most of the oil drilled out of Alberta and Saskatchewan. They hold vast quanties of oil trapped inside the holes (*pores*) in the rock, rather like water may be held inside a sponge.

In addition, the coral reefs provide evidence that at one time the climate of the region used to be much warmer than it is now. One of the results of that former warmth is that in some places, especially Saskatchewan, the lakes and shallow seas of the past often dried up under the hot sun. When this happened the minerals which had been dissolved in the water were left behind after the water had evaporated. Such mineral deposits are called *evaporites,* and they mark the location of former lakes and shallow seas which dried up. The most important type of evaporite deposit in Saskatchewan is *potash,* which is one of the three main types of rock fertilizer in the world, the others being phosphorous and nitrate. Saskatchewan's deposits of potash are amongst the largest in the world.

Figure 3-8 Note how the flat prairie land favours farming and road building.

Some of the famous lakes that are in the process of drying up at the present time are the Dead Sea and the Great Salt Lake. The Dead Sea is so called because the water is now so salty that it cannot support any aquatic life. Salt lakes have existed in various places at various times (as in Saskatchewan in the past), but one of the best known of recent times was Lake Bonneville in Utah, which has now completely dried up, leaving Bonneville Salt Flats as its only trace. The Salt Flats at Bonneville are so flat and so large that the world's land speed record attempts are regularly held there.

The Cretaceous rocks which lie over the Paleozoic rocks in Alberta and Saskatchewan mark the existence of a more recent sea. Indeed it was the last sea to cover this area. In the Cretaceous deposits there are also vast deposits of oil. One of the largest of

Figure 3-9 The high plains of Alberta.

these deposits (and one of the largest oil deposits in the world) is the Alberta Oil Sands. They are also known as the Alberta Tar Sands because the oil is so thick that it is more like tar than oil. It is also mixed in with loose sand, so that it is not possible to obtain it in the same way as normal oil is obtained. Also in the Cretaceous rocks are the remains of dinosaurs, for it was in the swamps at the edges of these Cretaceaus seas in Alberta that the dinosaurs lived and died.

*Calgary has a park with models of giant dinosaurs. It is called Dinosaur Park.*

In summary, the gentle slopes help to form the flat land; the harder strata form the Prairie Mountains; the buried coral reefs trap the oil and form the evidence for a previous hot climate; the once hot climate caused the formation of the present potash deposits; and the Cretaceous rocks are responsible for the Oil Sands and the dinosaurs.

**Figure 3-10    Diagrammatic Representation of the Prairies**

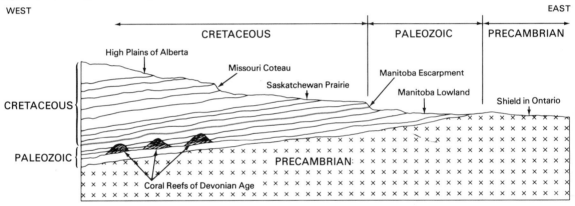

**Figure 3-11    Simplified Cross Section of the Prairies**

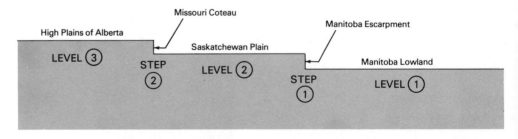

## The Mackenzie Valley

The differences between the Prairies and the Mackenzie Valley lie in land use, climate, and river drainage rather than in underground rock formations. The rocks are broadly similar to those in Alberta, except that they contain less oil. Nevertheless, they do contain *some* oil. The surface landscape, however, is quite different: the climate is harsher this far north and therefore farming is not practised. Instead the land supports vast quantities of forest. The river drainage is also different. In the Prairies the rivers flow eastwards, down towards Manitoba and eventually into Hudson Bay. In the Mackenzie Valley, on the other hand, the drainage is northwards, down towards the Arctic Ocean. Alexander Mackenzie spent a long time trying to reach the Pacific, as you know, but his main hope (the river named after him) flowed only into the Arctic Ocean.

### The Arctic Lowlands

The rocks are sedimentary in type and Paleozoic in age. In other words, they are identical in character with the rocks of the Prairies and the Mackenzie Valley. And, just like the others, they also slope gently away from the Shield (Figure 3-14). And again — like the Prairies and the Mackenzie Valley — the strata contain gas and oil. The Canadian Government is very interested in the gas and oil in the Arctic and accordingly owns nearly half an oil company which operates "down north". The oil company is called *Panarctic Oil.*

The first oil ever drilled in the Canadian northland was drilled at a place called Norman Wells in the Mackenzie Valley.

Indeed, Alexander Mackenzie initially called his river the *River of Disappointment.* Nowadays, however, people are pleased that it flows into the Arctic, for it not only brings relatively warm southern water into the Arctic region, but it also acts as a great artery of transportation between the north and the rest of the country.

**Figure 3-12**   Oil and gas extraction in Alberta. This is the Pincher Creek gas plant.

**Figure 3-13**   Drilling for oil and gas in the Arctic.

One of the reasons that the Canadian government is so keen to take part in northern oil exploration is that it thereby generates a Canadian *presence* in the Arctic. This is important, remember, because the Arctic regions could well be claimed by other countries if Canada does not appear to either want them or use them.

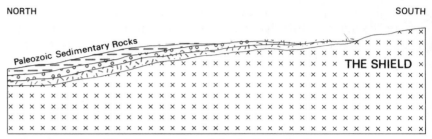

Figure 3-14   Simplified Cross Section of the Arctic Lowlands

• 6. Name the six lowland areas that are located around the edges of the Shield.

• 7. Write brief notes (two or three sentences each) to describe and explain:
   (a) Prairie Mountains
   (b) Evaporite
   (c) Two sources of oil in the Prairies

• 8. Refer to Topographic Map #2 on page 61.
   (a) What do you think the figure 506 means at point A? And the 578 at point B?
   (b) The figure at point C is a contour height in metres. Refer back to the text in this section and decide which of the three Prairie steps this region belongs to.
   (c) What is the difference in height between points C and D (in metres)?
   (d) What is the difference in height between points D and E (in metres)?
   (e) Write a description of the land you would cross if you travelled along the line between points F and G.
   (f) Using the information from the previous answers in this assignment say how you would describe this landscape to a stranger.
   (g) Point H identifies the intersection of two roads. What single word best describes the majority of roads in this entire area?
   (h) At points J and M there are differences in the roads from your answer to part (g). What are these differences? Can you explain them?

Figure 3-15   Topographic Map #2

For legend for Topographic Maps, see Appendix A, p. 344.

A

G Bethune 578
P

E D
557
Disley
M

608

506

J

576
Microwave 61

Microwave 46

BUFFALO POUND
PROV PARK

202

H

608

Rocky L

Stony Beach
Lake

F 301

lbeck

608

Stony
Beach 1906
Keystown
CANADIAN 1899 NATIC

Settling Beds

Eastview

Microwave
50
1915 CANADIAN PACIFIC 1891
P Po
Trans-Canad

Burdick

Microwave
91

Belle Plaine

Pasqua

39

Stelcam

Slow

339
P Drinkwater

B

C

Baildon

Scale 1 : 250 000
Contour Interval = 30.48 m
In metricating, an interval of 32 m has been used

Pitman 578

## C: THE ONTARIO LOWLANDS

The Ontario Lowlands (southern Ontario and the Hudson Bay Lowlands) are similar to those we have already looked at. The rocks are Paleozoic sedimentaries and the slope of the strata is away from the Shield.

An additional point of similarity in southern Ontario is the Niagara Escarpment, which faces the Shield in just the same way as the Manitoba Escarpment does. The Niagara Escarpment (Figure 3-16) is made of a resistant limestone called *dolomite*. Its existence — just like the Manitoba Escarpment — divides the region into different levels. In southern Ontario there are two levels: the lower one lying north and east of the escarpment and the higher one lying south and west of the escarpment (Figure 3-17).

Dolomite is known chemically as $CaMg(CO_3)_2$. It occurs in several parts of the world, and it takes its name from a mountainous area in northern Yugoslavia and Italy called the *Dolomites*.

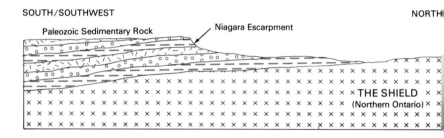

SOUTH/SOUTHWEST

NORTH

Paleozoic Sedimentary Rock    Niagara Escarpment

THE SHIELD
(Northern Ontario)

**Figure 3-16    Cross Section of the Niagara Escarpment**

**Figure 3-17    The Niagara Escarpment**

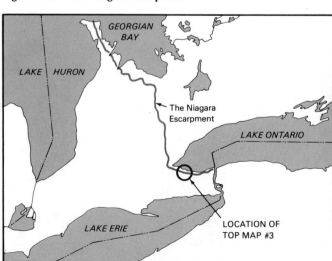

GEORGIAN BAY

LAKE HURON

The Niagara Escarpment

LAKE ONTARIO

LAKE ERIE

LOCATION OF TOP MAP #3

Yet another point of similarity between southern Ontario and the western and northern lowlands is that the Paleozoic rocks also contain oil. Indeed the very first oil well ever drilled anywhere in the world was drilled in southern Ontario — in 1857, at Oil Springs near Sarnia. Some oil is still obtained from these oil fields, but there is not much left now.

To add still further to the similarities between southern Ontario and the western and northern lowlands you should know that there are also very large evaporite deposits in southern Ontario, just like the potash deposits in Saskatchewan. The evaporites of southern Ontario are mostly salt, found in the Windsor and Goderich districts.

If you turn to the northern Ontario lowlands — called the Hudson Bay Lowlands — you will find that they are also made of Paleozoic rocks which dip northwards away from their surface contact with the Shield in the same manner as the rocks of the Arctic Lowlands (see Figure 3-14).

However, there are no escarpments in northern Ontario. The slope of the rock is so gentle, the deposits are so thin, and the land is so low lying that the harder strata do not stand out. Instead the landscape is almost flat, with a great deal of swamp. The swamp is called *muskeg*.

As far as fossil fuels in northern Ontario are concerned, there is only soft coal. There are drilling rigs in Hudson Bay looking for oil and natural gas, but the search has not yielded any new discoveries. So far soft coal is the only thing; it marks those areas where former swamps existed.

There is some dispute about the date and location of the very first oil well. This is partly because there is some dispute over what a well actually is. Is it merely a hole dug into the ground? Or is it a drilled cylindrical hole? Or what? The Oil Springs hole was a drilled cylindrical hole, and thus qualifies under the most stringent tests. Nevertheless, there are competing claims that the first oil well was drilled in Pennsylvania in 1858.

Muskeg is swampland with a few scattered trees, mostly *tamarack* and *black spruce*. It is the home and breeding ground for countless billions of mosquitoes.

- 9. Refer to Topographic Map #3 on page 64.
    - (a) What is the height in metres at A? and at B?
    - (b) Look at the contour glossary again. What type of landscape stretches between points M and N?
    - (c) What actual real name is given to the feature identified in your answer to part (b)?
    - (d) What single word best describes the majority of the roads in levels A and B? Compare this word with the one you chose for the Prairie roads in your answer to assignment 8 (g).
    - (e) Can you explain why the roads at points L and P are different from those you have just described?

- 10. Use *sentences and diagrams* to show all the features that the lowland regions so far studied have *in common*.

- 11. Write down the *differences* that exist among all the lowland regions studied so far.

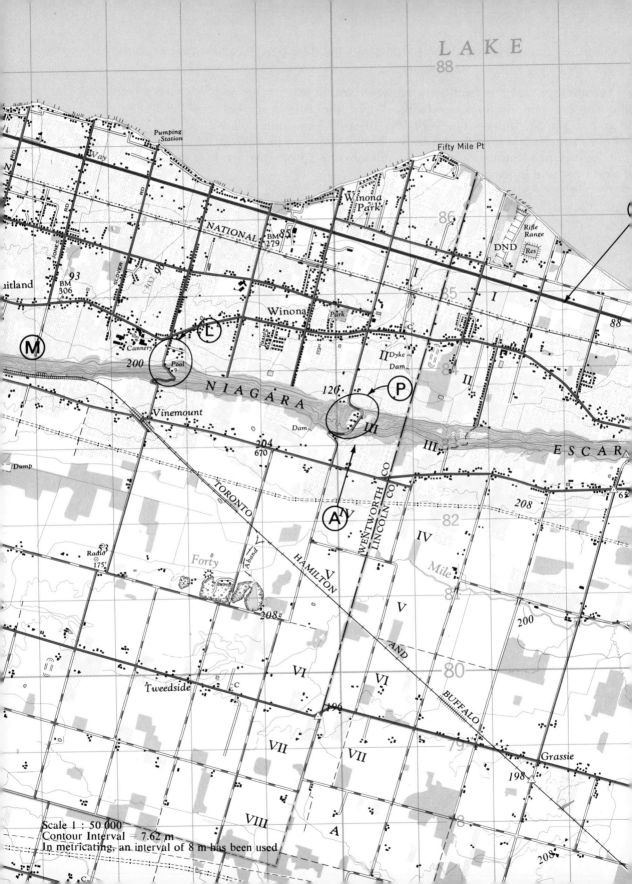

# CHAPTER 4

# THE PHYSICAL LANDSCAPE OF CANADA, Part II

## GLOBAL VIEW

You may wonder why the break is after six and not after five, since there are ten regions altogether. However, the group of six in Chapter 3 includes many that are alike, whereas the remaining four are all quite different from one another. So let us continue. You will remember that we were dealing with the several lowland regions around the surface edges of the Shield. The next and last of these lowlands is:

## A: THE ST. LAWRENCE LOWLANDS

This is a different sort of lowland from the others. The chief difference is its structure. Like all other lowland regions it consists of rocks of the Paleozoic and Mesozoic eras (see Figure 3-2 again), but the edge of the Shield along the northern side of the St. Lawrence Lowlands is very steep and rugged. Indeed the edge of the Shield here marks the existence of great cracks or fractures (called *faults*) in the crust of the earth. Since the southern edge of the St. Lawrence Lowlands also lies up against the steep faulted northern edge of the Appalachians, the whole St. Lawrence Valley is therefore an example of a *rift valley,* or a valley between two faults (Figure 4-1).

The upper deposits within the rift valley date chiefly from after the melting of ice during the Ice Age. After the ice had melted, the sea flooded into the rift valley, occupying the area between the Shield and the Appalachians. This sea was called the *Champlain Sea,* and into it were swept sediments from both the Shield and the Appalachians. After the sea had been pushed back by the rising land, these sediments (now compressed under their own weight) emerged to form the rocks of the St. Lawrence Low-

It was not called the Champlain Sea at that time, of course, because no one lived in the area then. And neither had Champlain been born.

**Figure 3-18   Topographic Map #3**                65

For legend for Topographic Maps, see Appendix A, p. 344.

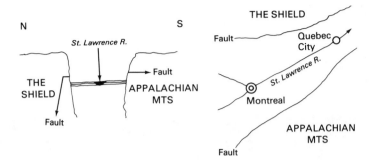

**Figure 4-1   St. Lawrence Valley Faults**

It is quite common to get igneous rocks protruding from inside the earth's crust, especially in areas which have fractures or faults. The East African Rift Valley, for example, has volcanoes; so it is not surprising that the St. Lawrence Valley has the Monteregian Hills.

lands. The surface land is therefore very flat indeed, almost as flat as the surface of a sea. But it is not *all* flat.

There are in fact several mountains: just little ones, but mountains all the same. The mountains are scattered, some in the Montreal area and some farther east. These mountains — collectively called the *Monteregian Hills* — are all of igneous origin. It is most likely that they were at one time formed *inside* the earth's crust, although close to the surface, and that erosion has since stripped off the less resistant rock strata that used to cover them (Figure 4-2).

**Figure 4-2   Origin of the Monteregian Hills (Mountains)**

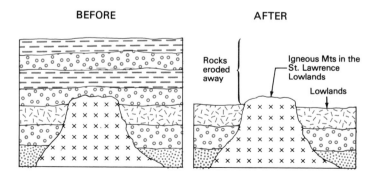

● 1. Refer to Topographic Map #4 on page 68.
  (a) Which contour line do you think separates the mountain from the lowland?
  (b) The lowland has been eroded away. What height do you think it might once have had?
  (c) What is the difference in height between points A and B?
  (d) Are points A and B in the mountain or the lowland?
  (e) Write a few sentences describing the differences in probable appearance between the mountain and the lowland. It is *not enough* to say that the mountain is mountainous and that the lowland is fairly flat. Ask yourself whether the slopes are steep or gentle, whether the mountain is large or small, and whether the lowland has any valleys in it.

# B: THE OUTER MOUNTAINS

### The Appalachians

The Appalachians are the main mountain system of the whole of eastern North America. They stretch all the way south to Georgia (Figure 4-6). The Canadian portion of the Appalachians occupies the Gaspé Peninsula of Quebec together with all parts of the Atlantic Provinces except Labrador. The rocks are chiefly Paleozoic in age, and sedimentary and igneous in type. They were crumpled by earth movements to form a range of mountains at the end of the Paleozoic era and since then they have been worn down so that there are now no high mountains left. Instead there are low rolling hills and broad, nearly flat valleys (Figure 4-7). Mixed in with these are extensive areas of roughly rounded low plateau, marking the existence of masses of igneous rock (mostly granite) which have been exposed by erosion.

During the Ice Age the whole region was pressed down by the weight of the ice which covered the area. Since the Ice Age the ice has melted, thus causing the sea level to rise. The land, however, has not yet fully *rebounded* to its original level. Parts of the Appalachian region are therefore still under the sea. The parts that are under the sea are obviously those that were lowest to start with — such as the mouths of rivers, the lower ends of valleys, and low lying basins and hollows (Figure 4-7). Figure 4-8 shows very clearly the general appearance of the drowned coast of the Appalachian region. You can see at point A the roughly rounded igneous rock which still stands out as hilly ground. Point B shows an area where the sea has flooded in over the lower end of a valley, now forming a sheltered bay, while point C shows an example of the rocky nature of much of the coast.

It is also quite common for masses of igneous rock to be incorporated into the folds of a fold mountain system. When the strata are disturbed to the extent that they are in a mountain building period, then the unsettled nature of the crust permits large masses of molten rock from the interior to spread upwards and become trapped in the folds of the crustal rock.

The earth is not solid, even though it may appear to be. The crustal rocks are fairly solid, but underneath them the rock is much more fluid. The fairly fluid rocks under the crust are called the *mantle*, and it is quite possible to think of the continents as being like rafts floating on the fairly fluid (and heavier) rocks underneath. However, if the rocks of the crust have a great deal of extra weight put upon them, as by masses of ice, then they will be depressed a little into the fairly fluid mantle. And when the ice melts away, the crustal rocks will rebound upwards. The time scale for all this to happen is naturally a long one: indeed the rocks of Canada are still rebounding even though the ice melted away about 10 000 years ago.

Lumber Yard

231

20

le Déboulis

Motel

Theatre

269

III

II

16

107

49

Limite de la Ville de Beloeil

24

Waste Pits

Sugar Refinery

CANADIAN

229
116

Cement Plant

PETI

A

291

95

Beloeil

Police Station

Trans

C

Campsite

Orchard

Or

Arena

Golf Course

Hospital

Shopping Centre

Curling Rink

Town Hall

Town Hall

Trans

Marina

St-Hilaire Est Sta

Mont St-Hilaire

(St-Hilaire Est PO)

St-Hilaire Sta

C

40

Orchard

Or

Or

F 81

MONTAGNE DU BRÛLÉ

400

La Quenouillière

240

264

MONT ST-HILAIRE

LE PAIN DE SUCRE

400

216

400

136

Hospital

Lac Hertel

Orchard

26

100

sterville

Shopping Centre

Lumber Yard

18

BM

223

20

Or

Orchard

176

240

195
195
59

Jokers

Filtration Plant

Otterburn Park

Or

Nursery

Orchard

Or

Or

Orchard

80

Orchard

Or

68
5

chy

ILLE DE CHAMBLY
NTÉ DE ROUVILLE

187

158

48

RANG DES TRENTE

Orchard

Nursery

RANG DES ÉTANGS

Limite de la Ville de Mont-St-Hilaire

42

Or

431

Campsite Reservoir

Poultry Farm

32

PAROISSE DE ST-MATHIAS

456

B

Oil Pipeline

2 Lines

173

Ditch

I

Trail

229

Golf Course

Scale 1 : 50 000
Contour Interval — 7.62 m
In metricating, an interval of
8 m has been used

**Figure 4-4** Low, rolling hills and broad, flat valleys in the Appalachian region. This is the Matapedia Valley.

**Figure 4-5** Tiny fishing village of Petty Harbour, Newfoundland.

**Figure 4-3    Topographic Map #4**

For legend for Topographic Maps, see Appendix A, p. 344.

**Figure 4-6   Major Mountain Areas in North America**

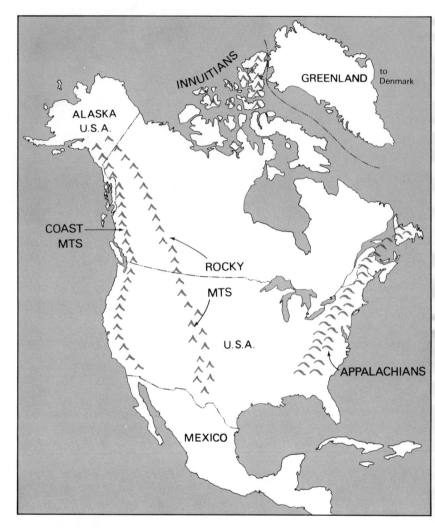

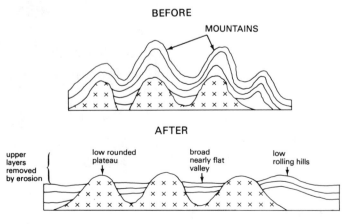

**Figure 4-7   The Appalachians**

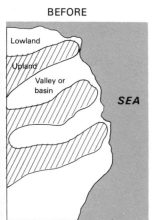
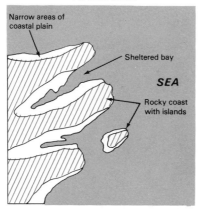

Figure 4-8 **Coastal Submergence (Drowning) in the Appalachian Region**

## The Innuitian Mountains

During the Mesozoic era (Figure 3-2) the rocks of the northern-most islands, especially those of Ellesmere Island, were folded up by earth movements into mountains. The folding and tilting of the rocks can be easily seen on the land — whenever it is not covered by snow — because there is no vegetation and no soil in these high latitudes. The Innuitian Mountains, as they are called, are very high. They reach up to about 3000 m. Because of their height and their closeness to the North Pole, the Innuitian Mountains are usually covered with snow. In many places there are permanent glaciers.

Mesozoic: meso = middle; zoic = life. Mesozoic is a term applied to the middle range of fossil ages, and the rocks which hold these fossils.

## The Cordillera

The cross section (Figure 4-9) gives you some idea of the variations within this last physical region. You can see that it is not uniform

You will remember from Chapter 2 that soil is formed from the mixing of shattered rock fragments with the remains of decayed vegetation. In the Innuitian region the lack of vegetation inhibits the development of soils; mostly the ground is covered with shattered rock fragments only.

Figure 4-9 **Cross Section of the Cordillera**

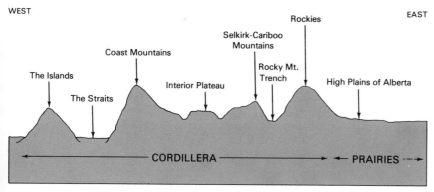

throughout. There are indeed several subsections within the main region. Let's take them one by one:

*The Islands*  The largest is Vancouver Island, but there are other groups farther north, chiefly the Queen Charlotte Islands, just south of the Alaska border. All the islands are quite mountainous.

*The Straits*  There is a narrow stretch of water separating the islands from the mainland. It marks the location of a great downfold (*syncline*) in the rocks, which has now been submerged by the sea. The straits have various names in different parts, but the best known are Juan de Fuca Strait and Georgia Strait. These are both shown in Figure 4-10.

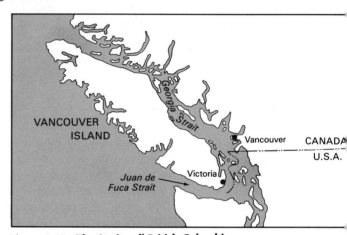

**Figure 4-10   The Straits off British Columbia**

Vancouver Island is named after Captain George Vancouver, an English sailor and explorer of the 18th century. He spent much time exploring the west coast of North America.

Grouse Mountain is a famous ski area, much used by people from Vancouver, which you can see as you ski down the slopes.

The most famous of the western canyons is the Fraser Canyon, cut by the Fraser River.

*The Coast Mountains*  These stretch all along the mainland coast from just north of Vancouver (at Grouse Mountain) to the main Alaska border at 142°W, where the highest mountain in Canada is located (Mount Logan, just over 6000 m). The Coast Mountains are all very high, averaging about 3000–4000 m. Even though they are cut into by numerous fiords, they still form a difficult barrier to cross. Figure 4-12 illustrates the general appearance of a fiord cut into the Coast Mountains.

*The Interior Plateaus*  Behind the Coast Mountains lies an extensive area of high plateau country. Several rivers drain through the plateaus and they have all cut quite deep valleys into the plateau surfaces. Some of the valleys are so deep and narrow that they are called *canyons* and *gorges*. Figure 4-13 shows you the typical appearance of a plateau canyon.

*The Selkirk-Cariboo Mountains*  These form the eastern or inland edge of the Interior Plateaus, opposite to the Coast Mountains. They are not so high as the Coast Mountains, but they are very rugged and they are as a result just as difficult to cross. Indeed, you may know about the tremendous difficulties the Can-

**Figure 4-11  Topographic Map #5**

For legend for Topographic Maps, see Appendix A, p. 344.

Scale 1 : 50 000
Contour Interval    7.62 m
In metricating, an interval of 8 m has been used

adian Pacific Railway faced when it was trying to find a route throughout these mountains in the 1880s, and about the surveyor, Rogers, who spent several years in the mountains before he finally found a way through (now called Rogers Pass).

*The Rocky Mountain Trench*   This is one of the curiosities of nature. It is a huge valley, caused by fracturing (*faulting*) of the rocks. It stretches from the 49th Parallel in the south all the way through British Columbia into the Yukon Territory. Many rivers flow along it before they eventually escape through gaps in the mountains at its sides: the Rockies to the east and the Selkirk-Cariboo to the west (Figure 4-17).

*The Rocky Mountains (The Rockies)*   You may be surprised to find that the Rockies are only part of the Cordillera. Many people think that all the western mountains are grouped together as the Rockies, but it is not so. From Figure 4-9 you can see that the Rockies are only the easternmost edge of the Cordillera, and not

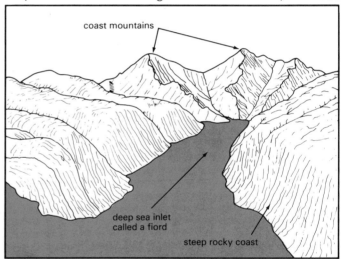

**Figure 4-12　A Fiord**

coast mountains

deep sea inlet
called a fiord

steep rocky coast

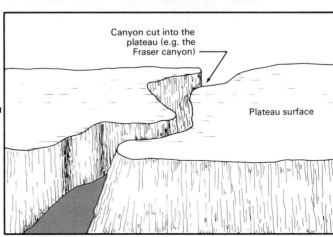

**Figure 4-13　A Canyon Cut into a Plateau**

Canyon cut into the
plateau (e.g. the
Fraser canyon)

Plateau surface

even the highest part at that. The highest mountain in the Canadian Rockies is Mount Robson, just under 4000 m. Compare this with Mount Logan in the Coast Mountains (how high?). Not only are the Rockies not the highest mountains but they are also not the most difficult of Cordillera mountains to cross. There are three major passes linking British Columbia and Alberta. Can you name them from Figure 4-19?

For comparison, the highest mountains in the world are Mount Everest at 8862 m, Godwin-Austin (K2) at 8625 m, and Kanchenjunga at 8612 m.

- 2. Refer to Topographic Map #5 on page 73.
    - (a) What do you notice about the size and shape of the coastal plain?
    - (b) What do you notice about the probable appearance of the land in area A (is it rounded, flat, hilly, steep, gently sloping, or what?)

- 3. Refer to Figure 4-14.
    - (a) Describe the sorts of landscape that are found at points R, S, and T.
    - (b) What type of landscape region is pictured in the photo?
    - (c) Can you think of the advantages this type of landscape might offer to the people who live there?
    - (d) What do you think the disadvantages to people might be? You should give examples of the ways in which the things you think of might act as disadvantages; for example, if the rocky land is thought of as a disadvantage, then you should say why the rocky land would be a disadvantage. Would it restrict farming? And so on.

**Figure 4-14** Farming-fishing village of Torbay, Newfoundland.

**Figure 4-15**   The Coast Mountains north of Vancouver.

**Figure 4-16**   The Fraser Canyon at Skihist.

**Figure 4-17**   Rogers Pass, discovered in 1882.

**Figure 4-18**   Spectacular scenery in the Rockies.

**Figure 4-19    The Rocky Mountains in Western Canada**

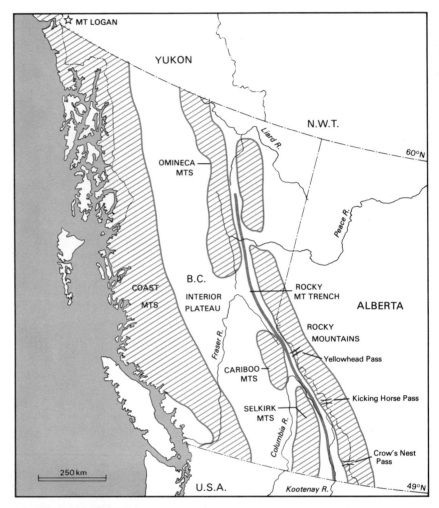

The Ice Age was not like a long lasting winter. Every year had its normal seasons of winter and summer, and during the summers the snow and ice would melt away a little. However, the summers were not warm enough to melt away the ice completely, and so every winter there would be a little more ice at the start and a little more again at the end. Over the years, therefore, the total amount of ice on the ground gradually accumulated into huge masses which became *glaciers*.

## C: GLACIATION

About 1 000 000 years ago the climate became colder. No one knows why. But the effect was to permit the winter snow to remain on the ground right through the summer, then being added to by more snow the following winter. Over the years the amount of snow which accumulated in this way became very large — and also very heavy. Under the weight of the snow in the upper layers the lower layers gradually turned to ice. In this way they eventually formed huge glaciers. The glaciers gradually covered the entire country, scraping and grinding their way out of the hills and mountains and out of the Northland. In time they covered all the lowlands.

In many places the glaciers scraped away *(eroded)* the soil and the softer rock, leaving behind bare rock and irregularly shaped hollows. Many parts of the Shield were glaciated in this way and the bare rock and the irregularly shaped hollows can still be seen. Look back at Figure 3-2 and Topographic Map #1 again, just to refresh your memory. After all, the ice only melted away about 10 000 years ago and that is not very long in geological time. The hollows now contain lakes in some places, but in other places the lakes have been filled in by marsh. Can you spot examples of these lakes and marshes in Topographic Map #1? The entire landscape shown in Topographic Map #1 is an example of what is called a *glacial abrasion surface*.

In the high mountains the glaciers did not cover all the land. Some of the highest peaks stood up prominently through the ice. Thus the effects of the glaciers in the mountains were slightly different than on the Shield. In the mountains the valleys were deepened and made into a *U-shape;* the spurs were also often sharpened into knife-like ridges called *arêtes;* another feature was the formation of large hollows called *cirques* in the sides of mountains. Figure 4-22 shows these features.

The very high peaks which stuck up through the ice are called *nunataks*.

When the ice eventually melted about 10 000 years ago it left behind a great amount of rock debris which had been scraped away from the ground somewhere else. The debris is called *till*. It is fairly hummocky, with lots of small oval shaped hills called *drumlins*. Often, however, there are long, low ridges of glacial material called *moraines*. Most of southern Ontario is covered by *till plains,* and there are some good examples of drumlins near

**Figure 4-20   Drumlins and Moraines in Southern Ontario**

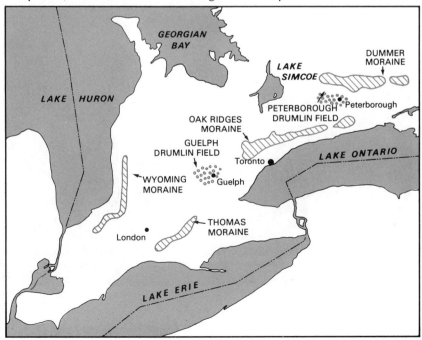

**Figure 4-21** Persistent, permanent ice. This is part of the great Columbia ice field in the Rockies.

both Peterborough and Guelph. Those near Peterborough in fact are world famous. Moraines stretch right across southern Ontario. from west to east, chiefly between London and Toronto.

**Figure 4-22** An aerial view looking down on Lake Louise, Alberta.

Figure 4-23  **Topographic Map #6**

For legend for Topographic Maps, see Appendix A, p. 344.

This fairly flat land is typical of a TILL PLAIN

**Figure 4-24** Flock of sheep grazing on farmland near Richmond, Ontario. In the distant background are some farm buildings. Note the old log fences surrounding the pasture.

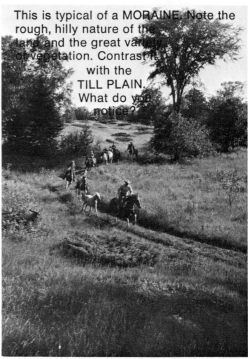

This is typical of a MORAINE. Note the rough, hilly nature of the land and the great variety of vegetation. Contrast it with the TILL PLAIN. What do you notice?

**Figure 4-25** A group of riders galloping through the countryside on the Frontier Ranch near Arnprior, Ontario.

● 4. Refer to Figure 4-26. What sort of landscape features are shown at points A, B and C?

● 5. In not more than about a page of writing say what you think are the problems that people would face in trying to live in the type of area shown in Figures 4-22 and 4-26. Say also what you think some of the ways are that people would use this type of area.

● 6. If the climate became colder again — as some people claim is happening — then what do you think the effects on Canada would be? Try not to write more than about a page, but include in your answer some mention of farming and some mention of where people live.

● 7. Refer to Topographic Map #6 on page 81.
   (a) What type of landscape do you think is shown on the map?
   (b) Identify the feature shown at point A.

**Figure 4-26**   In the Alberta Rockies.

• 8. Using the information in Chapters 3 and 4, try to write a few sentences to define or describe each of the following terms. You should use diagrams to help you, as well as actual examples, wherever you can.

(a) arête
(b) cirque
(c) Shield
(d) glacial abrasion surface
(e) Rocky Mountain Trench

(f) escarpment
(g) sedimentary rock
(h) fossil fuels
(i) moraine
(j) fiord

## CONCLUSION

Canada is certainly a country with an extremely varied physical landscape. It ranges from knife-edged mountains to featureless marsh, from great mountain ranges to vast tracts of flat prairie, from drowned coasts to exposed rocky plateaus, and from glacial abrasion surfaces to rounded hummocky till plains. It is a fascinating place, this Canada of ours.

# CHAPTER 5

# CANADA'S POPULATION
## CHANGE

## INTRODUCTION

The world's population is increasing by about 75-100 million per year. That's approximately 10 000 to 12 000 per hour.

The world's population is about 4.5 billion; Canada's population is just over 23 million.

As you read this single sentence the world's population will have increased by about 10–12 persons. That represents about 10 000 to 12 000 per hour: extra people, not extra babies; births minus deaths. About one in 200 will eventually live in Canada. Half of them may actually be born here, but the other half will probably come as immigrants.

Can you calculate from these figures just how many extra people Canada will gain each and every hour? Half will come from maternity hospitals across the country, and half will come by planes from various places around the world. Which way did you come?

Now, read the following article about the growth of Ontario's population, and answer the questions which follow it.

# Immigration From Abroad Seen Major Influence

Growth in Ontario's population from now on will be influenced more by immigration from other countries than by births in the province or by people moving to or from other provinces, according to a planning report tabled yes-terday by Treasurer Darcy McKeough.

The report pointed to several problems caused by the distribution of the province's population. Between 1951 and 1971, the percentage of the population living in the Hamilton-Toronto-Oshawa area increased from 36 per cent to 43 per cent; the number of people living in towns and cities grew from 73 per cent to 82 per cent in the same period. The total population of Ontario rose from 4.6-million to 7.7-

million in the 20-year period.

Four-fifths of those immigrating have settled in Central Ontario, particularly in Toronto, Ottawa and Hamilton the report said. Only a quarter of the people living in rural areas farm for a living, and in 1971 there were 130 000 of them, compared with 200 000 in 1951.

Most people (57 per cent of the labor force) now work in service industries, rather than producing goods—a reversal since 1951.

The federal Government's review of immigration policies "has opened the possibility that the flow of immigration to Canada may come to be varied to achieve desired rates of population growth," the report said.

Ontario's population will reach nearly 10 000 000 by 1986 and 12 000 000 by the year 2000, the report predicted.

What it all means is "inflated land and housing prices, heavy servicing costs, fiscal strains" in Southern Ontario, resulting from "an intense competition for land." Urban people are finding it "increasingly difficult and costly to reach uncrowded outdoor recreation areas."

Meanwhile, other areas are growing too slowly. In the north and east, particularly, there is "instability and even long-term decline" in the economy.

"As a result of the differences, there is a widen-

ing gap in social terms: in composition, population structure, and the intangibles collectively termed 'lifestyle,'" the report said.

"While total uniformity is certainly not a desirable objective, the emergence of an Ontario sharply divided in its identities, values, and concerns is not a prospect to be viewed with equanimity." The report said the province "does not by any means have a free hand in dealing with such problems," because growth is linked with "enormous capital investments."

The Government "can influence, but cannot dictate, where people choose to live," and the same is true of where companies choose to locate, the report said.

from the *Globe and Mail*, April 9, 1976

1. (a) By how many people did the population of Ontario increase in the 20-year period from 1951 to 1971?
   (b) What was the average increase in population per year?
   (c) If the rate of increase continues according to your answer above, what will Ontario's approximate population be in the year 1986? And in the year 2000?
   (d) What does the report predict that Ontario's population will reach by 1986? And by the year 2000?
   (e) There should be a slight difference between your calculated figure for 1986 and the report's predicted figure; there should be an even larger difference between the two figures for the year 2000. What do you deduce from the nature of these differences?

2. The report states that "only a quarter of the people living in rural areas farm for a living." What do you think the rest do?

- 3. The report also states that "most people now work in service industries, rather than producing goods." Can you give at least two reasons to explain how it is that we have even more goods produced now than we used to?

- 4. Can you describe at least two other things that the report states are happening in Ontario?

You will probably have realized by now that not only Ontario's but Canada's population is not the same as it used to be. The people do not live in the same places; they are not of the same ethnic origins; their numbers are very different; and they do different things for a living. These changes are taking place all the time. Even today, people are still changing the areas where they live, so that there are increasingly more in some places and fewer in others. The total number of people is also still changing. The ethnic composition of the population is not fixed for all time either. It has changed in the past, and it is changing still. And, as far as peoples' occupations are concerned, the pattern of so many engaged in farming and so many employed in factories is by no means established for the future. Like all the other aspects of population (*distribution, quantity,* and *composition*), the *employment* picture has changed considerably in the past, and is still changing. Let us have a closer look at all these four aspects in turn.

## A: CHANGES IN THE DISTRIBUTION OF POPULATION

The *distribution of population* means "which parts of the country support most people, and which parts support fewest people." In Canada, the parts which support most people *now* are not the same as those which used to support most people 100 or even 200 years ago. The parts of the country which are occupied and used by people are called the *ecumene.* You can see in Figure 5-1 that the area of the ecumene has not stayed the same throughout Canada's development. In 1871, just after Canada became a nation (Confederation was in 1867), the ecumene stretched over the Maritimes and through the St. Lawrence Lowlands into southern Ontario. Most of the West was fairly empty. There were some Indians in the West, and some Inuits in the North, but not many. The land was generally uninhabited. Figure 5-1 indicates that by 1911 there had been a great expansion of the ecumene into the Prairies and southern British Columbia. This is because the "opening up" of the Prairies occurred mainly in the first few years of this century (between 1901 and 1913). Since then there have not been any

The term *ethnic* refers to cultural qualities such as religion, language, history, and customs. It does not mean the same thing as *race.* The term *race* applies only to qualities which are passed on by heredity, such as shape of head, type of hair, colour of skin.

The word *ecumene* derives from a Greek word meaning *the inhabited world.*

The emptiness of the areas occupied by Indians and Eskimos can be gauged from the fact that their numbers were counted in thousands across the entire country. Their impact upon the environment was exceedingly small, partly because of their small numbers and partly because they lacked a sufficiently powerful technology. Thus to the Europeans it seemed as if the Indians and Eskimos made very little use of the land they occupied.

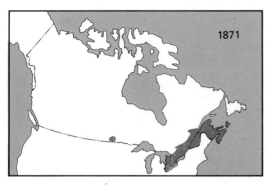

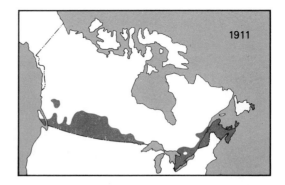

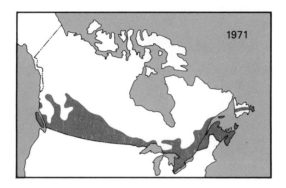

Figure 5-1  The Growth of Canada's Ecumene, 1871-1971

major changes, but if you look closely at the map for 1971 in Figure 5-1 you can probably see some differences in the ecumene between 1971 and 1911.

Within the ecumene the population is very unevenly scattered. You could travel through some parts of it and see very few people in one place. For example, some parts of Saskatchewan and British Columbia have very few people — perhaps a small settlement every 30–40 km, or maybe even farther. On the other hand, there are places within the ecumene which are so crowded with people that some local politicians claim that there should be no more additions. Parts of Toronto are like this. One of the problems in Canada today is indeed precisely this contrast: some places are fairly uninhabited while others are heavily populated. Do you remember what was reported in the article about the distribution of population in Ontario? Would it not seem logical for people in the populated areas to move to the fairly empty places, so as

The present day emptiness of parts of the land is attributable to the fact that in some places, e.g., interior British Columbia, people have not yet moved in, while in other places, e.g., southern Saskatchewan, people have already moved out.

**Figure 5-2**   The "opening up" of the Prairies. **Here,** new settlers move into south Saskatchewan in 1909.

There are arguments from some people that all immigrants ought to be forced to go and live in some of the empty areas; that they should be forbidden access to places such as Toronto that are considered to be already crowded.

One of Toronto's persistent problems under these conditions is the provision of enough accommodation for its residents. Part of the answer lies in more housing and more apartments, but part also lies in subdividing existing homes into rooms.

to even up the numbers in the different areas? However, it does not work that way! What seems to be happening is that people are leaving the empty places, thus reducing further those populations, and coming to live in the already populated places, thus making them even more crowded. (What sort of area do you live in — a sparsely or heavily populated one? Is that where you intend to live in the future?)

There are reasons for this apparently illogical behaviour by people. Fairly uninhabited places cannot offer as much in the way of social amenities such as theatres, stores, big league sports, and so on as populated places can. And for people who live in fairly empty places, the nearest doctor may be many hours' distance away. In a populated place, on the other hand, a doctor may be in the same block. Also, in a heavily populated area there are lots of different types of jobs to choose from, whereas in a sparsely populated one there may be only a small choice of jobs. It is for reasons like this (there are several others) that many people move from the relatively empty areas to those that are already heavily populated. Thus Toronto gains an *additional* 30 000–40 000 people a year, even though many people who live there think that it is already crowded enough.

The most densely populated places in Canada are the large towns and cities, particularly Montreal, Toronto, and Vancouver. Other towns such as Calgary and Halifax are also fairly crowded.

**Figure 5-3** Toronto . . . "places which are so crowded . . ."

These, then, are the places that are attracting the population, while the remoter areas of the countryside lose population. This process whereby people move from the countryside to the towns is called *urbanization*. It is a major movement in Canada. Figure

**Figure 5-4** Near Jasper: What sorts of jobs could there be in an empty place like this?

5-6 shows you how the country (rural) and town (urban) proportions have changed over the years.

Figure 5-6 is an example of a *multiple line graph*. A line graph shows you information by means of a line (as opposed to bars or circles). A *multiple line graph* is one that has two or more lines on it. In the case of Figure 5-6 the lines represent the rural percentage

**Figure 5-6    Rural-Urban Proportions, 1891-1971**

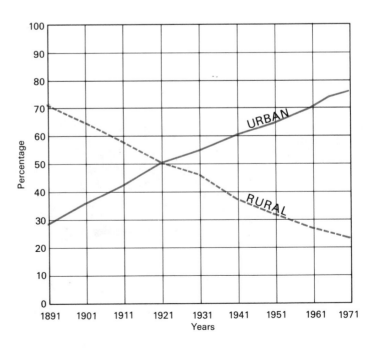

of Canada's population, and the urban percentage. You can see that the two situations have virtually been reversed. In 1891 over 70% of the population lived in the countryside, while in 1971 over 70% lived in the towns and cities. This trend of urbanization has not yet stopped. Some people are even forecasting that by the year 2000 perhaps 50% of Canada's entire population will live in just three metropolitan areas: Montreal, Toronto, and Vancouver, although Figure 5-7 suggests that the proportion is more likely to be about 40%, given the continuation of present trends.

This method of forecasting the future, i.e., projecting from past and present trends, is very commonly used, but it is not very accurate. Indeed, nothing is very accurate: we simply cannot predict the future by any means whatsoever. Nevertheless, it helps if we can get some idea of what might happen; so we project. However, bear in mind that such a projection does not guarantee that the projection will happen. It might be quite wrong, on either side.

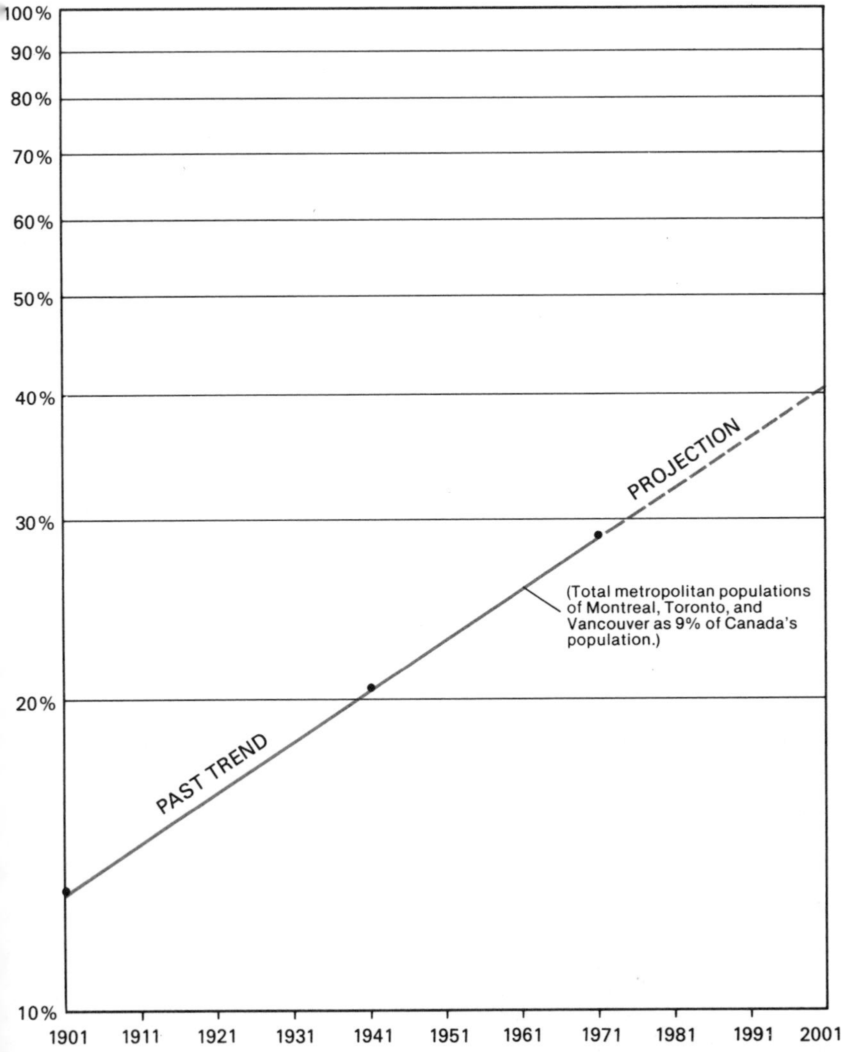

(Total metropolitan populations of Montreal, Toronto, and Vancouver as 9% of Canada's population.)

Figure 5-7   Total Metropolitan Populations of Montreal, Toronto, and Vancouver as a Percentage of Canada's Population

The first country to become urbanized was England. It was followed by other countries in northern Europe, notably Germany.

England was also the first country in the world to undergo an agricultural revolution and an industrial revolution. The urban revolution was the third of the great social revolutions of eighteenth and nineteenth century England.

The minimum number of people in a given area necessary to support the existence of a particular activity is called the *threshold population* for that activity. For example if it takes 1000 people to support an all-day milk store then the threshold population for a milk store is said to be 1000 people. In a city of 20 000 people there will likely be 20 milk stores, but in a rural area with villages of 200 people there will likely be a milk store in only every fifth village. How would you calculate what the threshold population for a high school with 1000 students would be?

The phenomenon of urbanization is not confined to Canada by any means. At one time or another it has affected several countries in the world, and it is beginning now to affect many more. By the end of this century it is doubtful if there will be any countries left that have not experienced some degree of urbanization. In relation to those countries which experienced urbanization earlier than Canada did, we can probably say that Canada's process of urbanization is in its final stages. The pattern appears to have been established in other countries that are already urbanized that a maximum percentage of about 85 characterizes the end stages of the process. By 1971 Canada had already reached a percentage of 76, as Figure 5-6 shows, and so does not have much farther to go. We can make these statements with a fair degree of confidence because urbanization has happened in other countries, and we can note their experiences. Further, urbanization is not an isolated process; it occurs in relation to other processes of change that are also at work, such as industrial economic development.

The relationship between urbanization and industrial economic development is relatively straightforward. As a society develops from an agricultural economy into an industrial economy there is a shift of people from the farms to the towns. One reason is that

**Figure 5-8**  Farming methods are now greatly improved in efficiency, and fewer farmers are therefore needed.

the methods of farming are greatly improved in efficiency (for example, more use of farm machinery), and therefore fewer people are needed. The second reason is that the growth of industry requires the availability of a large labour force and a large market in concentrated areas where factories can be built.

Urbanization has generated benefits and created problems in all areas where it has occurred. Among the benefits we should note are the gathering together of a substantial labour pool for the development of mass production, and also the collection of sufficient numbers of people to provide market support for a wide range of sophisticated activities, such as higher education, advanced health care, major league sports teams, and international travel facilities. Among the problems of urbanization are overcrowding, pollution, high cost of land and housing, traffic congestion, and crime. However, so long as people value the benefits more than they resent the problems, urbanization will continue; but that is not to say forever. A time eventually comes when the problems assume such proportions that they cannot be overcome by the benefits. At that time, urbanization will slow and eventually cease. And in time some of the existing urban residents will leave; the towns will thus contain a diminishing number of people.

The cessation of urbanization does not mean that towns will cease to exist. It simply means that they will cease to grow at a rate faster than the population as a whole. After all, urbanization is the process of transferring an increasing proportion of a country's population to the cities. When urbanization ceases, the towns either grow at the same rate as the general population, i.e., they maintain but do not increase their share of the total population, or they actually lose population, i.e., they experience a declining share of the total population. This last condition is also met if the towns grow more slowly than the general population.

**Figure 5-9** Housing to accommodate urban people.

Metropolitan areas in Canada are still in the stage of offering more benefits than problems, although problems certainly exist. People thus still wish to move into Canada's major cities from elsewhere, either from other parts of Canada or from other countries. However, the inward migrants are facing increasing difficulties placed in their way by a growing number of local residents; such difficulties involve mostly controls on building (such as restrictions on building heights) and road construction, which thus make it more difficult for people moving into cities to buy houses or rent apartments at affordable prices, as well as to commute easily if they live some distance away.

The classic examples of such difficulties were the actions of Toronto's City Council in the 1970s in banning high rise building construction which effectively limited apartment construction, and in stopping the building of the Spadina Expressway.

For a case study of the causes and effects of urbanization, let us take a close look at Vancouver. The first urban developments took place in the mid-1860s, when coal was extracted and shipped from Coal Harbour (Figure 5-10) and lumber was collected and sawn at the Hastings and Granville Sawmills.. At this time the intended administrative centre for the mainland region of what was still a British colony was New Westminster. Vancouver thereby never gained a major administrative function. In 1884 the south shore of Burrard Inlet, as far west as Coal Harbour, was selected by Van Horne as the location of the western terminus of the new transcontinental Canadian Pacific Railway. The first transcontinental train actually arrived in 1887, just a year after the newly chosen terminus had changed its name to Vancouver. Van Horne's decision to locate the transcontinental rail terminus in what was to become Vancouver was based on a number of considerations, but most importantly the easy access from the interior coupled with the availability of sheltered, silt-free, deepwater harbour accommodation. The harbour aspect was not a dominant one at the time, however, because the chief purpose of the railway was to connect British Columbia politically with the rest of Canada rather than connect the rest of Canada economically with trading opportunities in the Pacific.

British Columbia did not become a province until 1871. Before that it was run as a British colony, with two administrative centres. New Westminster acted as the mainland centre, while Victoria acted as the administrative centre on Vancouver Island. After the region became a province, administration was centralized in Victoria, which is still the provincial capital.

Indeed, the early years of Vancouver show that the railway did not assume any great trading importance; it was little used for linking Canada with the Pacific. Instead, early Vancouver grew on the lumber and sawmill industries. Around 1900 Vancouver also grew as a result of the Klondike gold rush, and many new residents were attracted from eastern Canada, as well as from Japan, China, and India. By 1912 Vancouver's population had reached 122 000, but the rapid growth of the early decades could not be maintained in the face of a sparsely settled hinterland and by 1913 people were accordingly beginning to leave Vancouver. Hundreds of buildings were vacated, and the depopulation process was

The Klondike gold rush in the Yukon attracted people from all over the world. The main trouble they had was in reaching the Klondike. Most set out for the goldfields from bases in Seattle or Vancouver, since those were about the closest places where they could buy their final supplies.

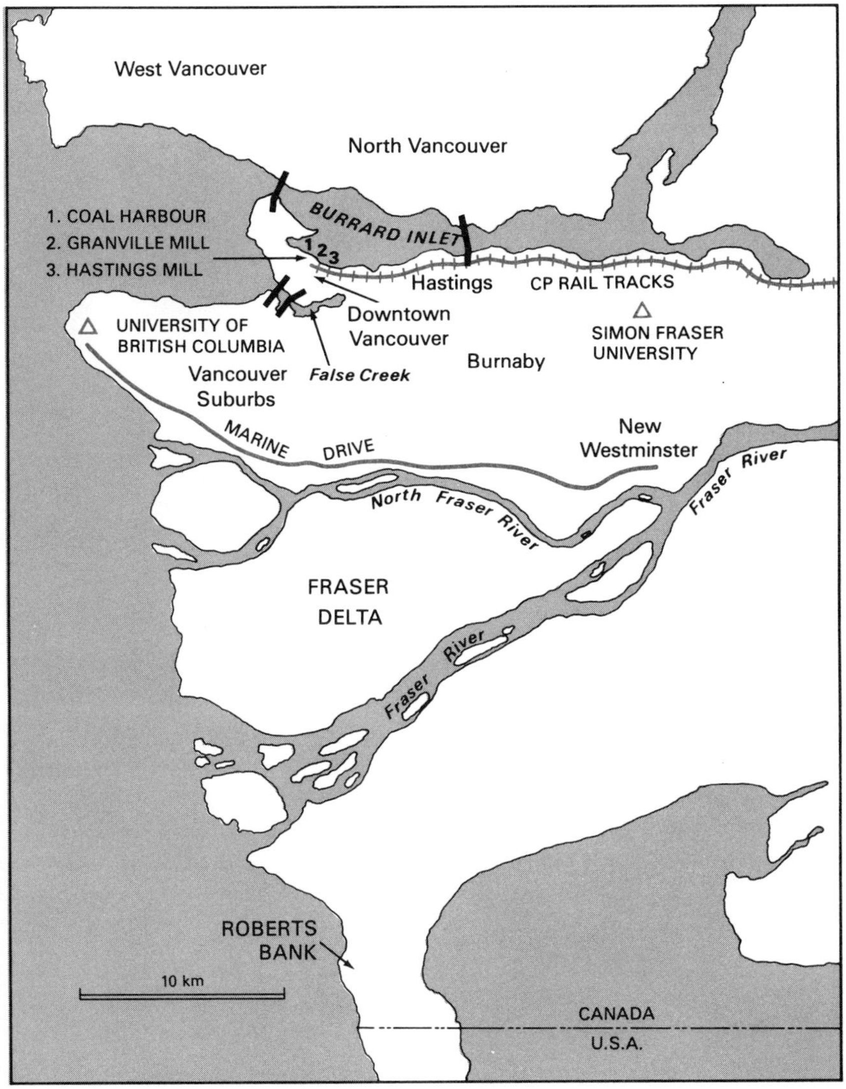

Figure 5-10   Vancouver

West Vancouver

North Vancouver

BURRARD INLET

1. COAL HARBOUR
2. GRANVILLE MILL
3. HASTINGS MILL

1 2 3

Hastings    CP RAIL TRACKS

△ UNIVERSITY OF
BRITISH COLUMBIA

Downtown
Vancouver

△
SIMON FRASER
UNIVERSITY

Vancouver   *False Creek*
Suburbs

Burnaby

MARINE   DRIVE

New
Westminster

*Fraser   River*

North   Fraser   River

FRASER
DELTA

Fraser   River

ROBERTS
BANK

10 km

CANADA
U.S.A.

accelerated by World War I (1914-1918) which took many people of British ancestry to the war in Europe. By 1916 Vancouver's population was down to 96 000. However, the opening of the Panama Canal and the end of World War I both prompted the renewal of growth. It now became possible for Vancouver to think of markets in Europe, and some prairie wheat began to move to Europe through Vancouver instead of via Montreal. Canada's economy also began to mature, and as an instance of this maturity there was a developing motor industry in Canada. Unfortunately there was no known oil, so this had to be imported through

It was mostly Alberta wheat that moved out through Vancouver, of course, because Alberta was the farthest province from the Great Lakes shipping route.

**Figure 5-11** Vancouver. Urban traffic congestion: a necessary evil?

Vancouver from oil fields in California. Vancouver thereby gained an oil refining industry. Gradually the sawmills began to vacate their locations on Burrard Inlet as land was becoming too valuable for their operations. False Creek became the major industrial area.

**Figure 5-12** Part of Canadian Pacific's rail facilities near the site of Coal Harbour in Vancouver.

As time passed Vancouver became increasingly the home base of many of British Columbia's huge resource industries. The offices of mines and lumber camps, transportation links and sawmills were gradually concentrated in Vancouver, and Vancouver therefore rapidly became a commercial and managerial centre. Meanwhile the mining camps and sawmills assumed a more remote location. Vancouver, by contrast, became a centre for higher education, for arts and entertainment, and for a vast variety of high level services. Moreover its links to other places became increasingly worldwide in character. On the one hand the sales of Canadian wheat to China and Russia through the 1950s and 1960s opened up new links, while the rise of Japan as a major world economic power caused a significant shift in Canada's general view of the

An example of Vancouver's development of a higher education function is its housing of two universities: Simon Fraser University and the University of British Columbia.

**Figure 5-13** Vancouver has become a commercial and managerial centre.

world from a predominantly European perspective. Vancouver became Canada's chief port, surpassing Montreal in the 1970s.

Part of the success of Vancouver as a world port has stemmed from its ability to open up new harbour accommodation in response to changing world markets. When Japan grew as a power in the 1960s, Vancouver was able to channel much of Canada's growth of resource exports by expanding its port facilities into the Fraser delta. For much of its early growth, indeed, Vancouver had been constricted by the narrowness of the peninsula between Burrard Inlet and False Creek. Expansion had been forced to take place eastwards towards Burnaby, northwards across Burrard Inlet

Roberts Bank is a new superport, built at the end of the 1960s to accommodate the largest Japanese superships. Its main trade is coal, mined in the interior mountains in the Crow's Nest Pass area, and shipped down to Roberts Bank by a continuously operating series of special trains. The trains never stop, even when they are loading and unloading their cargo. They slow down, but there are specially designed cars and loaders/unloaders which do not necessitate stopping. Six trains are always on the move at any one time, and each day a train unloads at Roberts Bank. Once a week a Japanese supership calls in, and loads up to take the coal to Japan.

Macmillan-Bloedel is one of the world's largest forestry companies.

to North and West Vancouver, and southwards across False Creek to Marine Drive along the north shore of the North Fraser River. The expanding Asian markets for commodities such as wheat, lumber, coal, sulphur, oil, and gas, together with Japanese innovations in the construction of superships, caused Vancouver to expand to the Fraser delta itself, and southwards even to Roberts Bank.

Within a hundred years, between the 1860s and the 1960s, Vancouver had moved from a settlement with a couple of sawmills to a major metropolitan area with the headquarters of one of the world's largest forestry companies, as well as a whole range of other metropolitan functions. And the attractions of the city continue to draw people in. Unforunately there are problems connected with the growth of the city. One of the most severe problems is the shortage of land for expansion. British Columbia is a scantily populated province, but it is also one with little inhabitable land. Most of the available land exists in the lower Fraser Valley, which is now dominated and perhaps threatened by the growth of Vancouver. A ready solution to outward expansion into farmlands has been to build upwards, thus minimizing land demands, and this has happened extensively in the central core of Vancouver. Some people, however, object to high rise develop-

**Figure 5-14**   Vancouver: ". . . a major metropolitan area . . ."

**Figure 5-15** Vancouver. A ready solution is to build upwards.

ment, and the construction of skyscrapers has thus been subjected to a strong local political opposition. Another problem has been the pollution of the waters around Vancouver by the important lumber industries. A solution to this has been found by persuading the lumber industries to vacate their False Creek sites, and move into the interior, or at least to the Fraser river and away from downtown Vancouver. False Creek is now the scene of a new urban renewal project, providing fashionable homes for people.

Yet another problem faced by Vancouver, along with all major metropolitan areas, is internal transportation. All cities face the problem of how to get suburban workers to and from downtown jobs, but Vancouver's problem is particularly severe because of the peninsular nature of its downtown area. Ferries used to be very popular for use by commuters, but they have been largely replaced by bridges. The bridges are, however, inadequate for today's growing traffic.

What is the answer? Should the city be prevented from growing? Should no one else be allowed to move into the region? Should suburbs be allowed to expand over the surrounding farmland? Should high rises be fostered, so as to pack more people into a given area?

Is there an answer?

What do you think?

• 5. In view of the fact that Canada's total population was only 7 200 00 in 1911 and yet had grown to as many as 21 600 000 by 1971, what do you think happened to Canada's ecumene between 1911 and 1971?

• 6. Make two columns on your answer page. In the first column write down all the reasons you can think of to explain why people would want to leave those parts of the ecumene which are fairly empty. In the second column write down the reasons that attract people to areas that are already crowded.

• 7. (a) Why do you think most early Canadians were rural dwellers?
     (b) What is the relationship between *place* of work and *type* of work?

• 8. Do you think it is likely that Canada will become entirely urban? If so, why? If not, why not?

• 9. Read the article, *The Grain Train Won't Stop Here Anymore*, and try to write two accounts, not more than one page each:
     (a) Imagine you lived in Eskbank when it was a thriving centre. What was a typical day like?
     (b) If you were the doctor in a small town what would you be thinking of as you saw more and more businesses close down and the inhabitants leave?

# The Grain Train Won't Stop Here Any More

ESKBANK, Sask. — This is a ghost town. Once a thriving community with two banks, a dozen businesses, three tough hockey teams, a baseball team and two daily trains, Eskbank is a desolate example of what is happening to many small communities in Saskatchewan, emptied by the trend toward larger farms and larger cities.

The last resident left months ago, but at dusk an automatic device still turns on the hamlet's three street lights. When dawn comes, the lights go out.

Apart from the occasional curious passerby, the only signs of life under those lights are skunks and rats. The shells of two of the business establishments stand out against the

Prairie skyline. One is a two-story boxline structure that once was a bank: the other is the familiar, false-fronted general store.

**No Resident Buyer**
Eskbank, 40 miles[1] northwest of Moose Jaw, still has three grain elevators — but no resident grain buyer. He left last spring

[1] 64 km

when his employer, Mc-Cabe Grain Co. Ltd. of Winnipeg, sold its two elevators to United Grain Growers Ltd. All three now are owned by Saskatchewan Wheat Pool, whose agent visits the area twice weekly to deal with the farmers.

The tiny community was founded in 1913 — by accident — during the completion of the Grand Trunk Railway branch line from Moose Jaw northwest to Riverside. A railway crew sidetracked a carload of groceries at this point instead of farther up the line. The owner decided to build his store where the groceries were piled and that point became Eskbank.

Four years later he sold out to Mr. and Mrs. J. L. Gibson, who now live in Moose Jaw. They operated that general store until they retired in 1959. The couple who bought it gave it up five years ago and so Eskbank's first business venture was also its last.

During its half-century of life the hamlet had two general stores, a combined butcher shop and pool room, an ice cream parlor, a blacksmith, an auto garage, a lumber yard, an implement agency and two farm fuel suppliers. There were also two banks, the Bank of Hamilton and the Merchants Bank. Merchants was taken over by the Bank of Montreal in 1921 and the Bank of Hamilton by the Canadian Bank of Commerce in 1923.

Although Eskbank's population never exceeded 100, it was a lively spot on Saturday nights, according to Rupert Pottruff. Farmers and their families descended on the hamlet in such numbers as to double its regular population.

In the Nineteen Twenties most of the farms in the rich wheat country that surrounds Eskbank were original 160-acre[2] homesteads with approximately four families on every section of Prairie land. A section is 640 acres.[3]

As those who could not make a living from a quarter-section left farming, those who remained expanded their holdings. The minimum acreage locally now is 800 acres.[4] Most are larger. For instance, the Pottruff farm comprises almost 1500 acres.[5]

Because the old Grand Trunk line — now owned by Canadian National Railways — is among those to be abandoned, Eskbank probably would have died anyway.

People are moving to larger centres, causing the demise of small communities. The abandonment of railway branch lines will encourage this movement.

On Jan. 1, Saskatchewan had 652 hamlets, in addition to self-governing urban communities, 362 villages, 128 towns, and 11 cities. To achieve the status of a self-governing village a hamlet must have a population of 100 but it does not revert automatically if its population drops below that figure. A hamlet's affairs are administered by the rural municipality.

**Only Seven Increases**

A comparison of the 1961 and 1966 census figures shows that of 62 villages with populations of 100 or less, only seven had increases in population. The declines ranged to a maximum of 64 per cent.

To qualify as a town, a village must have a population of 500 or more. Of the 128 towns, 25 recorded population losses of up to 14.68 per cent. Twenty-four just about held their own.

Towns in purely agricultural areas fared the worst. Those situated near potash and petroleum developments forged ahead with population increases ranging from 15 per cent to 186 per cent in five years.

It has become axiomatic

2 65 ha
3 260 ha
4 324 ha
5 607 ha

that if a community has a hospital (and, preferably, a doctor) and sewer and water systems, it will continue to live.

The old-age security program is giving a new lease on life to countless small hamlets and villages. Long after they have been denuded of business enterprises, they are becoming entrenched as small residential centres for recipients of monthly cheques from the federal Government. Property taxes paid in these small centres are only a fraction of those exacted from homeowners in larger centres.

**Acquired Water System**

Within a few miles of Esk-bank are several hamlets that survive even though they failed to match Eskbank's one-time prominence as a business centre. One of them is Darmody, which had a population of 34 on Jan. 1. It is clinging to life because it has become a residential centre for retired persons and area farmers. Darmody acquired a water system this year with financial assistance from the province and it is looking forward to a long life even though its only business enterprise is a grain elevator.

Some provincial Government administrators view Eskbank's demise as a blessing, not a tragedy. Their formula for tidying up the somewhat chaotic situation among the scores of expiring smaller communities is to speed their demise so that the province's urbanization will be concentrated in a relatively few centrally situated communities. Some even envisage the Government paying the cost of moving houses to these central locations from expiring smaller centres.

It is argued that the reduction in the number of urban communities would cheapen local government administrative costs as well as the costs to the provincial Government of providing such services as highways and hospitals.

Special to the *Globe and Mail*, December 19, 1968

## B: CHANGES IN THE QUANTITY OF POPULATION

We find the number of people living in an area by counting them. In a country this process of counting is called a *census*. Most countries hold a census every ten years. Canada holds a major census every tenth year, so that as you can see in Figure 5-16 there were full censuses in 1851, 1861 . . . 1961, 1971, and so on. The very first census of Canada was held in 1670 by the French in Quebec. Indeed in 1670 the French were the only inhabitants in Canada, except for small numbers of Indians and Inuits. The 1670 census was followed by others at different times, but in all these early censuses there were never many people to be counted. Canada was a big empty land. Even at the time of Confederation in 1867 there were only 3 500 000 people in Canada. As we saw in Figure 5-1, most of them lived in the east: the 1871 ecumene stretched from the Maritimes to southern Ontario. But even so the total number of people was very small. There are more people today, for example, just in Montreal and Toronto put together.

Canada's population did not cease to grow in 1971 merely because the last major census was held then. The population continues to grow. In 1976, for example, the population surpassed 23 000 000, and people talked of a population of about 40 000 000 by the year 2000.

**Figure 5-16    Population Growth**

| Census Year | Population |
|---|---|
| 1851 | 2 436 297 |
| 1861 | 3 229 633 |
| 1871 | 3 689 257 |
| 1881 | 4 324 810 |
| 1891 | 4 833 239 |
| 1901 | 5 371 315 |
| 1911 | 7 206 643 |
| 1921 | 8 787 949 |
| 1931 | 10 376 786 |
| 1941 | 11 506 655 |
| 1951* | 14 009 429 |
| 1961 | 18 238 247 |
| 1971 | 21 568 311 |
| 1976** | 23 231 000 |

\*    1951 data include Newfoundland for the first time.
\*\*  estimate

from *Canada Year Book*

You could try a projection of the data in Figure 5-16 to see how well the forecast of 40 000 000 fits in. As with all future forecasts there are many who agree with a particular figure, but also many who disagree. For example, there were many people who talked of a population of 30 000 000 by the year 2000. What does your projection show?

Why does Canada's population grow? There are two basic reasons: one is that the number of births exceeds the number of deaths in any given year, and the other is that people immigrate to Canada from other countries. Let us have a look at these reasons in turn. First the excess of births over deaths. If you look at Figure 5-17 you will see that the birth rate in Canada has decreased significantly in the last 50 years. In 1926, for example, there were 24.7 live babies born for every 1000 people in Canada. Since the total population of Canada in 1926 was about 9 500 000, you can readily calculate the number of live babies actually born. Divide 9 500 000 by 1000 to find out how many 1000s there were in the population; the answer 9500. Then multiply this answer by 24.7, because there were 24.7 live babies born for every 1000

The birth rate data in Figure 5-17 show that in addition to the general decline in the rate between 1921 and 1976 there was a considerable rise in the rate between 1941 and 1961. This rise was caused largely by World War II and its aftermath; it was called the *baby boom*.

people in the population. The answer this time is 234 650 (9500 × 24.7 = 234 650). This means therefore that in 1926 there were about 234 650 live babies born in Canada.

The difference between the birth rate and the death rate is called the *natural increase* rate. In 1961 the birth rate was 26.1/1000 (26.1 live babies per 1000 people in the population) and the death rate was 7.7/1000 (7.7 people died out of every 1000 people in the population). The natural increase rate was therefore 18.4 per 1000. This means that if there were 1000 people at the start of the year, then the natural increase of 18.4 would bring the total to 1018.4 people at the end of the year. In 1961 the total population of Canada was about 18 200 000. Could you calculate how many additional people there would be at the end of a year from that census? Do it this way: divide the total population by 1000 in order to find the number of 1000s in the total population. The answer is 18 200. Then multiply this answer by 18.4 to find how many extra people were added by the natural increase. The answer is 334 880 (18 200 × 18.4 = 334 880). Therefore the excess of births over deaths in 1961 produced 334 880 extra people. This is the first way in which Canada's population grows through the years.

| Year | Births/1000 | Deaths/1000 |
| --- | --- | --- |
| 1921 | 29.3 | 11.6 |
| 1926 | 24.7 | 11.4 |
| 1931 | 23.2 | 10.2 |
| 1936 | 20.3 | 9.9 |
| 1941 | 22.4 | 10.1 |
| 1946 | 27.2 | 9.4 |
| 1951 | 27.2 | 9.0 |
| 1956 | 28.0 | 8.2 |
| 1961 | 26.1 | 7.7 |
| 1966 | 19.4 | 7.5 |
| 1971 | 16.8 | 7.3 |
| 1976 (preliminary) | 15.4 | 7.4 |

Figure 5-17   Canada's Birth and Death Rates

The second way in which Canada's population has grown is by immigration. Figure 5-19 shows you some immigration data since 1900. You can easily see that the number of immigrants has fluctuated from year to year. The smallest number of immigrants came in 1942, during the Second World War, but there were other small numbers during the 1930s too. Figure 5-18 shows you another line graph, this time illustrating the immigration data and giving you some of the reasons for the fluctuations.

World War II started in 1939 when Germany invaded Poland, and Britain in turn declared war on Germany. The demand for soldiers effectively restricted the possibilities of immigration to Canada.

**Figure 5-18    Number of Immigrant Arrivals in Canada**

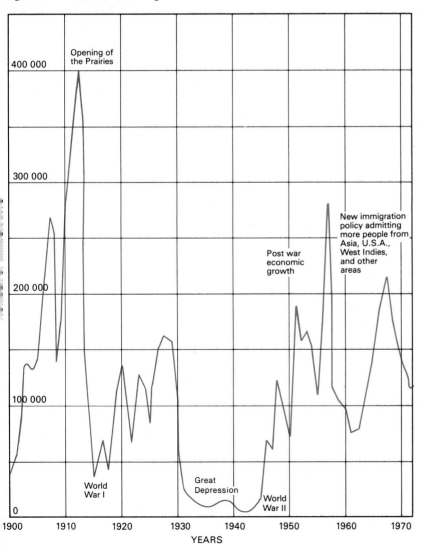

For comparison, the year of maximum immigration into the United States was 1914, when 1 218 480 people immigrated. The lowest year was 1933 when only 23 068 people immigrated. Why do you think the years and numbers are different from those for Canada?

**Figure 5-19  Immigrant Arrivals to Canada, from 1900**

| Year | Number | Year | Number | Year | Number | Year | Number |
|------|--------|------|--------|------|--------|------|--------|
| 1900 | 41 681 | 1920 | 138 824 | 1940 | 11 324 | 1960 | 104 111 |
| 1901 | 55 747 | 1921 | 91 728 | 1941 | 9 329 | 1961 | 71 689 |
| 1902 | 89 102 | 1922 | 64 224 | 1942 | 7 576 | 1962 | 74 586 |
| 1903 | 138 660 | 1923 | 133 729 | 1943 | 8 504 | 1963 | 93 151 |
| 1904 | 131 252 | 1924 | 124 164 | 1944 | 12 801 | 1964 | 112 606 |
| 1905 | 141 465 | 1925 | 84 907 | 1945 | 22 722 | 1965 | 146 758 |
| 1906 | 211 653 | 1926 | 135 982 | 1946 | 71 719 | 1966 | 194 743 |
| 1907 | 272 409 | 1927 | 158 886 | 1947 | 64 127 | 1967 | 222 876 |
| 1908 | 143 326 | 1928 | 166 783 | 1948 | 125 414 | 1968 | 183 974 |
| 1909 | 173 694 | 1929 | 164 993 | 1949 | 95 217 | 1969 | 161 531 |
| 1910 | 286 839 | 1930 | 104 806 | 1950 | 73 912 | 1970 | 147 713 |
| 1911 | 331 288 | 1931 | 27 530 | 1951 | 194 391 | 1971 | 121 900 |
| 1912 | 375 756 | 1932 | 20 591 | 1952 | 164 498 | 1972 | 122 006 |
| 1913 | 400 870 | 1933 | 14 382 | 1953 | 168 868 | 1973 | 184 200 |
| 1914 | 150 484 | 1934 | 12 476 | 1954 | 154 227 | 1974 | 218 465 |
| 1915 | 36 665 | 1935 | 11 277 | 1955 | 109 946 | 1975 | 187 881 |
| 1916 | 55 914 | 1936 | 11 643 | 1956 | 164 857 | 1976 | 149 429 |
| 1917 | 72 910 | 1937 | 15 101 | 1957 | 282 164 | | |
| 1918 | 41 845 | 1938 | 17 244 | 1958 | 124 851 | | |
| 1919 | 107 698 | 1939 | 16 994 | 1959 | 106 928 | | |

The reasons people have for immigrating to Canada are extremely varied. Some groups have come to avoid religious persecution in their homeland, (for example the Hutterites who are now settled in their own communities across Alberta). Others have came to avoid political persecution, such as the Ugandan Asians in 1972–73, and the Czechoslovakians in 1968. Still other groups have come to gain a better social or economic standard of living. Why did you or your ancestors come?

On the receiving side, Canada has many reasons for accepting immigrants. One of the basic reasons is that Canada has continuously wanted more people to help populate the country, so as to create a nation with its own territory. As we saw in regard to the Arctic in Chapter 1, empty lands are a temptation to other countries. Another reason is that Canada has long wanted to make its industries more economic, and a larger population would help to do that by forming a larger market. Canada has also always welcomed the infusions of new ideas and fresh skills and enthusiasms brought by immigrants.

At various times, however, immigrants have had to contend with hostility from people already living in Canada. During the 1930s, for example, there was deep-rooted hostility towards all new immigrants on the basis that they were competing with residents for

The Hutterites came originally from Austria, via Russia. They came because they feared persecution, and sought a peaceful communal farming life instead. They take their name from Jakob Huter, their founder in Austria in the 16th century.

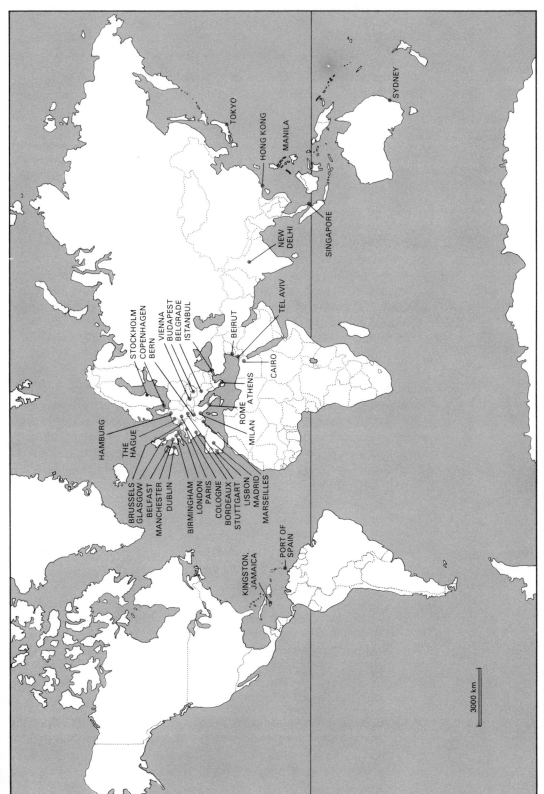

**Figure 5-20  World Distribution of Canadian Immigration Offices**

TOKYO

SYDNEY

HONG KONG

MANILA

SINGAPORE

NEW DELHI

TEL AVIV

CAIRO

BEIRUT

STOCKHOLM
COPENHAGEN
BERN
VIENNA
BUDAPEST
BELGRADE
ISTANBUL

ATHENS

ROME

MILAN

HAMBURG

THE
HAGUE

BRUSSELS
GLASGOW
BELFAST
MANCHESTER
DUBLIN
BIRMINGHAM
LONDON
PARIS
COLOGNE
BORDEAUX
STUTTGART
LISBON
MADRID
MARSEILLES

PORT OF
SPAIN

KINGSTON,
JAMAICA

3000 km

In the 1930s most people already in Canada resented immigrants because they felt there were not enough jobs to go round as it was. In the 1960s, on the other hand, jobs were plentiful, and more people were needed than there were people already in Canada, so immigrants were welcomed.

Immigration Officers play a crucial role in implementing government policy. When the government wishes to lessen immigration, the Officers can process applications more slowly, and vice versa.

already scarce jobs. During the 1970s another round of hostility started, partly because of the changed nature of the immigrant ethnic mix, and partly because of the growing fear of crowding, pollution, and depletion of resources.

Federal government policy towards immigrants has varied from time to time, in part as a response to public feelings. During the 1930s, for example, the government did not encourage immigration. During the 1960s, on the other hand, the government did much to encourage immigration, even abandoning its old quota system based on certain numbers for each nationality. Instead, the government introduced a points system, based on the idea that anyone who could gain a minimum of 50 points out of a possible 100 on such criteria as years of education, age, knowledge of French and English, job skills, and job availability could immigrate to Canada, from any country in the world. Accordingly, during the 1960s Canada began to attract immigrants from many non-traditional sources. The chief destinations of these immigrants were to places where there were jobs, namely Ontario, British Columbia, and Alberta, with smaller numbers elsewhere. Within the provinces of destination, the major attractions were the large metropolitan areas, particularly Toronto, which absorbed nearly 30% of all immigrants. However, with the anti-growth mood which developed in the 1970s the federal government again modified its immigration policy. It did not alter the worldwide pattern of sources which had been developed in the 1960s (Figure 5-20), but it did impose ceilings. The ceilings were publicized as being flexible, although figures of about 100 000 to 150 000 were widely mentioned by government officials. Exactly how this policy will work, we do not yet know. Presumably if the public generally demands more immigration, the ceilings will be raised, and *vice versa*.

- 10. Draw a line graph to illustrate the data in Figure 5-16. Remember: a line graph shows the data by means of a line, so look carefully to see how Figure 5-2 is drawn. You must put the years along the horizontal axis, taking care to keep the scale accurate. This means that you should watch how you plot the data for 1976.

- 11. Calculate the number of deaths in Canada in 1926. Take the death rate as 11.4 per 1000, and the total population as 9 500 000. How many more live babies were born in 1926 than there were people who died?

- 12. Using the data for 1971 in Figures 5-16 and 5-17, calculate the number of extra people produced by natural increase in Canada during that year. Compare your answer with the 1971 figure for immigrant arrivals in Figure 5-19. Which is the larger figure?

- 13. Use Figure 5-18 to answer the following questions:
    (a) Why was immigration low during the years 1914–18?
    (b) Why was immigration high during the period 1902–13?
    (c) Why was immigration low during the 1930s?
    (d) Why was immigration high during the 1950s?
    (e) Why was immigration high during the years 1964-72?

- 14. Can you think of some of the reasons for people to immigrate to Canada? If you know any immigrants, can you find out why they or their families came to Canada?

- 15. Read the article below and give *your* opinion on the matter of whether Canada's population should be limited to about 30 million at some time in the future. You should give reasons for your opinions.

- 16. In 1976 Canada decided to introduce a ceiling system for immigrants. Can you suggest the arguments that people who want to raise the ceiling would use? Do you agree with them? If not, why not?

# 30 Million People Limit for Canada Urged

**By Leone Kirkwood**

Zero Population Growth of Canada believes Canada's population should not exceed the 30 million mark and this limit should not be reached for 60 years.

Members of ZPG decided at a weekend meeting that if the population does not go over 30 million, the present, comfort-able lifestyle of Canadians can continue.

ZPG, with chapters across Canada, is concerned that the population growth plus industrial activity will soon result in people not having enough resources for the present living standard.

The meeting, on the University of Toronto campus Saturday and yes-terday was the first with provincial chapters represented.

It was strictly a working session; no speeches. The group exchanged ideas on how to get their message across to the public, on the co-operation or lack of co-operation they were getting from municipal and provincial governments.

The members also elected the first Canadian director, Chris Taylor, professor of interdisciplinary studies, University of Toronto.

ZPG feels the national average should be 2.1 children per family.

"This means," said John Archer, one of the directors, "that some families could have one child, some three, some none." The group also believes that immigration should match emigration.

At present, Canada's population of 22 million is increasing yearly at a rate of 1.5 per cent and would double in 45 years.

Mr. Archer and his associates feel that Canadians now are becoming uncomfortably aware that there are a lot of people around.

The imbalance showed strongly in the postwar baby boom when schools became overcrowded and there were not enough teachers to go around.

Other problems are inadequate e m p lo y m e n t, housing, transportation and recreational facilities.

Other recommendations, or policy statements, at the meeting included easy access for all persons to family planning, sterilization and abortion and social acceptance of the no-child, one-child and two-child families.

Alec Adams, Toronto chairman, said couples are still under pressure, particularly from their parents, to have children whether they want them or not.

The group also wants less insistence on economic and material growth on the ground that not all growth is necessarily good. This particularly applies to urban areas where the quality of life is affected by overcrowding.

The ZPG members are not asking that only Canadians voluntarily control the birth rate. But they said that if developed countries like Canada set an example, then the developing countries can be encouraged to do so.

They agreed among themselves that one of the problems in Canada is that everyone thinks Canada has so much space that there is room for plenty of people.

However, Prof. Taylor, in a background paper released at the meeting, said the wide open spaces theory is misleading.

Statistics show there are 10 acres[1] of land available to every world citizen and 100 acres[2] for every Canadian. But Canadians do not have equal access to 100 acres. Some wealthy people may have two homes, one in the city and one in the country. Others are crowded.

Another factor is the value of the acreage. One hundred acres in the north cannot support people — a short growing season for crops plus muskeg instead of rich soil — as 100 acres in the south can.

Milton Anderson of Calgary said gas and oil reserves are being depleted so quickly that they will be gone within 20 to 50 years at the present rate of depletion.

If that happens, Alberta will become a have-not problem, he said. But most people, when told of this still have great faith in technology and are unaware that much of technology is based on natural resources.

Mr. Adams said that many people have the attitude of "Well, I won't be around when that happens." But there must be a concern for humanity and for the lifestyle of future generations.

1 4.0 ha

2 40.5 ha

from the *Globe and Mail*, October 16, 1972

# C: CHANGES IN THE COMPOSITION OF THE POPULATION

The term 'native people' is used to describe the first immigrants. There are no native people in the sense that early people developed here; there are only immigrants. The first immigrants were the Indians, followed much later by the Inuits, and then much later still by the Europeans, and lastly by people from all over the world. Because the Indians and Inuits were already in Canada when the Europeans arrived, and because the Europeans at that time knew no better, the Indians and Inuit came to be called 'native people'.

Indeed, Indians were called Indians because the first Europeans thought they had reached India. Eskimos were called Eskimos by the Indians; the word means *flesh-eaters* in Indian. The Eskimos call themselves *Inuit*. Indians call themselves by their tribal names, such as Cree, Blackfoot, etc.

The Indians came first, possibly 10 000 to 15 000 years ago. They came from the south, migrating northward as the ice sheets retreated. The origin of the Indians before the Ice Age is obscure: they may have migrated from Asia across the Bering Straits and then gradually have spread out across the Americas, being forced farther south as the Ice Age occurred, or they may have migrated across the Pacific into south and central America, and then colonized northward as conditions permitted.

Four main types of economy were developed by the various groups of Indians who occupied Canada (Figure 5-21).
a. Forest-cultivation in the St. Lawrence–Great Lakes region.
b. Forest-hunting throughout the entire eastern and central forest regions outside the above cultivation areas.
c. Plains-hunting across the treeless (southern) Prairies.
d. Forest- and coast-hunting along the west coast.

Forest-cultivation was practised in clearings, usually on a shifting cultivation basis, chiefly by the Huron, Mohawk, Iroquois, and associated tribes. A typical village has been reconstructed at Midland, Ontario. Reliance was placed on corn, tobacco, beans, sunflowers: and this reliance on a food supply whose quantity could to a large degree be controlled enabled tribal groups to be quite large. Fish were hunted in the rivers and lakes to supplement the crops, while deer and moose were hunted in the forest.

Midland, Ontario, is located on the southern shore of Georgian Bay. It is well worth visiting.

Forest-hunting was practised almost everywhere in those wooded zones which were beyond the range of corn cultivation. Deer, moose, caribou, and fish were the staples. The size of tribal groups was limited by available catches.

Both forest-cultivation and forest-hunting had many things in common: long houses and wigwams, birch-bark canoes, clothing of skins, snow shoes, toboggans. The real difference was in the greater stability and wealth afforded to the cultivators by the availability of corn.

The difference between a wigwam and a tepee rests in the material of construction: wigwams are made of twigs and leaves, tepees of skins.

Plains-hunting relied on the buffalo, which were usually caught by stampeding them over a break in the plains. Food, clothing, and shelter (skin tepees) were all gained from the buffalo. When guns were introduced by Europeans, the Plains Indians caught many more buffalo; the Europeans also slaughtered many buffalo, and at one time there were thought to be only 13 left. The Indians who had relied on the buffalo became almost extinct themselves, and the tribal remnants sought refuge in reserves.

Forest- and coast-hunting by the West Coast Indians was based on the vast and rich salmon runs, supplemented by deer and moose. Life was relatively easy; and settlements were permanent instead of (as elsewhere) nomadic. Tribal groups were, however, relatively small, chiefly because of the severely broken relief in the mountains.

**Figure 5-21    The Distribution of Canada's Native People**

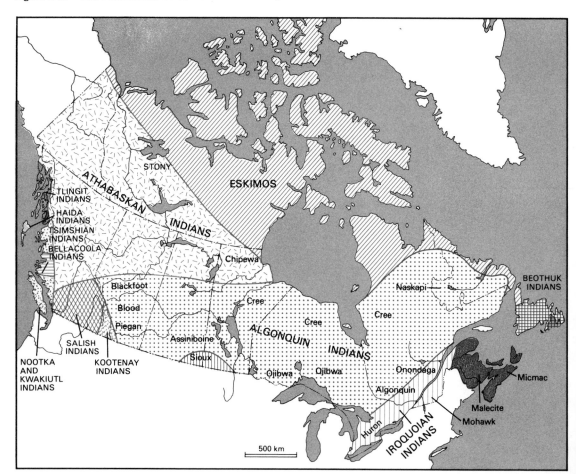

**Figure 5-22** A reconstructed Indian tepee on the Alberta prairie.

It is estimated that when the Europeans came there were about 200 000 Indians scattered in small bands across Canada. Contact with Europeans reduced the number to about 125 000, chiefly because of disease and fighting; and the number stabilized at that figure for many decades. Only since World War II has the number begun to increase significantly — and there are now about 250 000 Indians. The federal government, through its Department of Indian Affairs and Northern Development, is responsible for aid to Indians; it provides help in the form of roads, housing, schooling, wells, power, medical care, sanitation, social security, and so on. It is also trying to get the Indians to take care of these things for themselves: the Community Development Program is aimed at giving Indian associations the right to determine their own provision of various community services. The first major handover of such provision was made in 1969 to the Manitoba Indian Brotherhood, and other agreements have since been made with Indian associations in Nova Scotia, New Brunswick, Saskatchewan, and Alberta.

Despite the various forms of government assistance, the gradual abandonment of the old lifestyles is producing what the rest of Canada regards as poverty. Training of Indians for modern jobs progresses slowly, and there is much modern-type unemployment.

Disease was a serious killer. The native people had built up no resistance to such common European diseases as influenza and tuberculosis, and so they died in large numbers.

The James Bay project
is a scheme to develop
power in the lands to
the southeast of James
Bay. The plan requires
the flooding of some
land to create reser-
voirs, but the land is
traditional Indian
hunting land. A federal
court case resolved
the issue in favour of
the James Bay project,
but with guaranteed
hunting rights to be
maintained in certain
areas and a large
amount of monetary
compensation to be
paid to the Indians.

The names of the early
cultures (pre-Dorset,
and Thule) refer to
areas where the find-
ings of artifacts
occurred. Cape Dorset
is one of the areas
where finds of early
Eskimo life occurred.


HBC = Hudson's Bay
Company

Many Indians reject the demands of a modern economic state
such as Canada; they prefer to maintain their old lifestyle, in the
face of pressures to change the old land use patterns (as in the
James Bay Project). Some of the more enterprising Indians, however, have accepted the facts of change, and have set up co-
operatives to cater to the demands of a modern state — such as
in rearing fur-bearing animals, or logging, or forming dance
troupes, or in marketing handicrafts.

The Inuit arrived in Canada around 3000–2000 B.C. They came
from Alaska, where the first evidence of their occupancy of
North America is to be found, thus clearly indicating their northeast Asian origins. They subsequently spread across the rest of the
Arctic region to the east. A gradual development in their tools,
language, artifacts, clothing, and artwork can be traced from their
original *pre-Dorset* culture, through the *Dorset* and *Thule* cultures,
to the *Modern* culture, which is now itself gradually being replaced
by a *Mechanical* culture.

The first contact of Europeans was with the Thule-culture
Eskimos, who relied heavily upon whaling for sustenance; and
since the Europeans also wanted whales there were clashes to the
disadvantage of the Eskimos. The Thule culture gradually died,
and was replaced by the Modern culture, which was characterized
by a reliance on seals, together with additional supplies from
caribou, fish, and birds. Life was very precarious, and survival was
not guaranteed — starvation was indeed fairly common, even well
into the 1950s. The Modern culture was supplemented by the
Hudson Bay Company fur trade in certain places, and in general
the Eskimos who traded with the HBC were happy because they
received valued guns in exchange for white fox furs. From the turn
of the century to about 1950 fur-trapping was a very important
activity for many Eskimos; but around 1960 the sealskin trade had
become more important. Semi-nomadic Eskimos who still rely on
hunting (for seals, fish, caribou, birds) are still in the Modern
culture.

Hunting and trapping are nevertheless in decline, especially since
the start of significant federal interest in the Arctic in 1955 or so.
"Cottage industry" is taking over: such as the formation of co-
operatives for canning and marketing Arctic Char, for making and
selling Eskimo clothing, for sculpture, and for other handicrafts.
In addition, many Eskimos are working with mining and oil/gas
companies. The federal government in fact offers cash incentives
to firms to employ Eskimo labour. And the government itself
sponsors direct employment of Eskimos in weather stations and
DEW-line bases. Housing is federally funded, as are hospitals and

The federal govern-
ment began to be
seriously interested in
the Arctic in the 1950s
because there was
some fear that
Americans and
Russians might want
to move in.

schools; but increasingly the federal government is handing over powers to Northwest Territories authorities in Yellowknife. The policy of collecting semi-nomadic Eskimos into widely-spaced townships is being pursued to help in their adaptation to a mechanical-urban culture (see Figure 5-24). One result of contact with Europeans was initial decimation through disease; but Canadian authorities have now largely overcome this problem. Federal health care has also resulted in a baby boom among the Eskimos, whose birth rate is currently 38/1000 — the highest in the world, and way above the Canadian average of 15/1000. Numbers are therefore growing very rapidly, and the old lifestyles are now non-sustainable. There are possibly about 20 000 Eskimos in Canada: 500 in Manitoba, 1300 in Labrador, 3800 in northern Quebec, and the rest in the Northwest Territories.

The old lifestyles could support only a certain number of Eskimos, and even then starvation was quite common. Nowadays there are vastly more Eskimos than there used to be, and there is just no way they could all survive under the old lifestyle.

One attempt to maintain the modern culture with some degree of continuity occurred in the Mackenzie Delta: reindeer were introduced from Scandinavia, and herding was started, with the idea of supplying meat on a regular basis throughout the northwest Arctic. This was in 1935. The reindeer are still there, and there is still some herding, but the experiment failed: settled herding proved unpopular with the Eskimos, whereas snowmobiles proved to be extremely popular.

**Figure 5-23** Indian houses near James Bay.

**Figure 5-24** An eskimo working in the mechanical culture.

The Eskimos and the Indians did, however, fight each other on occasion, chiefly in those areas where they came into hunting contact, namely the Mackenzie Delta and eastern Labrador.

The first Europeans to come regularly to Canada were fishing groups from Portugal and England. These groups were not very interested in settling in Canada, so it was not really until the French came in 1602 that Canada began to get European *settlers*. For over 150 years the French governed the country. They traded with the Indians, settled all along the St. Lawrence Valley, and explored widely across the rest of Canada. In 1759, in the Battle of the Plains of Abraham (just outside Quebec City), the French were defeated by the English. Canada then came under the control of the British Empire, but the French inhabitants continued to live in the country, particularly in Quebec, the land they had first colonized. And in 1867, of course, French and English joined to create the formal union of Canada.

However, during the time that Canada has been inhabited, the last 10 000 years or so, we find that the composition of its population has changed quite considerably. First there were only Indians. Then there were Indians and Eskimos. Then there were Indians and Eskimos and French. Then there were Indians and Eskimos and French and English. This process of adding ethnic groups to the total has not finished.

During the period from 1900 especially there has been a tremendous change in Canada's ethnic mix. Many other groups have been added to the total, including in the early years many other

European groups such as Ukrainians, Germans, Swedes, Danes, Russians, Italians, and so on. In the later years there have been other European groups such as Greeks, Portuguese, Hungarians, and Czechoslovakians. However, the greatest changes have occurred chiefly since 1967 (the 100th anniversary of Confederation). Look at the table in Figure 5-25. You can see that from 1967 to 1972 the European portion of Canada's immigration went down from 72% of the total to 42% of the total. This was a big change, because it had always been over 70% until 1967. Instead of Europeans, Canada began to take in larger numbers of people from Asia, the West Indies, and other parts of the world. In 1971–72, for the first time in Canada's history, the numbers of Europeans coming in was less than 50% of the total immigrants. You can see therefore that the composition of Canada's population has changed drastically. There are now many different ethnic groups living within Canada. There are now more people of non-English descent than there are of English descent. This is why we said earlier that Canada was "mainly an English country" until about 1960. Since the 1960s there have been so many non-English peoples added that Canada is changing to a more international type of society.

Some people see the type of international society which is developing in Canada as a forerunner of what the whole world will be like at some time in the future. It is a society in which all cultures are free to retain some of their own individuality while at the same time giving some of it up in order to become part of a broader society.

| Year | Europe | Asia | USA | West Indies | Other |
|------|--------|------|-----|-------------|-------|
| 1960 | 79 | 4 | 11 | 1 | 5 |
| 1961 | 73 | 4 | 15 | 2 | 6 |
| 1962 | 72 | 3 | 15 | 2 | 8 |
| 1963 | 76 | 4 | 13 | 2 | 5 |
| 1964 | 73 | 5 | 11 | 2 | 9 |
| 1965 | 74 | 7 | 11 | 1 | 7 |
| 1966 | 75 | 7 | 9 | 2 | 7 |
| 1967 | 72 | 9 | 9 | 4 | 6 |
| 1968 | 66 | 12 | 11 | 5 | 6 |
| 1969 | 55 | 14 | 14 | 9 | 8 |
| 1970 | 51 | 14 | 17 | 9 | 9 |
| 1971 | 43 | 18 | 20 | 10 | 9 |
| 1972 | 42 | 19 | 19 | 8 | 12 |

Figure 5-25  Major Canadian Immigrant Sources, in percent

• 17. We can get another idea of just how the immigration mix has changed over the last few years by calculating what are called *index numbers*. In order to calculate index numbers we need to know the data for two different dates, so let us use data for 1967 and compare it with data for 1972. In this way we can see what the pattern of immigration was like before it really began to change, and also what it was like after a five year period when the changes had begun to occur.

**percentage of Canada's immigrants arriving from:**

| year | Europe | Asia | U.S.A. | West Indies | Other | total |
|------|--------|------|--------|-------------|-------|-------|
| 1967 | 72 | 9 | 9 | 4 | 6 | 100% |
| 1972 | 42 | 19 | 19 | 8 | 12 | 100% |

Index numbers are widely used to measure changes in the quantity of all sorts of things over a period of time. One of the best known index numbers is the *cost of living index,* which tells you how the prices of things have changed over a period of time.

Index numbers are calculated in this manner: take the information for *1972* and multiply it by 100. Then divide your answer by the information for 1967. This last answer is called the *index number for 1972,* with 1967 as the *base year.* Let us do one as an example. First, for Europe; take the 1972 information (42) and multiply it by 100. The answer is 4200 ($42 \times 100 = 4200$). Then divide this answer by the 1967 information (72). The answer is 58.3 ($4200 \div 72 = 58.3$). This last answer is called the index number for 1972, with 1967 as the base year. Now calculate index numbers in the same way for Asia, the U.S.A., West Indies, and Other. The index numbers you have just calculated tell you quite a lot about the way immigration into Canada is changing. If the number is *over 100* then it means that the item is increasing, and the more the number is over 100 then the faster it is increasing. If the number is 200 then the item has doubled, and if it is *over 200* then it has *more than doubled,* and so on. On the other hand, if the number is *below 100* then the item is decreasing, and the more below 100 it is the faster it is decreasing.

● 18. Using the index numbers from the previous assignment, answer the following questions:
  (a) Which of Canada's immigrant sources decreased between 1967 and 1972?
  (b) Which *two* of Canada's immigrant sources increased most between 1967 and 1972?

## D: CHANGES IN THE OCCUPATIONS OF THE POPULATION

The earliest inhabitants of Canada, the Indians and Eskimos, were mainly hunters. If they were unsuccessful in the hunt, they starved. Some are still hunters; but today no one really starves. Life in Canada has changed.

The first major change in Canadian life occurred when settled farming was introduced. The need for permanent occupation of the land led to conflict between those who wanted to farm and those who wanted to hunt. The farmers won. The land was accordingly surveyed and settled, and the government advertised for new colonists to come and farm the land. Most early settlers therefore became farmers. They acquired their parcels of land and learned how to farm in the Canadian environment. This was difficult even for people skilled in farming, for the Canadian environment posed problems with the length of its growing season, the nature of its soils, and the types of crops suitable for growing; but it was a more frightening prospect for the majority of the settlers, for they had not farmed before they came to Canada. Nevertheless, they struggled and succeeded, and Canada became renowned throughout the world for its farmers.

Conflict was fairly subdued. There were no large battles or any such extensive fighting as occurred in the opening of the United States.

There was always a strong market among farmers, however, for labour saving machinery. Labour was frequently scarce in newly settled areas, and inventors were constantly busy trying to make machines that could be substituted for human labour. Farming therefore provided a ready market for much early industrialization. With the advent of large scale industrialization during the late 1800s many farmers left their farms, selling them to other farmers who could operate afterwards on a larger scale. The trek from the land into the cities was therefore caused by a change of jobs. Factory work gradually replaced farm work as the most dominant type of occupational activity.

We should note the importance of Massey and Harris in setting up one of the most important agricultural industries, namely the manufacture of farming equipment. Their firm has now grown to be, in Massey-Ferguson Ltd., one of the world's chief farm machinery manufacturers. World headquarters are in Toronto.

**Figure 5-26** Canada has become renowned for its farming.

**Figure 5-27** Farmers provide a market for labour saving machinery.

**Figure 5-28** Factory operations are also very efficient and relatively few people are needed to generate a large output.

Inventions did not cease merely because people now worked largely in factories. Indeed, they continued and factory operations therefore gradually became more efficient. The result of this increased factory efficiency meant not only that more goods could be produced by a single worker but also that a smaller proportion of the total population was needed to work in the burgeoning factories. Just as people had left the farm in an earlier time, so they now left the factories. They moved into a variety of service industries.

The service sector of the economy provides jobs which involve doing things for people rather than making things, although the distinction is not entirely clear cut. For example, selling goods in a store is a service occupation, as is dentistry. Other examples of service occupations are teaching, medical care, bus driving, telephone maintenance, and entertainment. The service sector now provides the bulk of jobs for Canadians. The economy has changed quite enormously from its early hunting stage. Even since its pioneer farming days, the country has changed greatly, as Figure 5-29 illustrates.

Primary economic activities may be defined as those which are closely related to the direct interaction of people with the natural environment, such as with farming, forestry, mining, fishing, and hunting. Secondary economic activities are more concerned with the processing of primary products and their ultimate manufacture into consumer or capital goods. For example, the processing of timber into paper is a secondary activity; so also is the manufacture of a book, which is a consumer good. Equally, the production of steel from mined ore is a secondary activity, as is the ultimate use of the steel in the manufacture of papermaking machinery, which is a capital good because it helps to make even more goods. Tertiary economic activity is concerned more with the provision of services than with the creation of goods. Thus transportation, which moves goods from place to place, is a service, and therefore a tertiary activity.

**Figure 5-29   Changing Employment Patterns in Canada**

|           | 1881 | 1901 | 1921 | 1941 | 1951 | 1961 | 1971 |
|-----------|------|------|------|------|------|------|------|
| Primary   | 51.2 | 44.3 | 36.6 | 29.3 | 20.7 | 16.8 | 8.4  |
| Secondary | 29.4 | 27.8 | 26.5 | 26.3 | 32.6 | 31.7 | 26.8 |
| Tertiary  | 19.4 | 27.9 | 36.9 | 44.4 | 46.9 | 51.3 | 64.8 |

Note: Primary means jobs in farming, mining, forestry, hunting.
Secondary means jobs in manufacturing, processing, construction.
Tertiary means jobs in all services.

● 19. Write a short essay explaining what factors might influence a person's choice of work these days.

● 20. Graph the data in Figure 5-29. Compare your answer with Figure 5-6. Can you explain the connection between the two?

● 21. Many aspects of Canada's population have changed, as we have seen. What are the relationships which exist between the various changes?

● 22. How do you explain Canada's change from a primary producer to a tertiary producer?

# CHAPTER 6

# NORTHERN ONTARIO

## SUPPORT OF LIFE

## INTRODUCTION

Other workers who live in Southern Ontario, usually Toronto, but who depend upon Northern Ontario for their living include all the management staff of the mining and resource companies that operate through-out the north. The reverse is equally true, however, even more so, if anything. For instance, not a single forestry worker could survive in the north if it were not for the existence of southern markets. Equally not a single northern miner could exist, nor a single northern motel owner. The south supports the north much more than the north supports the south.

What do you think about when you hear the words *Northern Ontario*? Do you think of cold, snow, blackfly, swampland, and barren rock? Or of forests, lakes, streams, waterfalls, clear sunsets, few people, and the cry of the loon? Perhaps you think of mines and logging camps, of pulp mills and railway tracks, and of vacations, hunting lodges, and trap lines? Or maybe of steel and flour mills, of canals and ports, and of hydro dams and tall smoke-stacks? You probably think of them all, of course, for they are all part of the picture of Northern Ontario.

Northern Ontario may be defined as the area shown on Figure 6-1, stretching from Hudson Bay in the north to Muskoka in the south (though some people would say that Muskoka is part of Southern Ontario rather than Northern Ontario). This great area covers 815 150 km², or nearly 90% of the entire province. How-ever, it supports directly only about 850 000 people, or just over ten percent of Ontario's total population (Figure 6-2). We should note, though, that many people who do not actually live in Northern Ontario depend on it for their jobs: metal researchers in Toronto, for example, or pulp and paper workers at Thorold. So the northern 90% of the province actually supports more than the ten percent of the population who in fact live there. Neverthe-less let us stay with the ten percent who live there· How *do* they gain a living? Why is it that *more* people do not live there?

**Figure 6-1 Counties and Towns in Northern Ontario**

It's always fairly diffi-cult to decide where the borders of a geographical region are. This is because a geographical region is formed from the complex interaction of many variables, for example, a certain type of rock, a par-ticular sort of land-scape, a special quality of climate, a distinctive culture, and a singular economy. The problem of borders is com-pounded by the transitional nature of change in many of these variables; for example, who can say exactly where a wet area becomes a dry area, or where a densely settled region becomes a sparsely settled region? The transition in these cases is gradual, and it is impossible to put a precise boundary around even one of the variables. When it comes to putting a boundary around a region which is characterized by special qualities in several variables, then the problem becomes almost impossible to solve. For this reason, it is not easy to de-scribe exactly the area comprising Northern Ontario.

## A: HOW DO THE PEOPLE OF NORTHERN ONTARIO GAIN A LIVING? PRIMARY ACTIVITIES

The people of Northern Ontario are engaged in many different occupations because of their wide variety of interests and oppor-tunities. It is normal to classify economic activities into three main groups — *primary, secondary,* and *tertiary.* We shall look at primary activities first. The reason for this is that primary activities are basic to all the rest; not only did they develop first, but they also help to support the others. Examples of primary activities include farming and mining. They are activities which are closely connected with the use of the land.

Remember, *boreal* means *northern;* n.b.=northern, boreal.

Bear in mind what we said earlier about transitions: Muskoka is *not* divided from the Boreal zone by a line which runs along the county boundary between Muskoka and Parry Sound. There is instead a gradual transition from the characteristics of the Boreal zone to those of the Modified Continental zone, and the transition is most noticeable in the Parry Sound-Muskoka area. The transitional nature of Parry Sound and Muskoka is emphasized by the fact that both are composed of a southward extension of the northern rocks, and yet both have economies which are largely northward extensions of the southern lifestyle. There is considerable overlap, and the boundary between Northern Ontario and Southern Ontario is certainly not a clear line along the Parry Sound-Muskoka border.

The example of Holland Marsh in Southern Ontario shows us that marsh, if drained, can be enormously fertile and very productive. Why is northern marsh not drained?

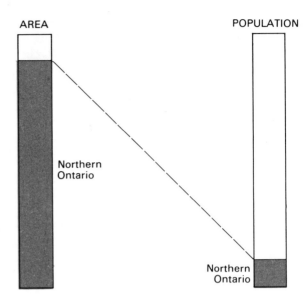

**Figure 6-2  Northern Ontario's Share of Ontario's Area and Population**

AREA

Northern Ontario

POPULATION

Northern Ontario

## Farming

Compare Figure 6-1 with Figure 2-4. You will see that most of Northern Ontario lies in the Boreal climate zone. The exception is the small county of Muskoka, which lies in the Modified Continental climate zone. In Chapter 2 you will also find the climate statistics for Kapuskasing, which is a fairly typical centre for Northern Ontario. If you compare them with the other statistics given in Chapter 2 you can probably see that Northern Ontario, as represented by Kapuskasing, has fewer months with average temperatures above freezing point than all the other regions except the Arctic.

The relatively low average temperatures and the short growing season in Northern Ontario mean that farming is not easy. Frost is a danger to crops both in late spring and in early fall; newly planted crops can suffer just as much as nearly ripened ones. A further climatic disadvantage is the rainfall. Even though there is adequate precipitation, it comes when it is not wanted, especially during ripening and harvesting time when the crops can be badly damaged by too much rain.

In addition to climatic disadvantages for farming there are also some landscape disadvantages. Figure 3-1 shows you that nearly all of Northern Ontario lies in the region of the *Canadian Shield*. You will see from Topographic Map #1 and Figures 3-5 and 3-6 in Chapter 3 that the landscape of the Shield is not suited to farming. It is generally too rocky, too uneven, or too marshy. Nevertheless, despite the disadvantages, there *is* some farming practised in Northern Ontario. It is carried out on patches of ground that were the silty floors of lakes at the end of the Ice Age. The largest of these lakes (there were many) was Lake Ojibway, but like many of the others it has now drained away. The silty lake floor still exists, however. Today, it is called the *Clay Belt,* and it lies in the region from Hearst to Cochrane (Figure 6-3). Unfortunately there is an abundance of acidic peat (decomposed vegetation) over the clay, and this — together with the trees — has to be cleared away before farming can take place. It is not easy. Even when the land *is* ready it is difficult to grow a wide variety of crops because the climate is so restrictive. Potatoes and hay are the chief crops, and many cattle are kept. Generally the region does not produce enough food, and extra food has to be imported into Northern Ontario, not only to make up the required quantities but also for the sake of some variety.

Many glacial lakes were caused by the meltwater from the ice being trapped between a rise in the land and the ice face itself. Eventually, when the ice melted away altogether, the ice-dammed lake automatically drained away. Other ice dammed lakes drained away by pouring out through channels which they cut for themselves across the rise in the land, such channels being called spillways or overflow channels. Still other meltwater lakes were tipped out of their hollows, or lake basins, as the land rebounded from its depressed state after the ice melted. Many of the largest glacial lakes have thus disappeared; but many others still remain.

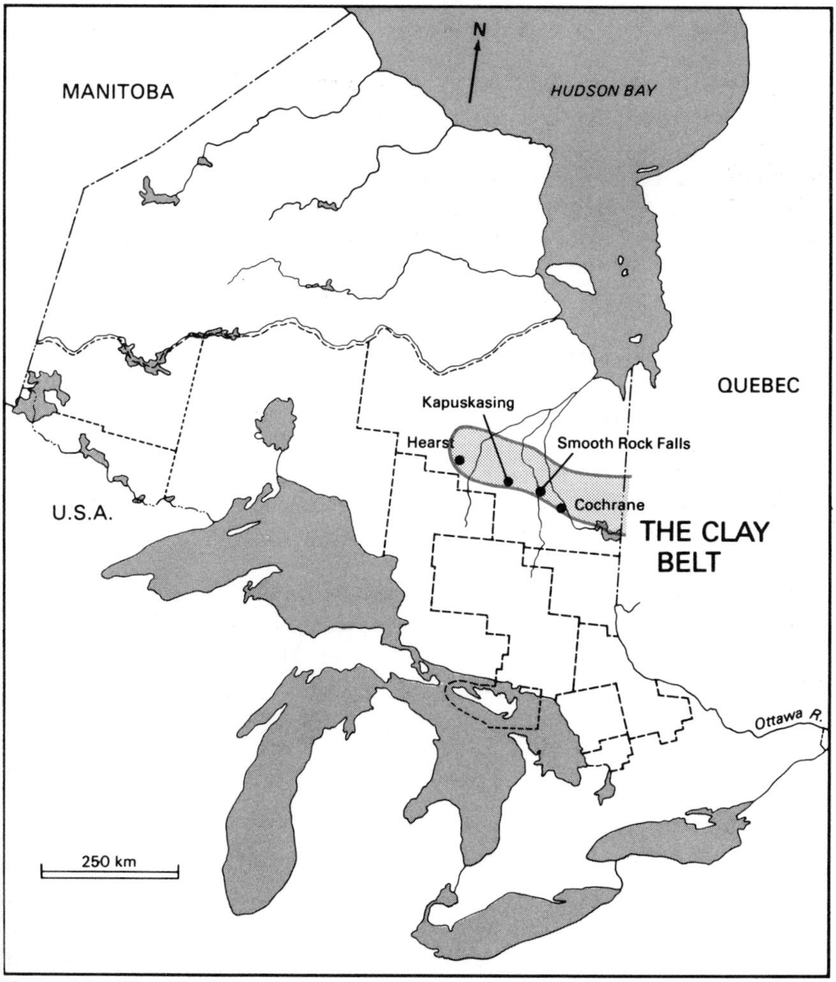

Decomposed vegetation is different from decayed vegetation. Decomposed vegetation, which forms peat, is usually waterlogged and does not benefit much from the action of bacteria and oxygen. Decayed vegetation, which produces humus, enjoys the positive action of both bacteria and oxygen.

**Figure 6-3   The Clay Belt**

# Cheap Land Lures Ranchers Up North

A newspaper report has noted a new and startling development in Ontario farming. Farmers are quoted as responding to a new call to the north, and are driving cattle 500 km north of Toronto to areas where land is not only cheap but plentiful. Douglas Maus, formerly of Ayr, 25 km south of Kitchener, is not untypical. He is one of Ontario's largest farmers, who is now setting up operations to compete with farmers in the U.S. Maus and his two younger brothers have recently finished a western-style round up in their experiment at cattle raising on the Clay Belt of northern Ontario.

What made the Maus boys turn to northern Ontario? "Cheap land."

According to Doug and his brothers, land in southern Ontario is becoming too expensive to raise cattle for market. So they moved north to the Clay Belt. "This land hasn't seen a plough in 30 years," Doug says. "We came up here to experiment and the first year of operation has seen some success."

The three brothers, along with Milo and Ross Schantz and Len Weeden have developed a 1000 ha ranchland operation in the Val Gagne area. Doug himself has picked up a further 500 ha in a block 30 km south. "We expect next year to have 1000 head of cattle on the northern spread," Doug says. "It will be a cow-calf operation, and we will ship the cows south for finishing on our home farm.

To A u g u s t a s Beauchesne, the government's agricultural representative in the area the move is "just great". Gus has three to four southern Ontario farmers visit him every week looking for land. "Land is growing in demand here; it's what we need." To Ted Gibson of the Cochrane Chamber of Commerce, the move north is wonderful. "We need the population," he says. Ontario's Minister of Agriculture says that the province is cooperating in the development of the north.

Northern Ontario has had some setbacks in the past, despite the early government offers of free land, a free cow, and free feed. One of the worst setbacks was the great fire of 1916, which swept across the north, killing hundreds. However, the fire also cleared a great deal of land for farming. Thomas Aitkens, with a family farm near Guelph, now has 500 ha of northern ranchland: "You just can't do it in southern Ontario where the price of land has gone sky high," he says.

## Forestry

Forestry came into Northern Ontario along with farming for the same reason: Southern Ontario appeared to be fully used and the best place to expand to was Northern Ontario (see the article *Cheap Land Lures Ranchers Up North*). In the south the forests were cut and cleared very early in Ontario's development because they occupied land that the pioneers wanted for farmland. But when the south was subsequently cleared and farmed then the pioneers turned to the north. The early northern forestry industry was therefore associated with the clearing of land for farming, as in the Clay Belt, where Hearst, Kapuskasing, Smooth Rock Falls and Iroquois Falls rapidly developed important pulp and paper industries (Figure 6-4). Other important forestry industries developed at about the same time (the 1880s and 1890s) near Lake Superior, where there was easy access to the then frantically growing U.S. market. Examples of Lake Superior pulp and paper mills include those at Thunder Bay, Nipigon, Terrace Bay, Marathon and Sault Ste Marie. Additional pulp and paper mills were later opened at Kenora, Dryden, and Fort Frances (Figure 6-4).

When settlers move into an area for the first time, they tend to settle on the best land for their purpose, leaving the other land empty. Later settlers therefore have to use this empty land, unless they can buy the first settlers out. Still later settlers face even more of a problem in that there is virtually no free land left, although the price they have to pay obviously varies according to the land they wish to purchase. Clearly, the most preferred land costs the most. As time passes, land thus acquires a price, and as population grows the price of land in preferred areas obviously rises. Indeed, you might even say that the price of land reflects peoples' preferences, and that land use in turn reflects peoples' abilities and wishes to pay whatever the market price is. There is just as much certainty that a cattle ranch in downtown Toronto would go broke, because no one would be able to afford the costly beef, as there is that a large office complex in the woods near Cochrane would remain empty and the builder go bankrupt because no one would wish to run a major commercial operation a great distance from other commercial operations.

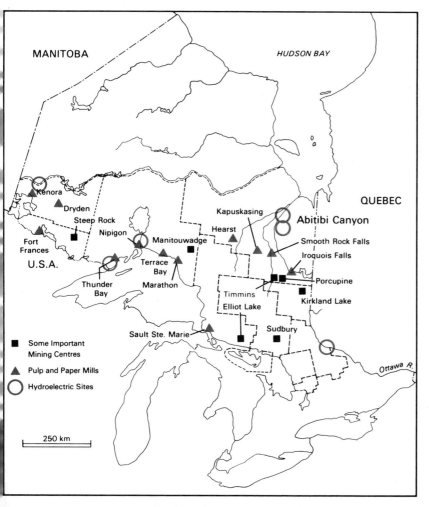

**Figure 6-4 Pulp and Paper Mills, Important Mining Centres, and Hydro Sites**

The pulp and paper industry *has* to be efficient, because it could not compete if it were not. Many other areas of the world are suitable for the growing of pulp and paper trees, and in most of these other areas the trees grow more quickly than they do in Northern Ontario, thus permitting a smaller area of forest to support a pulp mill of a given output (and thereby making transportation costs from the forest to the mill much cheaper, as well as reducing forest rental costs).

Such happy accidents are not so common nowadays. In the early prospecting days, most of the searching was done by individual propectors who were usually adventurers at heart. Very few were business people, or organizers of mining enterprises. As a result there was an almost party-like excitement surrounding most of the early discoveries. However, as mining became established, and the need for large-scale organization was seen, the days of the happy prospector gradually came to an end. Most searching is now done instead by highly trained company teams, operating with a great deal of technological assistance.

The products of the pulp and paper mills range from newsprint to fine tissues. Most of the products go into the U.S. market, but the industry is so big that it supplies markets in Europe and South America as well. The industry is also very efficient and could be expanded if the world demand for paper increases.

The chief problems facing the pulp and paper industry are the remoteness of the mills from large markets, the increasing distance of the cuttable areas of forest from the mills, and the relatively long time it takes for trees to grow in the Boreal climate. There are solutions to some of these problems of course: seedling trees can be planted in areas close to the mill that have already been cut over (this process is called *reforestation*), and research can be done into ways of making trees grow more quickly. Nevertheless the region is under strong pressure of competition from the southeastern United States, where trees not only grow much more quickly but are also much closer to major American markets.

## Mining

Mining developed largely by chance. Indeed one of the largest gold mines near Timmins (the Dome mine) was accidentally discovered by a man slipping on a hillside. Tom Flanagan was climbing up a slope when he missed his footing. As he slipped, his boot tore away the moss on the rock, revealing a tremendously rich gold deposit! Gold is not so important now as it was, but at the time it provided (a) the incentive for much prospecting and exploration, (b) the initial reason for the growth of towns, such as Timmins and Kirkland Lake, (c) the profits for investment in other mines producing other minerals such as lead, zinc, copper, and iron, and (d) the justification for the expansion of road, rail, and port facilities.

There are too many minerals for us to examine each one, and too many mining camps for us to note them all, so we will just select a few of the more important ones. However, before we do, let us note that mining is even more important to the people of Northern Ontario than forestry. Indeed for every person employed as a miner there are 12 others engaged in processing, transporting, and manufacturing the minerals. As you can see, then, mining is really very important.

Some of the more important minerals and mining camps (Figure 6-4) are:

(a) The Sudbury Basin centres for nickel, copper, and iron (Figure 6-6). The first metal produced here was copper, and the miners used to regard the nickel as an impurity. Indeed the word *nickel* in German (where many early miners came from) means a *troublesome being.* It got in the way — until a use was discovered for it in hardening steel. Now it is very important, and Sudbury is the world's largest producer. Reserves are huge, and production could be expanded if necessary. The same rock ores also yield iron, so the Sudbury region is additionally fortunate.

(b) Elliot Lake. This is a fairly new town, specially built to house workers in the uranium mines. With the increasing use of nuclear power by Ontario Hydro the future of Elliot Lake looks quite promising.

(c) The Timmins and Porcupine centres for zinc, copper, and gold. The decline of gold mining here has been offset by the development of one of the world's largest lead and zinc mines at Kidd Creek just north of Timmins.

**Figure 6-5**   This is the headframe of the Shebandowan nickel mine near Thunder Bay.

The origin of the Sudbury Basin is thought to have been a huge meteorite which crashed into the earth many millions of years ago when the rocks of the Canadian Shield were still not fully formed. The splashing and disruption caused by the impact were thought to have caused the earth at Sudbury to be bent into a basin shape, and to be partly filled in its lower layers by freshly molten rock from underneath the Shield.

Two of the largest companies operating in the Sudbury region are International Nickel Company Limited, called INCO for short, and Falconbridge Nickel. Both are Canadian companies, headquartered in Toronto; both are amongst the world's largest nickel mining companies (indeed, INCO *is* the largest).

There is some controversy surrounding the use of nuclear power for the generation of electricity. However, it looks likely that nuclear power will remain important, and maybe become even more important.

**Figure 6-6 A Simplified Sketch of the Sudbury Basin**

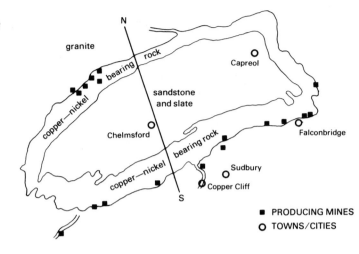

**Figure 6-7    Cross Section North to South Across the Sudbury Basin**

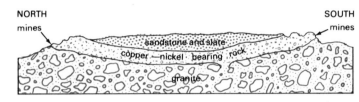

The Kidd Creek mine is so rich that it was worthwhile for the Canada Development Corporation to buy a controlling interest in the mine's owners, namely Texasgulf.

The reason that industry is close to markets rather than to raw material sources is that generally it is cheaper to ship raw materials than it is to ship finished products. Moreover, manufacturing operations require plenty of labour, which is more available at the market.

Mining companies also send out search and exploration teams. Searching for new resources is quite a big business in itself.

(d) Iron and gold at Kirkland Lake. Here too gold has virtually disappeared, but has been replaced by very profitable iron mining.

(e) Copper, zinc, lead, gold, and silver at Manitouwadge. This is a new development and is very rich.

(f) Iron at Steep Rock. This too is a new development. The iron ore is so rich (over 60% iron) that it was worth draining a lake (Steep Rock Lake) to get at the iron. Unfortunately, it is not a very large deposit.

Most of the minerals produced in Northern Ontario are used in industry. However, since industry is close to markets wherever possible, this means that most of the minerals are sent out of the area, usually to the U.S.A., where the chief industries are located. In order to keep transportation costs down, the minerals are usually *reduced* or *concentrated* in Northern Ontario (i.e., much of the unwanted rock is taken out of the ore). In some places, Sudbury for instance, the minerals are also *refined* (i.e., all the unwanted rock is eliminated), but this is an expensive process, and it is not done everywhere.

Another way in which people make a living through the mining industry is by prospecting and mapping. The Ontario Department of Mines sends out about 25 prospecting and mapping parties

**Figure 6-8** An ore crusher, to reduce or concentrate the ore.

each year. The work of finding and knowing the rocks and minerals of the Shield is by no means finished. It will take years, and who knows what discoveries may still be made?

**Figure 6-9** Part of a giant nickel refinery at Sudbury.

The fish become polluted by living in water that is polluted. One of the most serious pollutants in the waters of Northern Ontario has been mercury, leading to the fears of what came to be called *Minimata Disease*. Minimata is a place in Japan. There used to be a large factory emitting mercury waste into the sea near it, and when Minimata's fishing community caught and ate fish that had lived in these waters, they gradually became sick. The sickness was a disease of the nervous system that caused sufferers from it to lose control of their limbs, to go blind, and to become mentally deficient. Some of these symptoms appeared in Northern Ontario's Indians during the early 1970s, and many people suspected Minimata Disease. It was never proved; but mercury pollution was nevertheless legislated against.

## Indian Ways of Life

Hunting, trapping, and fishing are the traditional ways of life of the Indians, who were the first occupants of Northern Ontario. Animals were and still are hunted for meat and hides, while fish were and still are an important alternative foodstuff. Crops have never been grown widely because the climate is generally not suitable. Indians who still live in the traditional ways, though now on reserves, are finding that the old lifestyles are increasingly difficult to maintain in the face of water pollution which contaminates the fish and the temptations of welfare and city jobs. Not all streams are polluted, of course, but there have nevertheless been several instances (especially in Kenora Territorial District) where the provincial government has been forced to ban fishing to the Indians for the sake of their health. Deprived of their traditional support of life, many Indians have been forced to go on welfare or to seek jobs outside of the reserves. Others have created their own jobs within the reserves — for example, by acting as guides to non-Indians who wish to go on hunting or fishing trips. There are also some Indians who have set up co-operatives to produce various things. A good example of an Indian co-operative is *Widjiitiwin,* which was started by some Ojibway Indians near Kenora. Widjiitiwin produces logs and pulpwood for sale to the paper companies at Kenora and Dryden. It is a great success.

Other Indians gain an income from selling furs to dealers from North Bay, where the world's largest wild fur auctions are held (as distinct from ranch furs, where animals are bred in captivity and whose furs are sold chiefly in Montreal).

Altogether there are about 22 100 Indians living on reserves in Northern Ontario, or about 2.6% of the North's population. There are probably almost as many living away from the reserves, in various towns such as Sioux Lookout and Nakina. Thus about five percent of Northern Ontario's population is probably Indian in origin, compared with only about 0.2% of Southern Ontario's population.

The word *reserves* is the Canadian term; *reservations* is their name in the States.

● 1. Using the climate statistics in Chapter 2,
  (a) count up the number of months at each location with average temperatures above freezing point (0°C), and
  (b) note the average annual temperature.

(c) Rank the locations in order, with the one with the largest number of average monthly temperatures above freezing point (Vancouver) at the top. Where does Northern Ontario rank? How would you describe its climate in relation to the others?

*Can you remember what it is about the climate that makes it unsuitable for the growing of crops?*

● 2. Using the climate statistics in Chapter 2,
   (a) add up the precipitation figures for May-June-July-August-September for Kapuskasing, Regina, Toronto, Penticton, and then
   (b) add up the August-September portion only, and
   (c) calculate the August-September portion as a percentage of the May-June-July-August-September total.
   (d) Which place has the highest percentage of its summer rain during the ripening and harvesting time of August-September?

● 3. Which part of Northern Ontario does *not* lie in the region of the Canadian Shield?

● 4. Using the information in section A of this chapter, answer the following questions:
   (a) What is the silty floor of the former Lake Ojibway now called?
   (b) Give two reasons why Northern Ontario must import food.
   (c) What two things have had to be removed from the surface of the Clay Belt before it could be used for farming?
   (d) What are the chief crops of the Clay Belt?
   (e) Name four important pulp and paper towns in the Clay Belt.
   (f) Give two reasons why pulp and paper industries grew on the shores of Lake Superior.
   (g) Could the pulp and paper industry be expanded?
   (h) What problems face the pulp and paper industry today?
   (i) What is meant by the term *reforestation*?

● 5. Give four reasons why the discovery of gold was so important to mining in Northern Ontario.

● 6. (a) What mineral is produced at Elliot Lake?
   (b) What is the name of the world's largest nickel producing area?
   (c) What mineral is now produced at Kirkland Lake instead of gold?
   (d) Why is the iron at Steep Rock so important?

● 7. Despite the many disadvantages to farming in Northern Ontario, there is nevertheless one major advantage. Describe what it is, and say how it affects farming.

## B: HOW DO THE PEOPLE OF NORTHERN ONTARIO GAIN A LIVING?   SECONDARY AND TERTIARY ACTIVITIES

Secondary activities are generally concerned with the processing of raw materials and their eventual *manufacture* into **goods** of some sort. Tertiary activities, on the other hand, are not concerned with making things at all, but with *doing* things. Often, tertiary activities are described as being the provision of **services**, such as transportation, education, health care, entertainment, and so on.

### Manufacturing

Manufacturing in Northern Ontario can be described as basic: there are no transistor radio factories or car assembly lines. Nevertheless it is very important. Indeed if you add the different types of manufacturing together, it produces more value for the Northern Ontarians than either forestry or mining (though you should note that it depends on these two activities a great deal for its raw materials).

The chief types of manufacturing are (a) the production of steel and steel goods at Sault Ste Marie, (b) flour milling at Thunder Bay, (c) papermaking — as distinct from pulp — at various centres as shown in Figure 6-4, and (d) the manufacture of transport equipment (especially buses and rail cars) at Thunder Bay.

As you can see manufacturing is not widely scattered. It is mostly located in the large towns because it requires a plentiful labour supply.

### Hydro Production

Some people in Northern Ontario depend for their livelihood on power generation and transmission. There are many large silt-free rivers and there are therefore several large power dams, such as those in the Abitibi Canyon district (Figure 6-4) and around the northern edge of Lake Superior. (By the way, why do you think it is an advantage for the rivers to be free of silt? And how do you think they came to be like this?) Much of the electricity which is generated in the north is used in powering mills, mines, concentrators, and smelters, as well as in supplying some of the towns in Southern Ontario in addition to those in the north.

Remember that manufacturing of consumer goods requires both a large labour supply and ready access to market.

The chief types of manufacturing in Northern Ontario are clearly related to its major geographical characteristics. The processing of raw materials is the most important group, followed by the manufacture of transport equipment. This pattern makes sense in a region which is rich in raw materials and remote from large markets.

Perhaps the chief requirement for a successful hydro dam is regularity of water flow. The numerous lakes of Northern Ontario help greatly in this regard.

## Transportation

The upper Great Lakes waterway has long been important as a support of life in Northern Ontario. It increased in importance with the building of the locks at The Soo (properly called Sault Ste Marie) in the 1850s, and this importance was enhanced even further as the interior of the continent was opened up, culminating in 1959 with the opening of the St. Lawrence Seaway, giving Lake Superior access to the Atlantic Ocean. Numerous ports rely upon the waterway and its enormous traffic, notably Thunder Bay and Sault Ste. Marie.

Railway construction came later than the waterway and was not really needed until after British Columbia and, later the Prairies, had joined the Canadian nation. Then two transcontinental lines

*Sault* is an old French word for *rapids*. The frequency of French names along the shores of the Great Lakes is a relic of the days of the voyageurs, and the attempts by France to create a New France in the Americas.

*Superior* means *upper*. Lake Superior is the uppermost of the Great Lakes, in that it is farthest from the sea and the highest above it. Generally all the great lakes above the Detroit River are called the upper lakes, while those below the Detroit River are called the lower lakes. Which lakes are which, individually?

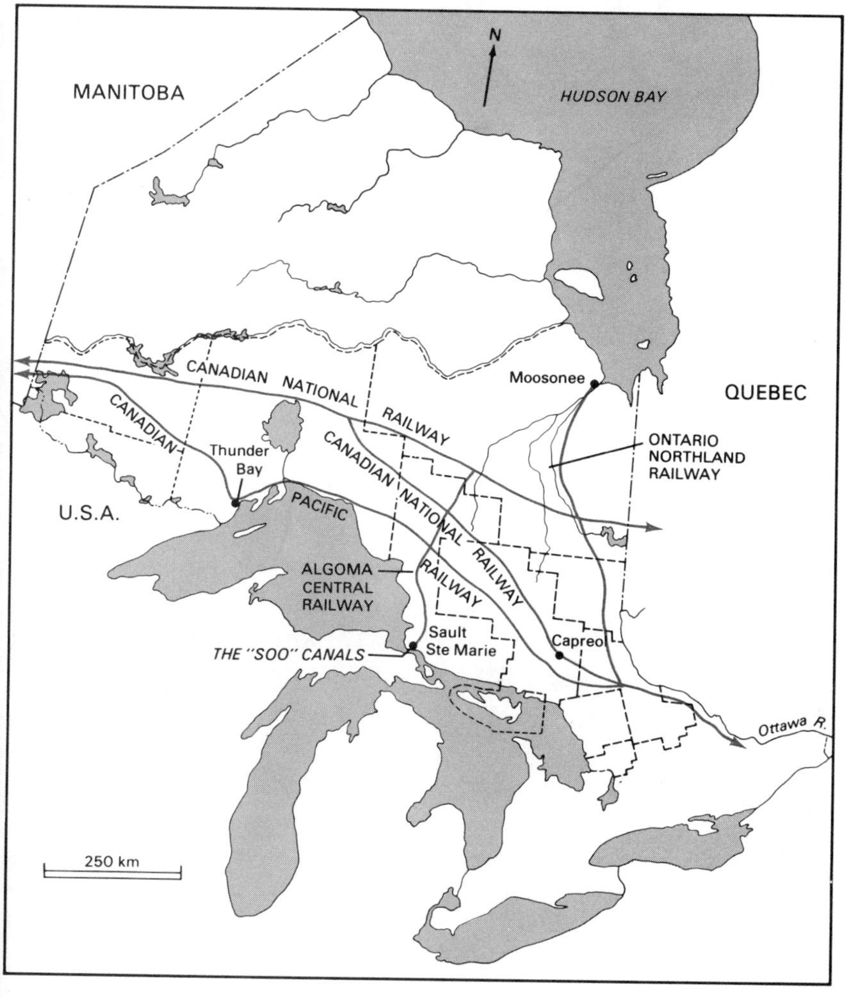

**Figure 6-10   Rail and Shipping Facilities in Northern Ontario**

**Figure 6-11** A ship entering the Soo canals from Lake Superior.

Thunder Bay had its reason for existence and growth in two things: first, it was the *head of navigation* on the Canadian side of the lakes, i.e., it was as far as you could go *up* the waterway before you had to transfer onto the land, and second, it was the closest point of navigable water for the produce being sent out of the landbound prairies. Sault Ste. Marie had its origins in its control of navigation passing through the Great Lakes between Superior and Huron, the more especially because of its rapids and the need for, first, portages, and second, locks. It also marks one of the few points where the Great Lakes system can be crossed easily between Canada and the United States.

were pushed across the Northern Ontario Shield, first by the Canadian Pacific Railway (CPR), and second by what later became the Canadian National Railway (CNR). Because the construction and maintenance of these railways was (and still is) enormously difficult (because of rocks and marshes and winter snow, which also produces spring floods when it melts) there had (and still have) to be

**Figure 6-12** The main street of Hornepayne, a railway town in northern Ontario.

a number of centres to look after the railways. Capreol is an example of such a railway town (Figure 6-10).

In addition to the two transcontinental railways there are also two local railways. These run from south to north. The most important for passenger traffic is the Ontario Northland Railway from North Bay through Cochrane to Moosonee, while the most important for freight is the Algoma Central Railway from Sault Ste Marie to Hearst (Figure 6-10).

People in Northern Ontario are less dependent upon road and air transportation than on waterways and railways. However, we

The Ontario Northland Railway is often nicknamed the *Polar Bear Express,* even though it does not pass anywhere close to areas containing polar bears.

Both of the local railways carry passengers and freight. The Polar Bear Express carries all the freight that's needed north of Cochrane, for there are no roads. On the other hand, one of the most famous trips on the Algoma Central is the passenger trip to Agawa Canyon.

**Figure 6-13** The Polar Bear Express of the Ontario Northland Railway.

should note that the Trans-Canada Highway has two routes across the Shield: a less important northern route through Cochrane and Hearst, and a more important southern route through Sudbury and Sault Ste Marie. As far as air transport is concerned, the chief population centre supported by supplying this service is North Bay.

## Tourism

After manufacturing, tourism is the second most important way in which the people of Northern Ontario earn their living. They do it by providing all the things tourists need and by looking after all the places that tourists visit. Thus they run hotels and motels, lodges and parks, gas stations and restaurants.

Most people do not work full time in providing services to tourists (though a few do). Instead they just earn more money when the tourists come. Most tourists come from the United States, in search of clean air, open lakes, and peace and quiet. Northern Ontario has a lot to offer, and the tourist industry could be greatly expanded if necessary.

**Figure 6-14** The passenger stop at Agawa Canyon on the Algoma Central Railway.

● 8. Describe the different ways in which pollutants from ore processing may be put to use in Northern Ontario. Refer to the article *Pollutants Turned into Fertilizer.*

● 9. Give reasons for the difficulty of maintaining railway operations across the Shield.

● 10. How is a town supported by *supplying* a service rather than by receiving it?

● 11. Look through sections A *and* B of this chapter and list all the life support activities that could be expanded. Do they conflict with one another in any way? If so, how? If choices have to be made between competing activities, what sort of considerations should there be?

# Pollutants Turned into Fertilizers

Reduce air pollution, make money and help grow food all at the same time.

This is a good combination in the Sudbury district where pollution of the air has been a problem for many years.

The smoke coming out of the tall stacks from the big ore reduction plants in the area puts a lot of sulphur dioxide in the air.

Canadian Industries Ltd., Montreal, takes some of the gases which otherwise would go up the stacks and turns them into sulphuric acid and liquid sulphur dioxide. Half the sulphuric acid produced goes into the making of chemical fertilizers.

The sulphuric acid complex of CIL is at the iron ore recovery plant of International Nickel Co. of Canada, Copper Cliff, the western suburb of Sudbury. This installation actually comprising three separate plants, is CIL's main production centre for this product in Canada. Capacity was increased from 300 000 tons to 700 000 tons[1] yearly in April, 1967, when No. 4 plant went on stream. This plant, when built, was the single largest metallurgical sulphuric acid plant in the world. Its raw material is the sulphur dioxide emanating from the roasters at Inco's iron ore recovery plant.

**Largest in World**

The liquid sulphur dioxide plant, located at Inco's Copper Cliff smelter has been producing 90 000 tons[2] yearly for the past several years. It is CIL's only liquid sulphur dioxide plant and is by far the largest plant of this type in the world, Joshua Fitch, works manager, said. Its raw material is the strong sulphur dioxide gas coming from an Inco flash furnace.

Recent selling prices were $31 per ton of sulphuric acid and $39 per ton of liquid sulphur dioxide, both fob Copper Cliff.

Capital invested in these plants is around $20 million. They employ about 130 in all (30 staff and 100 hourly rated employees). All operations are an around-the-clock basis.

Expansion, now under way, of Inco's iron recovery plant will make much more gas available. CIL is studying the possibility of further expansion here.

About half of the sulphuric acid produced goes into the making of fertilizers. A substantial portion is shipped to the company's fertilizer complex at Courtright, near Sarnia.

The other half of the production goes into a wide range of uses, such as in the uranium processing plants at Elliot Lake, 100 miles[3] west and in the titanium pigment, petroleum, chemical and pulp and paper industries and back into the nickel extraction industry.

Almost all of the liquid sulphur dioxide produced at Copper Cliff goes to the pulp and paper industry where it is used in making sulphite pulp.

CIL has a fleet of 300 tank cars with a capacity of 100 tons[4] of acid each for its Copper Cliff operations.

Much of the production goes out by 36-car unit trains. A considerable portion of sulphuric acid also goes out by tank trunks (as to the Elliot Lake uranium mines).

Simon Carves of Canada Ltd., Toronto, was the contractor for the $6–million No. 4 sulphuric acid plant.

[3] 160 km
[4] 90 t

[1] 270 000 t to 630 000 t

[2] 81 000 t

from *The Financial Post*, December 7, 1968

## C: WHY DON'T MORE PEOPLE LIVE IN NORTHERN ONTARIO?

There is a vast amount of space and there are many opportunities for expansion. What holds people back?

One reason is the newness of Northern Ontario. As Canada slowly gains population, so the *first* settled areas gradually fill up. People then start to settle in the *second* areas. Northern Ontario is a "second area" of this type, and it has not yet had the time or pressure to grow. In any event Southern Ontario is not yet really full, so there is at present no strong pressure to develop the north.

Another reason is the cold winter weather, which some people enjoy, but many do not. Yet another is the poor farming quality of the land and the climate, which means that food has to be imported, making it costly. And still another is the fact that not many people live there yet. Most people like to live where there are already many people, because then there are better stores, better entertainment, better health care, and so on. Look back to your answer to question 6 in Chapter 5 to see why existing population centres attract even more people and why relatively empty areas lose people. Northern Ontario is quite typical of such areas: it is growing in population very slowly indeed compared with Southern Ontario because more people are leaving Northern Ontario than are moving in. Not only that, but *within* Northern Ontario people are leaving the countryside and the small towns and moving instead to the few large towns such as Thunder Bay (population 115 000), Sault Ste Marie (population 80 000), Sudbury (population 90 000), and North Bay (population 50 000). Many towns advertise their attractions in order to obtain new industries.

It is more than likely that if food was grown locally instead it would be even more costly. Why is this?

If more people are leaving Northern Ontario than are moving in, how is it possible for the population to grow at all, let alone very slowly?

Why is it advantageous for a small town to grow?

● 12. One of the dreams that some people have about developing the northland is called the *Mid-Canada Corridor* idea. This is not concerned only with Northern Ontario; it is also concerned with other parts of Canada that lie in the Boreal zone. See if you can find out anything about it, and then — with reasons and examples — write about half a page saying what you think about the idea.

# CHAPTER 7

# SOUTHERN ONTARIO

## REGIONALISM

## INTRODUCTION

Why don't you try to write down a list of some of the things that come to mind when you think of Southern Ontario? Right now, that is, before you even go on to the next sentence.

What did you write down? Was it lots of people? Factories and industry? Cars? Expressways? Towns and cities? Many farms? Large lakes and beaches? Ports and trade? Pollution? High rise towers and large shopping malls? Recreation and sport? Good, they are all correct. However, what do you notice about your present list compared with what you thought of for Chapter 6? It's different, isn't it?

Of course; it's different because Southern Ontario is a different sort of region. What we have to do in this chapter is to examine just what it is that makes Southern Ontario a *region* that is identifiably different from other regions; in other words, why your list for Southern Ontario is different from your list for Northern Ontario, and why it would be different from lists for the Arctic or British Columbia or the Prairies or the Maritimes or Quebec.

There are many reasons, as you can imagine. We have already examined some of them: the climate and the landscape, for example. But there are others too, such as farming, industry, population densities, and trade.

We can look at these things in many ways. What we shall do first in section A is look at the various things as simple facts, so that you know the basic data, such as the population, the types of economic activities, and the locations of the cities. After that, section B will try to answer some of your questions. And then finally in section C we shall look at the role of Southern Ontario in the life of Canada: just how important is it, really?

A *region* may be defined in geography as a part of the earth's surface that has some quality or combination of qualities that make it recognizably different from other parts of the world. The differentiating characteristics may be physical in type, such as rock structure or climate, or they may be human in origin, such as ethnic composition, economy, language, culture, and form of government. Most frequently, however, they are a combination of several qualities, coming together in a unique blend to give the geographical region an individuality or personality of its own.

## A: BASIC DATA

Southern Ontario consists of the area shown on the map of the counties in Figure 7-1. You will notice that the boundary along the northern edge of Muskoka is marked with a broken line. Why do you think this is? Have a look back at the counties of Northern Ontario in Chapter 6 if you feel you would like a reminder.

Excluding Muskoka, the land area of Southern Ontario is approximately 110 000 km², or about 12% of Ontario's total area. The population was approximately 7 550 000 in 1976 (6 864 415 in 1971), thus creating a population density of about 70 people per square kilometre. This contrasts sharply with the population density in Northern Ontario of about one person per square kilometre. Southern Ontario is thus approximately 70 times more crowded than Northern Ontario.

The chief population centres of Southern Ontario are shown in Figure 7-2, but there are many more small towns and villages scattered across the Southern Ontario landscape—too many to show in fact. Figure 7-3 on page 144 gives you a better idea of how widely people are scattered, even though it does not tell you any names.

Figure 1-17 shows you some other population densities for comparison. What do you notice about Southern Ontario's population density in relation to some in Europe and Asia?

**Figure 7-1   The Counties of Southern Ontario**

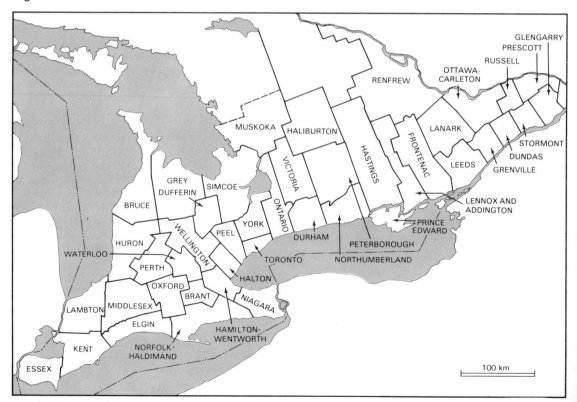

The people of Southern Ontario have created many different types of work for themselves. Many of them are farmers; indeed there are in total more farmers in Ontario than there are in any of the Prairie provinces. Even more are factory workers, and yet still more work in the service sector of the economy. Let us have a look at these in turn.

## Farming

Cattle form the basis of Southern Ontario's farming wealth. Mostly they are dairy cattle, particularly of the *Holstein* breed. The chief areas for specialized dairy farming are, first, eastern Ontario, which includes a broad band of counties eastwards from Northumberland, Peterborough, Hastings, and Renfrew to Prescott and Glengarry, and second, central western Ontario, especially a region centred around Oxford county. Despite these major concentrations, however, dairy cattle are to be found elsewhere in all counties of Southern Ontario. They compete with beef cattle for market dominance in a belt of territory stretching from Bruce and Huron counties across to the eastern dairy belt. They also compete with

Cash receipts from farming operations invariably show Ontario at the top, followed by Saskatchewan, Alberta, and then Quebec. The figures can be examined in any issue of the *Canada Year Book*.

**Figure 7-2   The Main Population Centres of Southern Ontario**

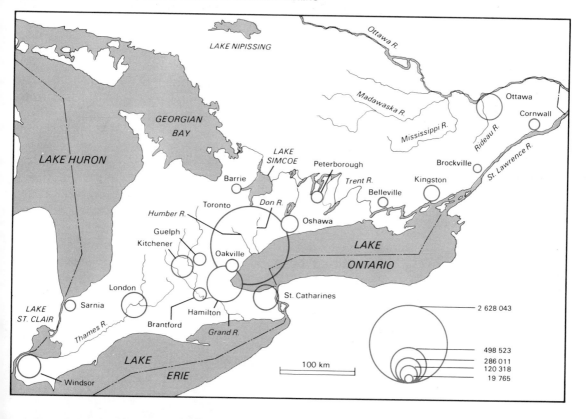

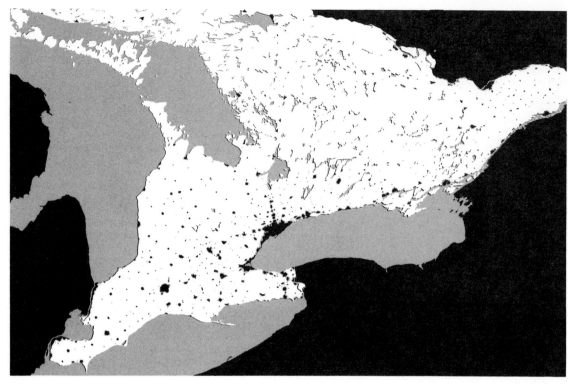

**Figure 7-3    Population Distribution**

Oxford county, chiefly in the Ingersoll district, has made a name for itself by frequently being the first area in Canada to pioneer advances in dairying techniques; it also has an excellent reputation as an area specializing in cattle for breeding purposes.

Peas and beans are examples of a type of vegetable called *pulses.*

hogs for importance throughout the counties of the large region around Oxford.

In all cattle and hog areas, however, most of the land is devoted to crops. The most important of these are corn and hay, with some barley and oats, which are mainly destined for use as feed. Crops are the main users of land in Southern Ontario, and although they are mostly grown for feed, some are important for use as human food as well. The chief food producing crop land is located in the extreme southwestern counties, notably Essex and Kent, but it also stretches eastwards to Niagara. Here the chief crops are called *field crops,* consisting mostly of various types of peas and beans, and *small grains,* chiefly grain corn.

In addition to the large scale users of land there are also some highly specialized but local users, namely the vegetable growers of Holland Marsh in York county, and the fruit growers of the districts downhill from the Niagara escarpment close to the moderating influence of the large lakes, that is, the Niagara peninsula and the Georgian Bay strip of Grey county. Finally there is also a major, although non-food, use of the land in the Norfolk-Haldimand region for the cultivation of tobacco.

There has been much talk of the loss of agricultural land in Southern Ontario. This is undoubtedly true, but it needs to be put into perspective. During the time of pioneer settlement, most pioneers were essentially rural dwellers; they sought and obtained land across the whole of Southern Ontario. Many managed to eke out a living from the soil, but the earth was not always generous, and as the years went by many pioneers, or the descendants of pioneers, abandoned their farms and moved to the cities. The high water mark of rural settlement was reached during the first bloom of pioneer life, but as society developed and towns grew, the tide of human occupation gradually withdrew from the less desirable parts. Even in the hundred-odd years of Ontario's farming life abandoned farms became quite a normal feature of the landscape. More recently, the rapid growth of urban areas has produced a loss of farmland in the more desirable areas as well, so that land losses have occurred in Niagara as well as in Peterborough and Haliburton. Whereas many people were quite happy to see less valuable land abandoned, they have not been quite so happy to see what they regard as prime agricultural land removed from farming. It should be noted, however, that much of the loss of prime farmland has not taken place as a result of urban growth and road building, although some certainly has. The chief reason for abandoning the farming of prime agricultural land has been economic: farmers of Southern Ontario have had to face certain facts, namely, that the land near cities has been more valuable to hold for eventual sale than it has been for continued farming, and that the products of specialized farms (such as those of the Niagara fruit belt) have had to face overwhelming competition from imports

The use of open pasture for cattle is not common in Southern Ontario. Instead cattle are kept mainly indoors, and fed regularly on specially prepared feeds which are grown and mixed on the farm. The reason for this is that the yields of milk and beef are much greater per cow when their feeding is carefully controlled; additionally, the use of land for growing feed is more productive than simply allowing cattle to graze on pasture.

Another reason for the idle farmland is that farm productivity has increased greatly over the years, and farmers now do not need to use as much land as formerly in order to obtain the same or more produce.

Much soil, especially towards the north and east, is gravelly and rocky.

**Figure 7-4**  Once farmland, this is now recreational land.

Both the Niagara fruitbelt and the Georgian Bay fruitbelt are located on the narrow strip of land which lies between the Niagara escarpment and the adjacent lake. Proximity to the lake ensures that the risk of frosts in fall is minimized, because the water retains its summer warmth longer than the land does. In addition, the location between the escarpment and the lake ensures that there is adequate air drainage, minimizing the risk of frosts developing in stagnant air pools during fall, winter, and spring. The Niagara fruitbelt, being farther south, has a wider variety of produce than the Georgian Bay fruitbelt. In Niagara, the chief crops are grapes and peaches, while at Georgian Bay the main crop is apples, especially *Northern Spies*.

from California and Florida, whose products flourish in more favourable climates than that found in Southern Ontario. Many farmers of specialized crops feel that it is hardly worth staying in business for the production of a crop for a few weeks in the summer while the farmers of California and Florida, and increasingly Mexico, can set up their operations for virtual year-round production. Accordingly a lot of land lies idle across Southern Ontario; it is out of farm production, although not necessarily lost permanently.

Another fact about Southern Ontario's farmers is that there are fewer of them than there used to be. This to a direct result of the equivalent fact that the average size of a farm has become much greater. Indeed, during this century the average size of Southern Ontario's farms has risen from about 40 ha to 80 ha, most of which is the result of the more efficient farmers buying out the less efficient ones.

### Industry

There are hundreds of factories across Southern Ontario, especially in the stretch from Windsor to Cornwall. The variety of goods manufactured is too great to be listed; you could fill a catalogue. At the western end of this manufacturing belt is Windsor, noted for cars (e.g., Chrysler) and car parts (e.g. Ford engines); at the eastern end is Cornwall, noted for hydro production and for the manufacture of chemicals, textiles, and paper. And everything is made in between, including more cars and car parts, and more electricity, chemicals, textiles, and paper.

**Figure 7-5** More cars: Ford at St. Thomas.

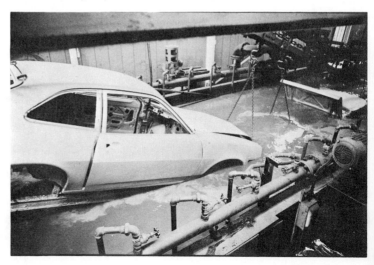

Manufacturing is not evenly spread along the Windsor-Cornwall line. It is concentrated in certain places, especially towns. Can you explain why?

Among the reasons favouring the concentration of industry in certain places we should note:

(a) The need for a large labour supply. Nowadays this means towns and cities, but in the early stages it meant rich farmland with many farmers, some of whom could leave their farms for factory work in the towns. This is one reason why many industrial towns are in good agricultural areas.

(b) The need to have access to as large a market as possible. This also means towns, especially if they have good transportation by rail, road, or water to other large centres of population.

(c) The need to have access to power supplies. This means that hydroelectricity, coal, or oil should be readily available, which in turn favours a factory location near water. The water may be important for hydro power, such as at Niagara Falls or Cornwall, or it may be important for use by coal ships and oil tankers, such as along the shorelines of the Great Lakes.

Coal is imported entirely from the United States; oil may come from Venezuela, the Middle East, Africa, or even the North Sea.

Figure 7-6 shows you the chief manufacturing areas of Southern Ontario. You can clearly see the Windsor-Cornwall line, and you can also see the concentration of industry in towns. The industrial towns themselves also appear to be concentrated more in *one* area than in any other. Can you see which area?

**Figure 7-6   Principal Manufacturing Centres in Southern Ontario**

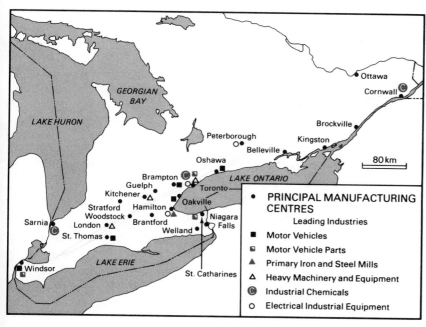

**Figure 7-7** Toronto offers a wide variety of services.

### The Service Sector

More people work in services than in any other sector. Every town has its stores, gas stations, law offices, medical centres, schools, banks, and so on. However, in Southern Ontario there are more of these than in most parts of Canada. Not only that, there are also more *major services* than elsewhere, for example, more universities, more specialized hospitals, more big banks, more department stores, and more expensive restaurants. Toronto offers more of these than other cities in Southern Ontario. Why do you think that is?

Toronto is the largest metropolitan area, but exactly *why* is this important for the development of services?

Why not make a list of all the services available in your town?

● 1. Study Figure 7-8 of the Ford Motor factory at Oakville, which is about half way between Toronto and Hamilton. From looking at the photo, can you suggest four reasons why this would be a good location for Ford?

● 2. Study Figure 7-9 of the Stelco works at Hamilton. Can you tell what advantages this location seems to offer for a steel works?

● 3. Study Figure 7-10 of Toronto's *Central Business District* (CBD). (a) Can you explain why the buildings are so tall?

**Figure 7-8** The Ford Motor factory at Oakville.

(b) What type of work do you think most people do in these buildings?

(c) What do you think the land in between the tall buildings is used for? Why is this so, do you think?

(d) Can you suggest any other uses that might be made of the lakeshore so close to downtown Toronto?

● 4. Figure 7-11 is of another part of Metro Toronto. What do you think it shows? Which type of housing do you think is more

**Figure 7-9** The Stelco works at Hamilton.

**Figure 7-10** Toronto's Central Business District.

wasteful of space: the single family homes at the top of the photo or the apartments at the bottom? What was your answer to part (a) of question 3?

● 5. Can you identify some of the towns and cities of Southern Ontario in Figure 7-3?

● 6. Using the information in this section, try to construct a map to show the distribution across Southern Ontario of the several types of farming described in the text.

**Figure 7-11** A Toronto suburb.

# B: ANALYSIS

The simple reason why there are so many people in Southern Ontario is that there are many job opportunities, and people live where the work is. However, *why* are there so many job opportunities?

In section A of this chapter, we divided the activities that people do into three categories; we can now use their official names, namely primary, secondary, and tertiary.

## Why There Are Many Primary Activities

What is the most common primary activity? That's right, it is farming. And what factors favour farming?

First of all, though not necessarily most importantly, the climate has to be suitable. It is hard to say what is meant by *suitable,* because what suits one crop might not suit another. The climate of Southern Ontario is not suitable for the growing of oranges, for example, but it is suitable for the growing of corn. In general, the warmer an area is the more suitable it becomes for growing a variety of crops, while the cooler it is the smaller is the variety of crops that can be grown.

Refer to Figure 2-2 in Chapter 2. What do you notice about the 20°C isotherm in relation to Southern Ontario? It is fairly obvious now that according to temperature you will get a wider variety of crops in the counties along the Lake Erie shoreline than you will in the counties next to Georgian Bay. Which are the Lake Erie counties? Which are the Georgian Bay counties? Look at your answer to question 6 in section A: can you name the main types of farm produce in the Erie shoreline counties? What do you think is meant by *field crops* (excluding grains)? And by *small grains* (excluding wheat)? These are all important along the Erie shoreline. Indeed the Erie shoreline counties are the main ones where these crops are the dominant farming type; elsewhere it is mostly livestock of one type or another, with corn for silage.

A second requirement for good farming is a suitable soil. Again, it is hard to say what *suitable* means. For example, the rich tobacco farms of Norfolk county thrive on a soil that is so sandy that corn would not grow in it. Generally, however, most of the soil in Southern Ontario is suitable for growing some sort of crop, even though it usually requires a certain amount of drainage and/or irrigation, or even if that crop may only be hay for cattle. This is a great contrast with Northern Ontario, where for the most part there is ofen no soil at all.

A third requirement for profitable farming is an accessible market. This usually means being located within short distances

The most suitable climate for the growing of corn is to be found in the west central parts of the United States, chiefly Iowa and Missouri; however, corn is a very tolerant crop, and it grows quite well for long distances away from its most ideal region.

*Silage* is the term used to describe the mixture of feed kept in a *silo,* and for use in feeding cattle.

In the days of the original pioneers the most common crop across all of Southern Ontario was wheat; indeed Ontario used to produce 95% of all of Canada's wheat around 1850. Wheat was grown widely on the sandy soils of Norfolk county, but the soils soon became exhausted by this repeated cultivation of a single type of crop (this practice is called *monoculture*). In time the sandy soils were abandoned as useless. It was only when later settlers moved in for tobacco cultivation that the sandy soils were coaxed back into fertility, and for tobacco the soils proved ideal because they warmed up very rapidly in the spring.

Gravel is usually mined very close to towns. It is needed by the construction industry, and it is very expensive to transport. Many townspeople object to the existence of gravel pits virtually in their own backyard, but the alternative is higher priced buildings Many people also object to the existence of limestone quarries along the Niagara escarpment, claiming that the escarpment ought to be preserved for its natural beauty. Again, the alternative would be higher priced buildings. What would your choice be?

The Ontario government has been pursuing a policy of restocking the lower lakes with trout and coho salmon. The policy has been quite successful, although commercial fishing is not likely to be restored for some time.

The production of power at Niagara Falls is not allowed to interfere with the important tourist trade of the area. Accordingly the water intakes and the power turbines are far removed from the actual Falls, and the volume of water going over the Falls is carefully regulated to keep it up to an acceptable level.

of large towns. And there are many towns in Southern Ontario.

Another primary activity found in Southern Ontario is mining, such as salt in the Windsor and Goderich areas, oil and gas in Lambton county and underneath Lake Erie, gravel in many areas where glacial gravel deposits exists, and limestone along the Niagara escarpment.

A third primary activity is fishing, especially along the Lake Erie shore, although this has suffered recently because of the pollution of Lake Erie.

### Why There Are Many Secondary Activities

In reality it is all to do with the Great Lakes and the St. Lawrence River system.

**Power** for industry comes from a variety of sources:

(a) Direct generation of *hydroelectricity* is carried out near Niagara Falls and Cornwall.

(b) The burning of coal, oil, or gas to generate what is called *thermal electricity* is usually carried out where the fuels are unloaded into the region of Southern Ontario. This generally means near the St. Lawrence River or Lakes Ontario and Erie, where coal ships, oil tankers, or pipelines can readily penetrate.

(c) The use of uranium to generate *nuclear electricity,* as at Pickering on Lake Ontario east of Toronto or at Douglas Point on the Lake Huron side of Bruce County. Large quantities of water are needed for cooling purposes, which is why nuclear generators are next to large lakes.

**Raw materials** are nearly all imported. Once again the shipping routes of the Great Lakes favour the easy importation of raw materials, either from Northern Ontario via Lakes Superior and Huron or from abroad via the St. Lawrence Seaway and Lake Ontario. Either way, the waterway acts as an industrial lifeline.

**Markets** for the products of the factories can be readily reached either in Southern Ontario itself or outside the region. Again the good transportation of the waterway is a great help, though it is aided by rail and road links which have been fairly easy to build over the flat till plains of Southern Ontario.

**Labour supply** for the factories has come from the well populated farming areas in the countryside of the region as well as from abroad. As the factories grew in the towns the people of Southern Ontario came to be increasingly concentrated in urban areas. And it was to the towns that most immigrants then came. Before industrialization many immigrants had sought farmland, but after industrialization most went directly to the towns; so the towns grew and industry prospered.

The St. Lawrence Seaway was opened in 1959. It replaced an older set of river locks, and opened up the Great Lakes to sea-going ships.

**Figure 7-12**   The Seaway lifeline. This is at Welland.

## Why There Are Many Tertiary Activities

One obvious reason is transportation, but you can probably think of several others. Doubtless you thought of trade, banking and finance, insurance, administration and government, communications, and entertainment, among other things. Did you know, though, that Toronto is Ontario's most important tourist attraction? More tourists come to visit Toronto than Niagara Falls! They come mostly from the United States, but there are many visitors from other parts of Canada too.

Like factory industries, most services are located in towns. They need a certain number of people in order to survive, so the towns are the obvious places for them. However, they then attract more people; so the towns grow. Most jobs in Southern Ontario are now in the tertiary sector (Figure 7-13), and they are nearly all in towns (Figure 7-14).

Suggest some examples of Canadian banks and insurance companies headquartered in Toronto.

The minimum number of people necessary to support a particular service is called the *threshold population* for that service.

Southern Ontario's population is now about 85% urban.

Fifure 7-13   Distribution of Employment in Ontario, by Major Categories (per cent)

|  | 1951 | 1961 | 1971 |
|---|---|---|---|
| Farming | 10.8 | 7.2 | 3.6 |
| Other primary | 3.0 | 2.7 | 1.8 |
| **Total Primary Jobs** | **13.8** | **9.9** | **5.4** |
| Manufacturing | 32.4 | 27.5 | 27.4 |
| Other secondary | 6.3 | 6.6 | 5.8 |
| **Total Secondary Jobs** | **38.7** | **34.1** | **33.2** |
| Transportation, etc. | 9.0 | 8.3 | 7.6 |
| Trade | 14.6 | 15.8 | 16.4 |
| Finance | 3.3 | 4.2 | 5.1 |
| Administration | 6.2 | 7.7 | 6.8 |
| Other services | 14.4 | 20.0 | 25.5 |
| **Total Tertiary Jobs** | **47.5** | **56.0** | **61.4** |
| **Total All Jobs** | **100.0** | **100.0** | **100.0** |

It is often very difficult to decide just what part of a population is *urban* and what part is *rural*. The census definitions are usually quite arbitrary, and are generally based on the fact that a single settlement must have at least 1000 persons in order to be considered urban.

Figure 7-14   Urban and Rural Distribution of Population, by Counties, 1971 Census data

|  | Urban + | Rural = | Total |
|---|---|---|---|
| Brant | 74 405 | 22 365 | 96 770 |
| Bruce | 17 575 | 29 810 | 47 385 |
| Dufferin | 9 865 | 11 335 | 21 200 |
| Dundas | 6 105 | 11 355 | 17 460 |
| Durham | 21 045 | 26 450 | 47 495 |
| Elgin | 34 135 | 32 475 | 66 610 |
| Essex | 246 560 | 59 840 | 306 400 |
| Frontenac | 73 605 | 28 085 | 101 690 |
| Glengarry | 3 240 | 15 240 | 18 480 |
| Grenville | 9 445 | 14 870 | 24 315 |
| Grey | 33 505 | 32 900 | 66 405 |
| Haldimand | 12 135 | 20 535 | 32 670 |
| Haliburton | 0 | 9 085 | 9 085 |
| Halton | 178 725 | 11 745 | 190 470 |
| Hamilton-Wentworth | 360 285 | 41 600 | 401 885 |
| Hastings | 67 130 | 32 260 | 99 390 |
| Huron | 19 590 | 33 360 | 52 950 |
| Kent | 60 830 | 40 290 | 101 120 |
| Lambton | 79 745 | 34 570 | 114 315 |

| | Urban | + Rural | = Total |
|---|---|---|---|
| Lanark | 26 495 | 15 765 | 42 260 |
| Leeds | 26 050 | 24 045 | 50 095 |
| Lennox-Addington | 8 795 | 19 565 | 28 360 |
| Middlesex | 240 325 | 41 690 | 282 015 |
| Niagara | 334 875 | 12 455 | 347 330 |
| Norfolk | 20 500 | 33 605 | 54 105 |
| Northumberland | 20 620 | 27 540 | 48 160 |
| Ontario | 159 865 | 36 395 | 196 260 |
| Ottawa-Carleton | 428 940 | 42 990 | 471 930 |
| Oxford | 44 870 | 35 475 | 80 345 |
| Peel | 238 650 | 20 750 | 259 400 |
| Perth | 37 575 | 25 400 | 62 975 |
| Peterborough | 65 390 | 22 415 | 87 805 |
| Prescott | 13 605 | 14 230 | 27 835 |
| Prince Edward | 4 875 | 15 765 | 20 640 |
| Renfrew | 56 240 | 34 630 | 90 870 |
| Russell | 6 440 | 9 845 | 16 285 |
| Simcoe | 104 370 | 67 060 | 171 430 |
| Stormont | 47 115 | 14 185 | 61 300 |
| Toronto | 2 086 015 | 0 | 2 086 015 |
| Victoria | 15 880 | 18 360 | 34 240 |
| Waterloo | 222 790 | 31 240 | 254 030 |
| Wellington | 76 960 | 31 620 | 108 580 |
| York | 134 765 | 31 290 | 166 055 |
| **Total for Southern Ontario** | **5 729 830** | **1 134 485** | **6 864 415** |

Source: Ontario Statistics
    Ministry of Treasury, Economics and Intergovernmental Affairs

● 7. Refer to the data in Figure 7-14. It shows the number of people who live in each county of Southern Ontario, as well as the number of urban and rural dwellers.

(a) Calculate the percentage of each county's population that is urban.

(b) On a blank county map, shade all those counties that have over 90% of their population in urban areas.

(c) In less than a page suggest explanations for the pattern of urban intensity that your map shows.

There is a major area of urban counties at the western end of Lake Ontario. Do you know the nickname for this zone of urban counties?

● 8. There are 184 different types of industries in Canada. How many can be found in Toronto?

## C: THE ROLE OF SOUTHERN ONTARIO

Southern Ontario is an important region. Even though it contains just over one percent of all Canada's land area it supports about 32% of the population. In addition it accounts for about 80% of Canada's fully manufactured goods, 50% of Canada's partly manufactured goods, 50% of Canada's banking activity, 50% of Canada's immigrant arrivals, 45% of Canada's insurance activity, 40% of Canada's buying power, 35% of Canada's construction activity, and 30% of Canada's farm income.

But even with its present important position, Southern Ontario is still concerned with expansion and growth. The government puts many advertisements into international magazines, inviting business companies from around the world to set up operations within Ontario. In practice, this means Southern Ontario.

Fully manufactured goods are those that can be bought and used in their final form, such as cars, aircraft, TVs, furniture, and clothing. Partly manufactured goods are those such as steel, plastics, and textiles, that are still to be made into something else.

Canada's major banks, in order of size, are
Royal Bank
Canadian Imperial
  Bank of Commerce
Bank of Montreal
Bank of Nova Scotia
Toronto Dominion
  Bank.

**Figure 7-15**    Did you know that Toronto is Ontario's most important tourist attraction? This is Ontario Place, on Toronto's lakeshore.

- 9. Draw a percentage bar graph, with ten bars, to illustrate the data at the beginning of this section.

- 10. We have tried to give you an idea of the character of Southern Ontario as a region. We have undoubtedly left several things out. What additional things can *you* think of that would help you in understanding the character of Southern Ontario?

**Figure 7-16**   Forest area outside of Toronto.

**Figure 7-17**   Toronto's parkland.

**Figure 7-18**   Urban highrises.

# CHAPTER 8
# THE PRAIRIE PROVINCES
## RESOURCES

The first permanent European settlement in the prairies occurred in 1812 at the junction of the Red and Assiniboine Rivers. This was the so-called Red River Settlement. It was started by a Scotsman, Lord Selkirk, who shipped the first settlers from Scotland. He wanted to provide a number of things, including a more permanent British presence in the continental interior, a new home for dispossessed Scots farmers, and a source of varied and regular food for the *voyageur* traders. The settlement had many problems in its early days, including plagues of grasshoppers as well as attacks by fur traders. The fur traders saw the settlement as the beginning of the end of their freedom to travel without hindrance. They were right.

## INTRODUCTION

The prairie provinces are Alberta, Saskatchewan, and Manitoba, as shown in Figure 8-2. They are the home of about 3 600 000 Canadians whose ancestry is as varied as the world itself. In addition to the Indians, who were the first to come and who now form about three percent of the prairie population, there are large numbers from Europe and Asia. Dotted over the prairie provinces there are communities whose origins were at one time in France, England, the Ukraine, Russia, Germany, Finland, Sweden, Estonia, China, Japan — just about every country in the world, in fact. Like a pervasive cement, however, the former influence of England helps to bind all together, providing a common form of communication, a common New World heritage, a common form of government, and a common language in an otherwise great diversity of cultures.

Figure 8-1, which shows data for Manitoba, gives an indication of the cultural diversity of the prairie provinces. Just what are the reasons, do you think, that have attracted people to the prairie from so many lands?

The simple answer is *resources*. The resources offered by the prairies are widely varied, and not all are what you might expect if you were asked to list them.

● 1. What do you think *resources* are? What do you think the resources of the prairie provinces are?

158

| Ethnic Origin | Percent of Provincial Population |
|---|---|
| English | 20.0 |
| Scottish | 12.9 |
| Ukrainian | 11.4 |
| German | 10.0 |
| Irish | 9.2 |
| French | 9.1 |
| Dutch | 5.2 |
| Polish | 4.8 |
| Scandinavian | 4.1 |
| Indian | 3.2 |
| Jewish | 2.1 |
| Austrian | 1.1 |
| Russian | 1.0 |
| Welsh | 0.8 |
| Italian | 0.7 |
| Hungarian | 0.6 |
| Czech and Slovak | 0.5 |
| Chinese | 0.3 |
| Finnish | 0.1 |
| Japanese | 0.1 |
| Caribbean | 0.1 |
| Others | 2.7 |
| **Total** | **100.0** |

Figure 8-1   Ethnic Origins of the 1970 Manitoba Population

## A: THE PAST

To the Indians the resources offered by the prairies were not the same as those offered to later populations. Indeed the range of resources provided by the prairies has varied continually through time, so that people of different time periods have made use of different resources.

The earliest prairie resources used by Canadians were the animals, chiefly the buffalo. The Indians of the plains, notably the Blackfoot, Piegan, Blood, Assiniboine, and western Cree, lived by hunting buffalo for thousands of years before the coming of the Europeans. The hunt was usually arduous because the Indians did not have horses. In fact, horses did not become common until

There are all different sorts of buffalo, such as the south Asian water buffalo, the Cape buffalo of Africa, and the bison of North America. The bison, or North American type buffalo, used to graze freely in giant herds over the short grass prairie which stretched from Texas to Alberta and Saskatchewan. Short prairie grass used to be called buffalo grass.

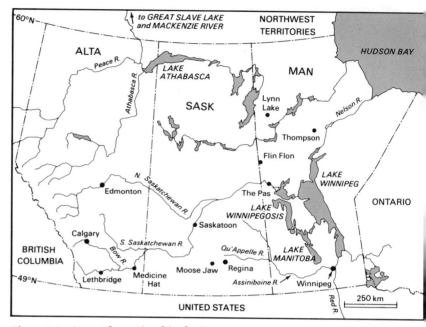

**Figure 8-2    Some Places Listed in the Text**

Tepees were made out of several skins cut to shape and stitched together. They were kept up by a series of long poles, of which two were generally longer than the rest. The longer poles were used to keep a flap open at the top so that smoke could escape. Similarly shaped homes made of twigs and leaves, widely used by the eastern forest Indians, were called wigwams.

Mostly beaver and muskrat.

they were introduced by Europeans, via Spain, Mexico, Texas, and the American West. For thousands of years, therefore, the prairie Indians hunted buffalo by various less efficient means. Sometimes they would dress up in wolf skins and crawl along as a wolf until they were close enough to use arrows and spears; at other times they would stampede the buffalo until the animals were either trapped in a pen or driven to their death over the side of a ravine.

Buffalo were almost the only prairie resource used by the Indians. The animals provided not only food but also clothing, shelter, and tools. Clothing of buffalo skin was usually too hot in summer, so an occasional alternative was the skin of the deer, either buck or doe. Buffalo and deer skins also provided material for moccasins and for tepees. Prairie Indians did not stay in one place, as the eastern forest Indians usually did; they were nomads, following the buffalo herds. They needed easily transportable shelter, which was provided by collapsible skin tents. Buffalo chips provided fuel for cooking, and also for winter warmth.

The first Europeans penetrated the prairies in search of fur-bearing animals. They used the great east-west valleys of the Assiniboine, Qu'Appelle, North and South Saskatchewan, and Peace Rivers as their major arteries. They found wealth in furs. Generally the richest fur regions proved to be in the northern and northwestern parts of the prairies, and for many years (most of the

700s and well into the 1800s) the rights of European ownership of the prairies were hotly disputed between the *voyageurs* and agents of the North West Company on one side and their rivals of the Hudson's Bay Company on the other. Such disputes were resolved by the amalgamation of the two companies in 1821.

Throughout the entire phase of European interest in furs, the Indians continued to rely on the buffalo. The Indians and European voyageurs generally co-operated in their exploitation of the animals. Indeed they developed a considerable trade with each other. Indians provided pemmican, which was a preserved form of dried buffalo meat, as well as furs which they had trapped for the voyageurs. In return the Europeans provided alcohol and rifles. The additional acquisition by the Indians of rifles from the voyageurs, combined with the earlier introduction of horses, led to much more effective hunting of the buffalo. The hunt became something of a sport as well as a means of survival. However, the advent of the Europeans, with their interest in furs and their range of goods available for trade, meant that buffalo gradually ceased to be such an overwhelmingly dominant resource for the survival of the Indians. The Indians had gained access through trade to some of the resources of the Europeans. Their resource base had widened.

The extinction of the buffalo as a resource was not caused only by the widespread use of horses and rifles, however. It was also caused by the changing land use forced on the prairies by the pressure of European immigrants. The prairies of Canada, cut off from population clusters in the east by the inhospitable barrier of the Shield, did not feel the pressure of large numbers of Europeans as early as the American prairies did. The American prairies were put under the plough long before the Canadian prairies were, and this is virtually what finally killed the buffalo as a resource. The buffalo, once hunted for their skins and meat, now became hunted for their bones. The hunt was merciless; untold numbers of buffalo were slaughtered, and their bones collected and piled up in a neat box-car sized lots at railway sidings. Indeed, for many years the new city of Regina's nickname was *Pile o' bones*. Buffalo bones became big business, and proved, after furs, to be the second largest export of the prairies. Most of the bones were shipped to Minneapolis for grinding into rich calcium fertilizer for use on the surrounding farms. The buffalo were therefore soon driven almost to extinction, and the old way of life of the prairie Indians ceased forever.

The way was thus opened for further prairie resources to be used, mainly the soil and the open spaces. The soil of the prairies

Contact between the fur traders and the Indians also resulted in the creation of a new group of people of mixed ancestry, the Metis.

Alcohol came to be known as *firewater* from the way in which its strength was tested. Many European traders used to water their alcohol before using it in trade, so that they were in effect trading in an inferior good. The Indians and Metis developed the practice of testing the strength of the alcohol they received by pouring some of it on to a fire. If the alcohol was heavily watered it would put the fire out, but if it was of high strength then it would flame up in the fire.

Buffalo hunters used to roam far and wide over the prairie, leaving their skinned victims to rot or be eaten by scavengers. They were followed by teams of bone collectors, who scoured the increasingly barren prairie in squeaky dust-covered carts.

Precipitation over the prairies varies between 300 mm and 500 mm per year. Most of it falls as rain during the summer, when it provides valuable moisture for the growing crops. Winter precipitation always occurs as snow.

Leaching is the term used for the downward movement of soluble matter in the soil. In areas of heavy rain, the movement of soil water is always downwards, and soluble material is washed out of the soil altogether, leaving just insoluble mineral particles behind. A heavily leached soil is not very fertile because it lacks some of the necessary fertile constituents.

Humus is the name given to the black organic material in a soil formed from the decomposition of dead vegetation. It is rich in fertile constituents.

Captain Palliser was sent by the British to survey the interior of the continent in 1857. He reported that a large triangular area of the southern prairie would be unfit for settlement and farming because it was too dry. The part that he so described is now called Palliser's Triangle.

was essentially that of a dry region, characterized by the upward movement of ground water through capillary action. Leaching was not a dominant characteristic. Instead, soil moisture was drawn to the surface, even after rain, and the soluble minerals in the soil therefore tended to accumulate at or near the surface of the soil. Where there was sufficient vegetation to provide a good supply of *humus*, the soil became black and fertile. It came to be called *black earth* or *chernozem*. Black earths are located, as shown in Figure 8-3, in a great arc stretching from southern Manitoba through central Saskatchewan to Edmonton in Alberta, and then south past Calgary to the U.S. border. Inside this black earth arc, to the south, lie the drier prairies of southeastern Alberta and southern Saskat-

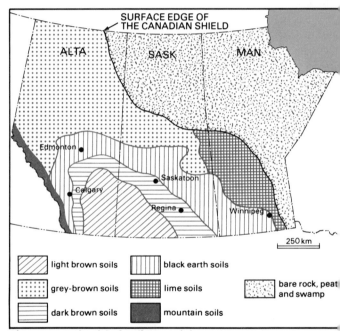

**Figure 8-3    Simplified Soil Map of the Prairie Provinces, showing the Black Earth Zone**
(see Chapter 2 for Soil Profiles)

chewan. This is the area where rain is insufficient even for long grass; it is the area of the short grass prairie, where vegetation is not sufficient to provide enough humus for black earth. The soil is only a *brown earth*, and in the driest parts, commonly called *Palliser's Triangle*, barely even that. Outside the black earth arc, on the other hand, there is too much soil moisture for black earth development. The richer vegetation, consisting of long grass and trees, provides plenty of humus, but this is to some extent negated by the leaching effect of the additional soil moisture. Black earth are therefore the product of a fine balance between soil moisture and surface vegetation: too little rain and there is not adequate vegetation; too much rain and there is leaching. Away from the black earth arc, soils therefore deteriorate in all directions.

In 1869 the Hudson's Bay Company traded the rights of European ownership of the prairies to the new nation of Canada. Land surveyors moved in, followed shortly by railway surveyors. The incursions of the land surveyors were resisted in vain by the fur traders and buffalo hunters. Eventually the land was surveyed, and farmers began to move in. They came from the American Mid-West, which was becoming overfilled with farmers, as well as from the already filled lands of the Eastern Townships of Quebec and southern Ontario, and from the economically and socially oppressed lands of the Old World. They were attracted by the offers of free land, made possible by the relative scarcity of population, and by the promise of rich harvests, made possible by the wide distribution of black earths.

Settlement fanned out to the west and northwest from Winnipeg, the gateway to the prairies. The black earths were soon occupied and farmed, and their attractions proved so great to the many inexperienced settlers that the lesser soils of the northern and southern prairies were also occupied and farmed. However, the droughts of the 1930s eventually proved to be too much for most dry land farmers, and many farms were abandoned.

Along with the abandonment of dry land farms came two other changes: one was the diversification of farming in the black earth zone, so that wheat came to be accompanied by hay, barley, oats, roots, vegetables and dairy cows; the other was the concentration in the dry zones on wheat, and, in the driest zones, on beef cattle. In a sense, the growing importance of beef cattle represented a return to the original interest in the first resource of the prairies, the animals. Most of the prairie dry land is in Saskatchewan, and it is not surprising therefore that Saskatchewan is the chief wheat province, followed by Alberta and Manitoba (Figure 8-8).

Railways were of crucial importance in the development of the prairies for farming and settlements. Settlers were carried in and grain was carried out, both at subsidized rates. The railways were so important that it is almost fair to call them a major prairie resource. One of the most important aspects of the railway as a resource has been the existence of a freight rate structure called the Crow's Nest Pass rates. Under this freight rate structure the railways have been legally required to carry wheat from the prairies to the ports at rates which were fixed in 1897. During the twentieth century these rates have proved to be a great boon to

In the early days settlers were granted free ownership of about 64 ha, called a quarter section. They could buy more if they wished for about $2.50/ha. They were required to work the land for five years and to put up a permanent home by that time. Their first homes were usually made of sod. A sod home was warm, but its roof often leaked.

Not many prairie settlers were farmers. Some were, but many were factory workers, store clerks, school teachers, gamblers, retired soldiers, and so on. The business of farming was a totally new experience for them. Many did not succeed, even where the physical conditions were not so unfavourable as in the Triangle. Others learned, however, and survived; some prospered.

Saskatchewan accounts for about 70% by value of all the wheat produced in the prairies. Alberta accounts for about 20%, and Manitoba for the remaining ten percent.

**Figure 8-4** Railways moved into the Prairies. This is the Qu'Appelle Valley in Saskatchewan.

prairie wheat farmers, enabling them to get their wheat to export markets much more cheaply than would have otherwise been the case.

**Figure 8-5** Saskatchewan is the primary wheat province.

● 2. What do you think are some of the effects on the railways of the Crow's Nest Pass rate agreement?

● 3. What do you think are some of the ways in which *other* farmers in the prairies feel about the Crow's Nest Pass agreement?

The importance of wheat to the growing prairie economy of the twentieth century cannot be exaggerated. Wheat was largely responsible for the growth of settlements, both large and small. It even spurred the further growth of places outside the prairies altogether, places such as Thunder Bay, Montreal, Halifax, St. John, and Vancouver, all of which became important as wheat *transshipment ports.*

**Figure 8-6** Wheat transshipment facilities at Montreal . . .

**Figure 8-7** . . . and at Vancouver.

**Figure 8-8   Major Prairie Farming Regions**

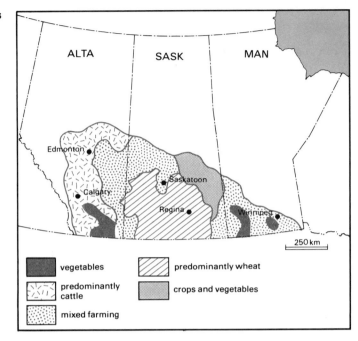

**Figure 8-9   The Growth of Population in the Prairie Provinces**

| Year | Alberta | Saskatchewan | Manitoba |
|------|---------|--------------|----------|
| 1891 | 3 000 | 3 000 | 153 000 |
| 1901 | 73 000 | 91 000 | 255 000 |
| 1911 | 374 000 | 492 000 | 461 000 |
| 1921 | 588 000 | 758 000 | 610 000 |
| 1931 | 732 000 | 922 000 | 700 000 |
| 1941 | 796 000 | 896 000 | 730 000 |
| 1951 | 940 000 | 832 000 | 777 000 |
| 1961 | 1 332 000 | 925 000 | 922 000 |
| 1971 | 1 628 000 | 926 000 | 988 000 |
| 1975 (est) | 1 788 000 | 925 000 | 1 021 000 |

● 4. Find out the difference between *transshipment ports* and *break of bulk ports*. None of the wheat ports are break of bulk ports (not for wheat, that is). If anything, they are collectors of bulk rather than breakers of bulk.

● 5.  Discover the meaning of:
     open ranges
     ranges
     townships
     sections
     quarter sections

● 6.  Graph and analyze the growth of population for Alberta, Saskatchewan, and Manitoba, as shown in Figure 8-9.

The rise of the wheat economy marks what might be called the end of the beginning of the prairies. In the space of 100 years they had moved from a hunting and trapping form of livelihood, characterized by nomads with a simple technology, to a system of settled cultivation, characterized by a complex mechanical technology. For a better understanding of the early prairies look at the following articles and answer the questions which follow them.

# Manitoba 1870-1970

By W. J. Megill

During the first half of the nineteenth century, only a few small settlements were made along the Red and Assiniboine rivers. The Selkirk settlers, Scottish crofters brought out by Lord Selkirk in 1812 to grow food for the fur traders, took farms near Fort Garry. The few farmers already in the area were mainly French-Canadians who had come out as voyageurs and settled in the country with Indian wives. Many of their descendants, the Metis, formed small farming communities farther from Fort Garry, but their main preoccupation was the annual buffalo hunt to make pemmican for the voyageurs. Despite difficult years the colony grew slowly and achieved some stability, but progress was limited by lack of communications and an outside market.

By mid-century, colonization in the United States to the south was beginning to reach the headwaters of the Red River, and the railway arrived at St. Paul. A cart trail and steamboats from St. Paul to Winnipeg supplied for the first time practicable communications with the outside. During the sixties the first main wave of settlement began. Scores of Ontario farmers looking for free land of their own were a major element, and the original French-speaking settlements were reinforced by "Massachusetts French" — farmers who had gone south to the United States and who repatriated themselves to Canada in a new French-speaking area. Other arrivals were a group of Icelanders who settled on the west side of Lake Winnipeg where they could both fish and farm, and two groups of Mennonites who settled east and west of the Red River.

The realization that something better than the canoe route between the head of the lakes and the Red River valley was imperative to offset the "pull to the south" of the St. Paul route, led the Canadian government to start construction of the Dawson Trail, a combined wagon and water route between Port Arthur and Winnipeg, at the same time as negotiations were going forward to take over the Northwest Territories from Britain. The first major party along the still-incomplete route was the military force despatched from Upper and Lower Canada to put down the Riel insurrection, since they c o u l d not travel through the United States.

At the time of Confederation, a pattern of area settlement by different ethnic groups had already emerged and was to remain substantially unchanged, except for the addition of the Ukrainians, who had not yet arrived. The English-speaking old Ontario settlers were along the Red River and west of it, having displaced many of the original Metis settlers from along the Assiniboine. St. Boniface, a c r o s s the river from Winnipeg, was French-speaking, as were the people of the small villages and farms in the southeast part of the province, east of the Red River. The German-speaking Mennonites had formed two colonies, east and west of the

Red River respectively, and the Icelanders were north of Winnipeg along Lake Winnipeg, with their principal settlement the fishing station of Gimli.

The fact that Manitoba actually became a province at this time, and not just the only settled portion of the new territories, was due in no small measure to the determination of these settlers to shape their own destiny as far as possible, rather than be subject to the whims of a central government. The Riel insurrection of 1869-70 was not just a struggle of French and Metis against Anglo-Saxon, as it was generally regarded in eastern Canada. The older inhabitants, whatever their origins might be, had a strong basic element of concern for the future of the area. They might not support the fact of rebellion, but the principle of local control was in the forefront of their minds.

Despite the difficulties of communications and the lack of transportation for grain to the markets of the east, the fertile lands of the Red and Assiniboine rivers attracted an increasing number of settlers, mainly from Ontario and the British Isles, in the decade following Confederation. As they pushed westward, pressure grew to enlarge the province, and the first boundary extension was

made in 1881. Also, the completion of rail connections from St. Paul, Minnesota, to St. Boniface in 1879 gave sharp focus to the fear that the rich traffic of the west would be drawn to the United States, and hastened the completion of the C.P.R., which reached Winnipeg from Fort William in 1882 and from the east in 1885.

The next ten years were a period of slow growth in numbers, mainly of British, but some of French stock. Instead of moving to the new land of the west, the sons of Ontario farmers were moving to serve the growing industry of the cities. There was, however, a steady consolidation of the land which was already settled, and a widespread move to mechanized farming, notably to seeding and harvesting devices. At the same time, a network of branch railway lines with their characteristic grain elevators was built; the general basis seems to have been to put each farmer within one day's haulage distance of a railroad.

Then in 1897 began the last wave of settlement which was to alter the basic composition of the province. The newcomers were mainly Ukrainians and Poles, and once again the pattern of settlement by ethnic "blocs" was repeated. By this time the grasslands were largely taken up, so they settled on bush lands, north of a line from the southeast corner of the province to Lake Winnipeg, in the interlake district, and in the Riding Mountain and Duck Mountain areas. Many did not go on the land, but swelled the labour force in Winnipeg and in the railway divisional towns of Brandon, Portage la Prairie and Dauphin. By 1913, the general pattern of settlement of the province was complete. Manitoba was not to be a melting pot of cultures within communities, but rather a province whose individual areas each held a predominant ethnic strain, which is still visible in the names of the members elected to both federal and provincial parliaments from the various constituencies.

from the *Canadian Geographical Journal*, Vol. 8, No. 2, August 1970

# Agriculture

The history of Alberta from the end of the 19th century is the story of agricultural development, a tale of hardship, perseverance and success as the sturdy settlers of the province undertook to wrest a livelihood from its virgin soil. With the establishment of p e r m a n e n t settlement, ranching progressed spontaneously in the naturally favourable environment of southern Alberta. Government authorities encouraged this trend with favourable land regulations and by 1883 there w e r e reportedly 75 000 head of cattle in what is now the Albertan territory. The introduction of ranching regulations and the appointment of inspectors to enforce them ensured the orderly growth of this profitable industry. For many years, the early settlers were entirely dependent upon the horse for transportation and farm work and horse raising developed concurrently with cattle ranching. In the nineties, a market was found for agricultural produce in the new mining districts west of the Rockies and soon mixed farming developed in the area between Calgary and Edmonton. In 1895, the Alberta Live Stock Growers Association was formed to encourage scientific ranching methods. Agriculture had become established as the foundation of Alberta's economy.

Following 1895, the prolonged downward movement of world wheat prices ceased and a long upward trend began. This reflected a recovery of general world prosperity, technological changes, and greater industrialization and urbanization in Europe and the United States. Wheat was in short supply as the movement from farm to city intensified, as real incomes rose, and European — especially British — farmers turned to market gardening. The rapid influx of settlers into Alberta was a concomitant of these developments.

In 1882, John Macoun, a botanist attached to a railway company, reported that in the previous year the total population of the territories later to become Alberta and Saskatchewan consisted of 5800 whites and Metis and 49 000 Indians. By 1901, the population of the districts of Alberta and Athabasca, which became the Province of Alberta in 1905, was 73 000. A decade later it had risen to 374 000, and there were over 60 000 occupied farms in the province. By 1911, the soils of the Peace River country in the northwest were being broken.

At this time, wheat was the staple product. The relative disadvantage of northern location was overcome by employing selective early maturing spring wheats. In areas where moisture was scarce dry-farming methods, i.e. growing methods intended to conserve moisture, were employed. The disadvantages of location and climate were in fact turned to profits as the hard wheat grown produced a more desirable flour than could be milled from soft varieties and thus came to command a premium. In consequence, the area under wheat in Alberta increased from 43 000 acres[1] in 1900 to 879 000 acres[2] in 1911.

The establishment of the wheat economy stimulated related activity in the secondary and tertiary sectors not only of Alberta but of other Canadian provinces as well. It required the accumulation of the considerable amount of capital equipment without which the large-scale production and marketing of wheat would not have been possible. The products of heavy industry were required in the construction of the necessary transportation facilities and also in the establishment of the thousands of farms which rapidly appeared on the prairies. Much of this capital equipment was obtained from the newly emerging industries in Ontario and Quebec. Lumber and its products came mostly from British Columbia. In this manner the wheat economy of Alberta and the rest of the prairie region played a strategic role in the early industrialization of Canada.

[1] 20 210 ha
[2] 413 130 ha

from the Canadian Imperial Bank of Commerce, *Commercial Letter,* September, 1965

- 7. Design a poster or a handbill showing the attractions of settlement in the Canadian prairies to a European of the 1900s.

- 8. Research the *Hutterites.*

- 9. What is the difference between a chernozem soil and a podzol soil?

- 10. What part did research into different types of wheat seed play in the development of the prairies?

- 11. Can you list the order in which the main immigrant groups arrived?

- 12. How did the opening up of the prairies for wheat cultivation affect the rest of Canada?

**Figure 8-10   Canada's Wheat Output, 1871-1976**

| Year | Production in Tonnes |
|------|---------------------|
| 1871 | 455 000 |
| 1881 | 880 000 |
| 1891 | 1 147 000 |
| 1901 | 1 511 000 |
| 1911 | 3 595 000 |
| 1921 | 6 165 000 |
| 1931 | 8 745 000 |
| 1941 | 8 568 000 |
| 1951 | 15 041 000 |
| 1961 | 7 713 000 |
| 1964 | 16 349 000 |
| 1965 | 17 674 000 |
| 1966 | 22 516 000 |
| 1967 | 16 137 000 |
| 1968 | 17 689 000 |
| 1969 | 18 267 000 |
| 1970 | 9 024 000 |
| 1971 | 14 412 000 |
| 1972 | 14 514 000 |
| 1973 | 16 458 000 |
| 1974 | 14 220 000 |
| 1975 | 17 078 000 |
| 1976 | 23 569 000 |

Source: 1976 Canadian Almanac & Directory

**Figure 8-11   Selected GPP Data for 1975**

| | Alberta | All Values in $ Saskatchewan | Manitoba |
|---|---------|------------------------------|----------|
| Gross Provincial Product: | 13 000 000 000 | 5 000 000 000 | 6 500 000 000 |
| Factory Shipments | 3 220 000 000 | 777 000 000 | 1 840 000 000 |
| Mineral Products | 6 000 000 000 | 890 000 000 | 500 000 000 |
| Farm Cash Receipts | 1 732 000 000 | 1 800 000 000 | 750 000 000 |

# A Bin Buster of a Year

World agricultural production soared in 1976. Estimates for the all-important grain crop indicate it was the greatest ever and depleted stock have returned to more normal levels. The record crop suggests a continuation of easing food prices, a welcome relief to consumers following the virulent food price spiral of 1972-1975.

Good growing conditions were the prime factor behind this year's bumper crop just as poor weather had led to the crop failures of the early seventies.

**Canadian Grain Crop**

On Canada's prairies, as in many of the other major growing areas of the world, weather conditions were just about ideal in 1976. Seeding operations got off to a fast start in the spring as warm, dry conditions permitted field work to begin earlier than normal. Rains arrived when required in early and mid-June to restore moisture levels and hot weather in July and August resulted in favourable crop development. Very little pest damage was reported throughout the summer and warm, sunny weather in the main harvest period in September provided a fitting conclusion to the season.

With the bulk of the crop now safely off the fields, the tally shows that the Canadian grain harvest was of record proportions. Total wheat production, at 866 million bushels,[1] surpassed the previous record set in 1966 by 5% and exceeded last year's good crop by a whopping 38%. A 17% increase in wheat acreage sown was a significant factor behind the increase in production from 1975, but higher yields per acre were an even more important contributor. Indeed, the wheat yield this year was 31.5 bushels per acre,[2] by far the highest ever, and for the first time in many years the Canadian wheat yield matched that of the United States. The yield, in fact,

[1] 23 569 000 t
[2] approximately 0.3 tonnes/ha

was 18% above last year and 30% above the 1965-74 average.

With the world wheat harvest this year also reaching an all-time high, world wheat stocks are expected to increase by as much as 30%. As a result, wheat prices have fallen steadily and significantly in recent months. In the first week of July the Canadian Wheat Board's asking price for wheat (No. 1 Canadian western red spring wheat) was about $4.50 per bushel[3] but by mid-October it had fallen to $3.30. While the general price downtrend is good news for consumers, the disposal of the huge crop amidst a background of rising world supplies could be a significant prob-

[3] 0.03 t

## Production of Principal Field Crops
### millions of bushels*
### millions of tonnes†

| | Average 1965-74 | 1975 | 1976 | Change 76/75 |
|---|---|---|---|---|
| Wheat | *586.8(16.0)† | 627.5(17.1) | 866.0(23.6) | 38.0 |
| Oats | 338.2 (5.2) | 289.6 (4.5) | 326.1 (5.0) | 12.6 |
| Barley | 386.7 (8.4) | 437.3(10.3) | 475.6(10.4) | 8.8 |
| Rye | 16.3 (0.4) | 20.6 (0.5) | 22.3 (0.6) | 8.3 |
| Flaxseed | 23.0 (0.6) | 17.5 (0.4) | 12.1 (0.3) | −30.9 |
| Rapeseed | 45.5 (1.2) | 77.1 (1.9) | 41.1 (1.0) | −46.7 |
| Mixed Grains | 90.2 (2.3) | 89.8 (2.3) | 86.0 (2.2) | − 4.2 |
| Corn for grain | 88.7 (2.3) | 143.5 (3.6) | 136.8 (3.5) | − 4.7 |

lem in the months to come.

Of course, this is not an unusual situation for Canada. Domestic stocks of wheat expanded rapidly in the late sixties as good Canadian harvests were combined with falling export sales, the result of increased production in other countries. To reduce these enormous stocks, land was taken out of wheat production under the auspices of the federal operation LIFT (Low Inventories For Tomorrow) program.

While there is little likelihood of wheat stocks reaching the former billion bushel peak by the beginning of the next crop year they could well double and reach the area of 600 million bushels[4] if exports fall 10% from the 1975-76 crop year total. In that year total wheat exports amounted to 449 million bushels,[5] an increase of 14% from the previous year, as sharply higher purchases by the Soviet Union (which bought 27% of all Canadian wheat exports) more than offset cutbacks by China and the United

[4] 16 330 000 t
[5] 12 220 000 t

Kingdom. This year, however, with the bumper crop in the Soviet Union and with a record grain harvest in China — Canada's largest wheat buyer, on average, over the past decade — the prospects for increasing exports appear slim. Although domestic consumption of wheat could increase during the current crop year as a result of falling prices, the potential increase would appear to be too small to have a significant effect on the size of carry-over stocks at the beginning of the next crop year.

Source: Bank of Montreal *Business Review*, November 1976

## B: THE PRESENT

- 13. Graph the data in Figure 8-10.

- 14. From the evidence in the article *A Bin Buster of a Year*, can you suggest some of the factors that would influence the amount of wheat that prairie farmers decide to grow from year to year?

Your answer to question 13 shows that wheat continues to be a major product of the prairies, now even exceeding the output of the golden years of the 1900s through 1920s. However, the data in Figure 8-11 show also that other things have become important too. The prairies have moved away from their former dependence on one resource only, whether buffalo or wheat; they have found and developed other resources, and thus broadened the base of their economy.

Perhaps the most important of these present resources is fuels, mainly oil and natural gas, but also coal and hydroelectricity. Fuels have long been important to the prairies, from the days when the early railways sought local supplies of coal. Some discoveries were quick, like those of the Crow's Nest Pass coal deposits;

An economy is the organization of activities by people to gain a living. In a simple economy people may do only a few things, such as hunting or farming, but in a more complex economy people have a much wider choice of things to do. The price of the increased choice in a complex economy is the loss of self sufficiency. Can you explain this?

The earliest trains were wood burning, but these could prosper only in forested areas. Clearance of forest meant a switch to coal burning locomotives, which were also ideal for the treeless plains of the west. In order to have enough coal to keep the trains moving, the locomotives used to carry several tonnes with them in a special compartment just behind the driving platform. The coal was fed into the furnace by a *fireman*.

**Figure 8-12** Canada's original oil field in Turner Valley.

others were lucky, like those of the Medicine Hat natural gas fields when early settlers were drilling wells looking for drinking water; still others were the result of prolonged and often heartbreaking effort, like the Leduc oil discoveries of 1947.

**Figure 8-13** One of Canada's largest oil refineries, at Edmonton.

The search for a large oil strike had been going on for years when the winter of 1947 rolled round. The oil industry was getting pessimistic, faced by dry hole after dry hole. Hundreds of wells had been drilled, and not one had looked even promising. In February, Imperial Oil decided it would try one more well before it stopped altogether. The well was Leduc. It struck oil. Hope was rekindled, other wells followed (which is why the original well came to be called Leduc #1 rather than just Leduc), and a new Canadian industry was born.

Before 1947, small quanitities of oil had been discovered, but none that amounted to anything of more than local importance. In 1947, Leduc #1 changed all that. Canada became one of the world's major oil producers. There are now thousands of producing wells in the Edmonton area, and new fields are constantly being discovered under the prairies. Oil is usually found in old buried coral reefs of Devonian age (see Chapter 3), but some is also found in anticlinal and faulted oil traps, as shown in Figure 8-14.

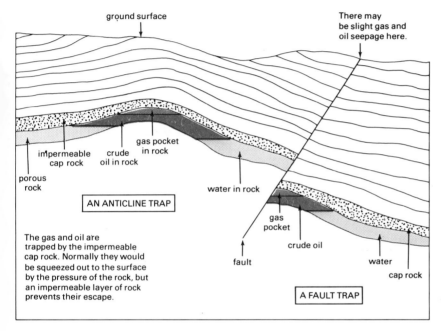

**Figure 8-14   Two Common Types of Oil Traps**

The 1947 discoveries led to the growth of secondary industry in the prairies. Steel plants developed to make pipes; pumping and drilling manufacturers came into business; petrochemical factories making plastics and fertilizers developed; engineering became important. The prairie economy began to be diversified. Farming eventually ceased to be the dominant activity.

Manufacturing in the prairies has continued to develop over the years, but it still remains smaller than most prairie towns would like. Despite the natural resource wealth of the region, the provinces lack both a large labour supply and easy access to a large market. As we have noted, the present population of the prairie provinces is only about 3 600 000, which is much less than half that of Ontario. In addition, the prairie population is well scattered, making transportation relatively expensive.

Secondary industry means manufacturing industry of one sort or another.

Many prairie towns advertise in papers like the *Financial Post*. They try to attract businesses to set up factories. What sort of attractions do you think they advertise?

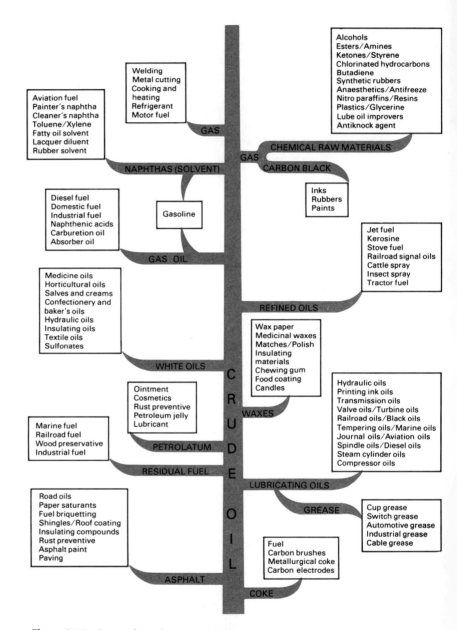

**Figure 8-15   By-products from Crude Oil**

**Figure 8-16   Seismic Method of Determining Underground Rock Structures**

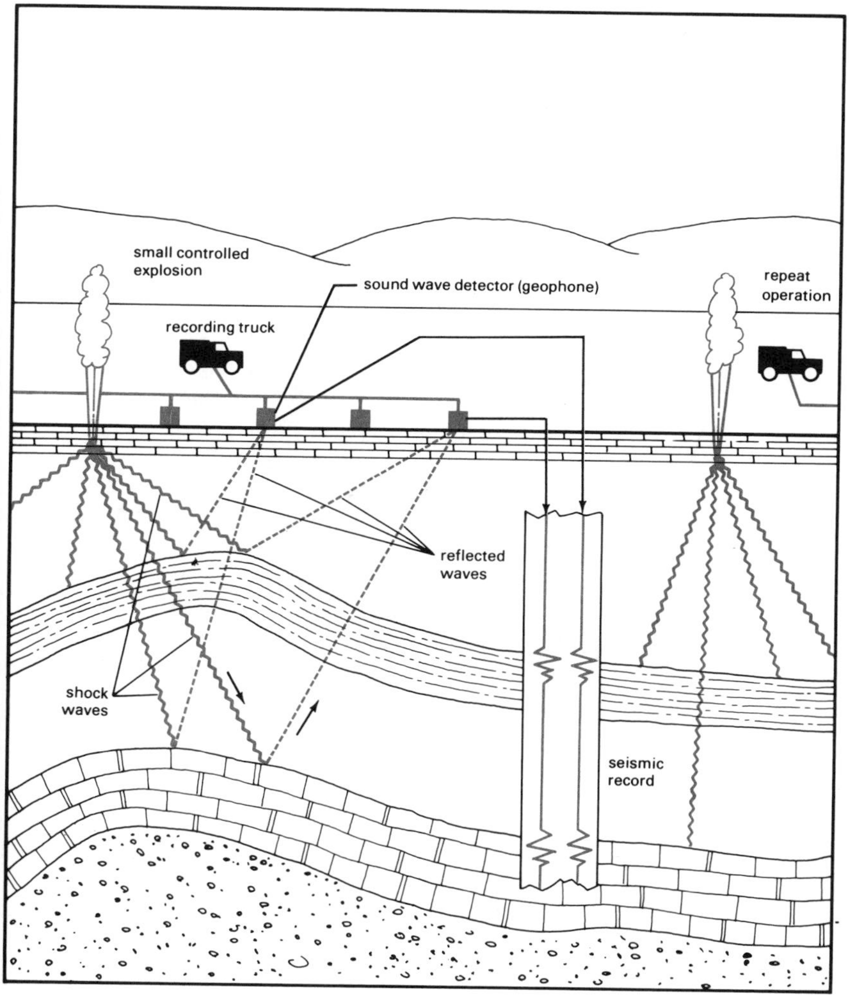

# Meat Processing on the Prairies

The meat processing industry, which ranks third in size nationally, is the single largest industry in the Prairies — ranking ahead of petroleum in dollar value, said Child.[1] Burns[2] is the single largest employer in Saskatchewan, with about 1000 people.

1 President, Burns Foods Ltd., Calgary
2 Burns Foods Ltd.

It has 21 plants in 11 locations in the three Prairie provinces, and revenue in Saskatchewan is larger than the entire potash production in dollar value.

# Alberta's Energy Future

By Thomas Kennedy
CALGARY — Coal is cast in a major role in the plan being designed by the Alberta Government to fully utilize all energy resources.

Coal, which fuelled industry almost exclusively 100 years ago but was pushed into near oblivion by oil and gas during the past 30 years, could again become a prominent energy source by virtue of a price advantage over its competitors.

The Alberta Energy Resources Conservation Board recommends it as the most appropriate fuel for future power stations in the province. The recommendations would mean development of more than one billion tons[1] of coal deposits— about 690 million tons[2] for use in thermal power installations over the next 30 years.

The switch to coal as the main fuel for power generation would also "liberate" up to 12 trillion cubic feet[3] of natural gas for export that would otherwise be burned locally to produce electricity. The gas can be sold at a better rate of return elsewhere, including Ontario.

The recommendations stem from the board's study of long-term provincial energy requirements, conducted last year. Its report on coal will be followed by a second volume to be based on a comprehensive public hearing, called for June 19, on the current and potential impact of the coal industry on the provincial economy.

Alberta's coal production — about 10.5 million tons[4] in 1972 — appears almost insignificant compared with its vast reserves, which are yet to be assessed with accuracy.

The province has known and readily accessible reserves of high-quality coal, suitable for steelmaking, of about 2.5 billion tons,[5] and lower-quality thermal coal reserves of about five billion tons.[6] The ultimate potential for both categories is estimated at several times those levels.

Almost two billion tons[7] of the thermal coal for power generation is found along a 100-mile wide[8] Calgary-Edmonton axis, and could be mined by open pit operations. And it is in this region that most of the demand for electric power is expected to materialize. (The projected vast plants for the Athabasca oil sands would generate their own power, mostly on-site).

Alberta has two major gas-fired power plants and several smaller installations, which together with thermal and hydro-electric facilities produced about 12 billion kilowatt hours of electric energy in 1972. The board estimates an average annual increase in demand of 8 per cent, to about 113 000 gigawatt hours by 2002.

Alberta's hydro-electric generating capacity, though not fully harnessed, is limited, but its coal potential is enormous and could create a major, capital-intensive and job-producing industry. Overseas demand has been responsible for the renaissance of the Alberta coal industry since the mid-1960s, but its growth in that direction is limited by transportation costs. In 1972 exports of high-grade coal, mostly to Japan, amounted to 5.6 million tons.[9] Coal industry estimates are that exports of high-grade coal will be doubled during the next 30 years.

Development of the mining industry as the board

[1] 900 000 000 t
[2] 621 000 000 t
[3] 340 billion m³

[4] 9 500 000 t
[5] 2.25 billion t
[6] 4.5 billion t
[7] 1.8 billion t
[8] 160 km

[9] 5 040 000 t

recommends would mean an investment in mines and equipment of billions of dollars and creation of several hundred permanent jobs.

Alberta could meet its long-term power needs at a lower over-all cost. Some utilities have asked for continued use of gas for local power generation, but the board is expected to discourage such considerations.

There is an almost insatiable demand for gas in North America of late, a market condition that would more than amply compensate the gas industry for any loss of growth in provincial demand.

The Alberta Government, which is expected to concur with the board's recommendations, would sooner see its gas exported. In the planned two-price system Alberta consumers are to get a rebate on their gas from export revenues.

In other words, Alberta gas is rapidly becoming too valuable to be used for such a low-quality end use as power generation.

Expressed in terms of millions of British thermal units[10] of heating value, coal costs about 15 cents per million BTUs, or $2.40 a ton, at today's average pithead prices. This represents a 20-cent advantage over

the volume of gas needed to yield the same heating value.

Coal prices will escalate over the next three decades to about 48.7 cents a million BTUs or $7.80 a ton. Assuming that gas will be priced according to its commodity value, the board puts gas prices, in its least painful calculations, at 39 cents a million BTUs in 1979, rising to 90 cents by the year 2002.

An upper estimate puts gas prices at $1.51 a million BTUs in the same year, compared with an estimated ultimate coal price of 81 cents a million BTUs or $13 a ton on a heat value basis.

The board expects that utilities will become "coal-oriented," and there is adequate regulatory authority to compel utilities to use coal instead of gas.

Ontario is a major consumer of Alberta gas and substantial volumes are used in power generation. Alberta producers and the provincial Government oppose this use and have claimed that Ontario utilities switched from coal to gas because the latter was securely available at low cost. Gas is being put to a similar use in California.

The 10 to 12 trillion cubic feet[11] that would be spared in Alberta by more

extensive use of coal locally represent about one-quarter of Alberta's current contracted reserves.

The new philosophy of the regulatory authority fits comfortably into Premier Peter Lougheed's multi-purpose strategy of enhancing the contribution of resources to the over-all economy.

The Government is engaged in a bid to increase gas reserves through higher prices, which will bring into a commercial category gas too expensive to produce at the previous prices.

Coal is also being considered as a source of synthetic gas supplies, although only on a long-term basis.

The renewed use of coal for power generation would conclude a trend that in the 1960s saw wholesale conversion of coal-fired installations to natural gas — an application now being blamed by producers for the present fuel shortage in the United States.

Increased use of the low-grade thermal coal would assist the economics of mining higher grade coal, either for the steelmakers of the world — prospects exist as far away as Europe if transportation can be made competitive — and for Ontario, where Alberta expects to market some of its intermediate grade coal.

[10] 1 BTU = 1 kJ (approx.)   [11] 280 to 340 billion m$^3$

Ontario imports about 14 million tons[12] of coal annually, according to industry estimates, and experts

[12] 12 600 000 t

here believe a good portion of these imports could be replaced by coal from Alberta.

Rail tariffs, now on the agenda of intergovernmental discussions, are the key to successful marketing of Western coal in Eastern Canada.

from the *Globe and Mail*, April 17, 1973

# Manitoba Industry

By W. J. Megill

Manitoba has the most diversified industrial complex of any of the prairie provinces, centred mainly in the Winnipeg-St. Boniface metropolitan area. The leading industries are meat packing, oil refining, dairy factories and clothing factories, in that order, and these four segments together account for about 28 per cent of the total value of production. Flour milling and other food processing plants are also important, but the whole field of fabrication of metals, wood and plastics is probably the key to future growth. An increasing variety of products is being made as industry is attracted by a central position, excellent communications and low cost electric power.

Mining is the growth sector in Manitoba, the value of mineral production having doubled during the past five years. Just as basic agriculture was displaced by manufacturing as the chief earner some 30 years ago, so mining will probably reduce agriculture from second to third place in the Manitoba economy during the early part of this coming decade. Northwest of Lake Winnipeg is the copper-zinc area, with the principal producers in the Flin Flon, Snow Lake, and Lynn Lake areas. To the northeast is the nickel belt, where production of electrolytic nickel started in 1960 at Thompson with an annual capacity of 75 million pounds,[1] and is expected to reach 170 million pounds[2] in 1970. Some precious metals are also extracted, and gold has been produced at Bissett, east of Lake Winnipeg, since 1932. Active prospecting is continuing in all known mineralized areas. In the southwest around Virden is the oil region, a useful addition to the economy but not as important as in the other prairie provinces.

[1] 34 million kg
[2] 77 million kg

Low cost power from hydro electric plants on the Winnipeg River has been for many years an important incentive for the location of industry in the Winnipeg area. The northwest is now served by a plant at Grand Rapids on the Saskatchewan River, close to where it enters Lake Winnipeg. The great remaining potential power source is the Nelson River, with about 7 million horsepower[3] available. A plant at Kelsey serves the nickel refinery at Thompson and one at Kettle Rapids is now being built. Power from Kettle Rapids and from further plants to be built on the Nelson will be transmitted to the south by ultra-high voltage direct current, to meet developing needs in the Winnipeg area and for export. Manitoba is also preparing for the nuclear age at the Whiteshell Research Establishment operated by Atomic Energy of Canada, Ltd., at Pinawa on the Winnipeg River.

[3] 5222 million watts (W)

from the *Canadian Geographical Journal*, Vol. 8, No. 2, August, 1970.

# Prairie Demand Highest For Technical Specialists

The Prairies have again ousted Ontario from its traditional position as the Canadian leader in the number of openings for engineers, scientists, accountants, executives and professionals, according to the latest survey by the Technical Service Council.

Vacancies in the west are heavily concentrated in Alberta where shortages of specialists continue, with vacancies for petroleum engineers outnumbering all other types as oil exploration activity and tar sands development continues to grow.

Many Alberta employers report difficulty in recruiting staff and are seeking help across Canada, the Council says.

It reports that nationally the number of job openings for executives and professionals increased by 12.7 per cent during the third quarter of this year but it notes that the rate at which new jobs were formed was little changed.

This suggests that "the increase was largely due to employers taking longer to fill their positions."

Because of the slack economy, employers are "unusually selective," according to N. A. Macdougall, general manager of the Council.

"Most are insisting upon directly related experience in order to cut training costs. Many are prepared to wait for a superior candidate," he added.

from the Toronto *Star*, October 20, 1976

- 15. Why do you think a scattered population is a disadvantage for the growth of industry?

- 16. What changes do you think are taking place in Alberta's energy picture?

- 17. Can you suggest the main reasons for Winnipeg's position as the chief manufacturing centre in the prairies?

- 18. Why is the demand for technical specialists high in the prairies?

As much as anything, the lack of large population clusters is an important cause of the lack of industry in the prairies. Inevitably, most of the existing industries are related more to the development of resources than to the supplying of consumer demand. For example, there are food processing industries, tractor making operations, fertilizer factories, and oil refineries, but not automobile makers or electric appliance manufacturers.

Special ships come from Japan to pick up very large cargoes of coal. They are called very large bulk carriers (VLBCs), and they carry cargoes of over 100 000 t on each journey. A special port was built at Roberts Bank, just south of Vancouver, to handle these VLBCs, and special handling and delivery arrangements had to be made to get coal from the Crow's Nest Pass down to Roberts Bank in the sorts of quantities needed to fill up a VLBC. Canadian Pacific runs six trains on a 24 hour schedule between the coal field and the port, so that at any one time a train is being loaded at the coal field, two more are at different stages on the journey down to Roberts Bank, one is at the port unloading its coal into a giant storage area, and two more are returning empty to pick up more coal at the coal field. Every week a VLBC comes from Japan and collects all the coal that has been brought down to the port.

Hydro stations do not need to be built in mountainous areas. It is more important that they get a large and regular volume of water passing through.

Meanwhile the resource base continues to expand. New sources of heavy oil and other non-conventional oils have been discovered in northern Alberta and Saskatchewan. Non-conventional oils are those which cannot be pumped in the ordinary way: heavy oils, for instance, must be injected with steam to make them fluid enough to be pumped; the Athabasca oil sands, on the other hand, must be mined like a metal. The non-conventional sources contain supplies sufficient to last Canada for hundreds of years at present rates of use. The problem is the cost of extraction and refining.

Coal is another important fuel. First exploited to power the transcontinental railways it went into decline when the railways switched to diesel traction. However, it is now becoming important once again, though for different reasons. Its two main markets are: (1) locally in the prairies for the generation of thermal electricity, and (2) overseas in Japan for use in steel mills. Figure 8-17 gives information on the fluctuating fortunes of the Canadian coal industry.

The energy picture in the prairies is rounded out by the abundance of hydroelectricity that they can generate. The prairie rivers generally flow from the Rockies eastwards to Hudson Bay. In doing so they fall some 2000 m. Many are easily dammed in fairly narrow valleys. Several hydro stations exist at various points along the rivers from Alberta down to Manitoba, with some of the very largest being built or planned on the Nelson river in Manitoba (Figure 8-18).

● 19. Figure 8-18 shows clearly that Manitoba contains most of the large hydro stations, yet this is where the land is lowest. There are several reasons, both physical and economic, for this. Can you suggest and explain any of the possible reasons?

The widespread drilling for oil and gas which occurred in the three provinces has generally improved our knowledge of the existence of other mineral resources too. For example, in Alberta small quantities of iron and salt have been found and used. In Saskatchewan the chief non-fuel mineral is potash. Indeed, some of the largest potash deposits yet found in the world lie in a belt between Saskatoon and Esterhazy (Figure 8-20).

In Manitoba, the minerals tend to be different from those in Alberta and Saskatchewan. Figure 8-19 suggests why. Manitoba, even in its more populated southern parts, contains a large proportion of the Canadian Shield, and the minerals there are more metallic in character than those of the sedimentary rocks in

Alberta and Saskatchewan. For example, one of the world's major known nickel deposits exists at Thompson. It was first put into production in 1960. In addition, copper and zinc are important at Flin Flon and Lynn Lake.

Mining, whether for fuels or for metals or even for evaporites, certainly provides the prairie provinces with yet another major resource.

One of the first mining prospectors into the area of Flin Flon happened to be reading a book on his journey north. The book was about the adventures of a character called Flintabbity Flontin, hence the name of Flin Flon.

**Figure 8-17   Canadian Coal Production, 1871-1970**

| Year | Production in Tonnes |
|------|---------------------|
| 1871 | 1 064 000 |
| 1881 | 1 537 000 |
| 1891 | 3 578 000 |
| 1901 | 6 486 000 |
| 1911 | 11 323 000 |
| 1921 | 15 057 000 |
| 1931 | 12 243 000 |
| 1941 | 18 226 000 |
| 1951 | 18 587 000 |
| 1961 | 10 398 000 |
| 1962 | 10 285 000 |
| 1963 | 10 576 000 |
| 1964 | 11 319 000 |
| 1965 | 11 589 000 |
| 1966 | 11 392 000 |
| 1967 | 11 123 000 |
| 1968 | 10 980 000 |
| 1969 | 10 635 000 |
| 1970 | 16 047 000 |

Source: Canadian Almanac and Directory

The prairie provinces are also making efforts to develop their forest industries. Most of their forest is in the Boreal climatic zone (see Chapter 2) in the northern parts of the provinces. It is most accessible in Manitoba, where the greatest forest developments have accordingly taken place. The centre is The Pas, which started life as a fur trading post, but which is now the home of a giant forest products complex, including a pulp mill, a kraft mill, a saw mill, and a machinery plant. However, severe financial problems trouble the industry, and its future is not entirely certain.

Boreal is a word derived from Greek mythology. Boreas was the god of the north wind, and over the years the word has come to be applied to anything northern, such as the aurora borealis. The opposite is australis, named after Auster, the god of the south wind.

**Figure 8-18 Major Hydro Sites in the Prairie Provinces**

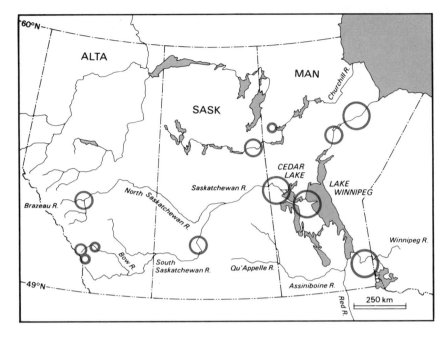

**Figure 8-19 Map and Section Showing Large Expanse of Precambrian Shield in Manitoba**

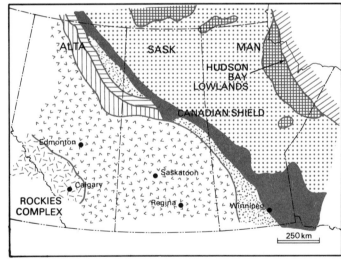

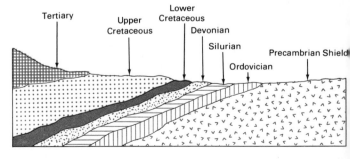

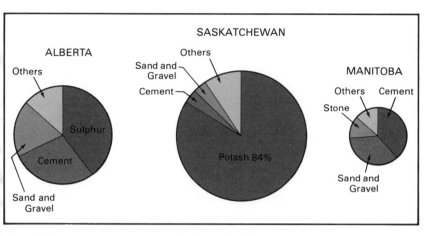

**Figure 8-20    Non-metallic, Non-fuel Minerals in the Prairies**

**Figure 8-21** A uranium mine at Rabbit Lake in north Saskatchewan.

**Figure 8-22** Part of the nickel refining operations at Thompson, Manitoba.

Winnipeg Goldeye became famous because the transcontinental trains used to take on supplies at Winnipeg, and thereby serve fresh fish to their customers in the middle of the continent.

Some irrigation is by open ditches, which are cheaper to construct than sprinkler systems, but an increasing proportion is by sprinklers, which are cheaper and more efficient to operate. With a sprinkler system, water can be pumped long distances, loss by evaporation can be minimized, and flow can be turned off at any time it is not required.

● 20. Why should the Boreal forest be most accessible in Manitoba rather than in Alberta or Saskatchewan? Accessible *from* what? And *to* what? Can you suggest some of the reasons for the financial problems of the forestry industry in Manitoba?

In the many lakes of the prairie provinces, fish form yet another resource. Lake Winnipeg was the first large lake to be fished commercially. It happened in 1882, when two men named Clark and Reid used a sailboat and a few nets. The practice spread very quickly, and rich hauls of perch, pickerel, pike, lake trout, whitefish, and Winnipeg Goldeye soon started to be made. In the 1970s the farming of fish also became important. Rainbow trout are now "planted" as fingerlings in farm ponds in spring, and harvested as marketable fish in the fall.

The *wetlands* of the prairie provinces, including lakes and marshes, are located mostly in the more moist northern and eastern areas, mainly in Manitoba and Saskatchewan. In addition to providing fish, they also act as both a permanent home and a migration staging post for hundreds of thousands of wildfowl. Duck hunting is a major seasonal activity.

But water in the prairies is important for more than fish and wildfowl. We have already seen its importance for hydro power; so we should now note its importance for irrigation. The earliest large scale irrigation projects started at the turn of the century, using water from rivers flowing eastwards from the Rockies. Today about five percent of prairie farmland is irrigated, mostly by sprinklers, enabling a wide variety of vegetables to be grown, in addition to richer crops of grain. The chief irrigated areas are in southern Alberta, near Lethbridge and Medicine Hat, and in southern Saskatchewan along the South Saskatchewan and Qu'Appelle Rivers, as shown in Figure 8-25. All prairie irrigation projects are run by the Prairie Farm Rehabilitation Administration (PFRA), which was set up in 1935 to combat the problems of the early 1930s drought years. The PFRA operates everything from major multi-purpose projects to individual farm ponds.

**Figure 8-23** Irrigated vegetable land near Lethbridge.

**Figure 8-24** A water management scheme on the South Saskatchewan River.

For many years, from 1930 onwards, Saskatchewan lost a few people each year, and its population slowly declined. However, in 1976-77, the trend was halted, and Saskatchewan actually began to gain population slightly.

In spite of the variety and richness of prairie resources, however, the three provinces are not overly populated. Indeed, Saskatchewan is barely holding its existing population. And within the prairies the rural areas are increasingly losing population in favour of the towns. This thinning of the rural fabric, however, can produce both negative and positive effects. For example, the drift from the land usually means that family farms become fewer, but it also means that the land may become more efficiently farmed by giant *agribusinesses*. For another example, urbanization means not only that the large cities become larger but also that the small country towns become smaller. In turn the small country towns can therefore provide fewer services to their surrounding countryside.

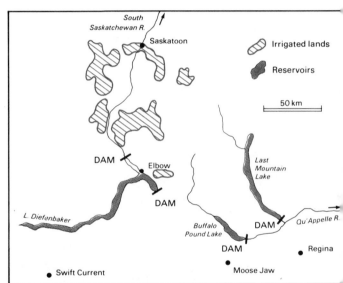

**Figure 8-25    The South Saskatchewan Irrigation Project**

- 21. If you were an urban dweller what would the greater increase in farming by agribusinesses likely mean to you?

- 22. What are some of the advantages of the larger towns in the prairies becoming even larger?

- 23. If you were the Premier of a prairie province what would you want to do about the drift of people from the country into the large towns?

There is one more current resource we should mention: the location of the prairie provinces in relation to the Canadian northland. Canada's interest in its northland has grown for a number of reasons over the last several years, but the greatest problem lies in the fact that the north is not easily accessible from the major population centres in the south. Figure 8-26 shows some of the problems and some of the solutions. You can readily see that the prairie provinces, especially Alberta, are in a good position for acting as the main southern supply base for the northland. Within Alberta there is no doubt that Edmonton, the northernmost large city as well as the provincial capital, is best situated to act as the main gateway to and from the north. As the northland develops so the prairie provinces will benefit.

The north is not easily accessible from anywhere in the south, except by air. Ground and water transportation are exceedingly difficult, although ground is less difficult in winter and water in summer; but air is best at both seasons.

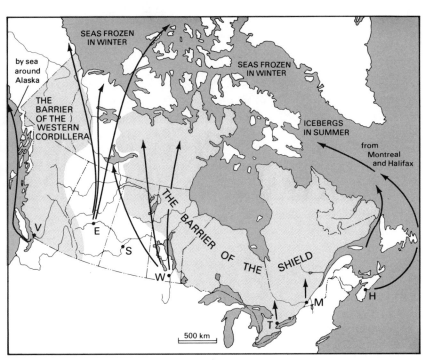

**Figure 8-26   The Locational Advantage of the Prairie Provinces for Access to the Canadian Northland**
Note especially the strategic advantage of Edmonton.

So far we have looked at several of the resources of the prairie provinces, including buffalo, furs, wheat, fuels, metals, forests, water, population movements, and location in relation to the northland. You will probably have noticed that most of these

resources have always been there, even though they have no
always been used, nor continue to be used. It is the abilities an
wishes of the people that have changed.

**Figure 8-27**   Transporting prairie resources.

● 24. What do you think would be a good definition of  
      *resource?*

● 25. Do you think that what is a resource now will continue t  
      be a resource? Should present resources be conserved for  
      future that might not want them? *Will* the future want them  
      Should we waste resources?

# CHAPTER 9

# PACIFIC CANADA

## SUPPORT OF LIFE

## INTRODUCTION

Along with Ontario and Alberta, British Columbia is one of the provinces that persistently has levels of personal income above the average for the whole of Canada. This makes it one of the wealthier parts of the world. Certainly, in general terms, the people of British Columbia live well.

In specific terms it is slightly more difficult to say exactly how much better the people of Pacific Canada live in relation to the people of other areas. However, some indicators are shown in Figure 9-1.

When British Columbia celebrated its centenary (the union of Vancouver Island with the mainland) in 1966, the Royal Bank *Monthly Letter* commented, "With its vast power resources, its rapidly growing population, its carefulness in conserving resources, and its abundant human energy, its prospects for continuing prosperity appear unlimited."

Figure 9-1   Some Comparative Indicators of Standards of Living, All Quantities per Thousand Population

|  | Pacific Canada British Columbia | Average for all Canada | Atlantic Canada | |
|---|---|---|---|---|
|  |  |  | Nova Scotia | Newfoundland |
| Motor vehicles | 510 | 418 | 393 | 247 |
| Telephones | 50 | 47 | 38 | 27 |
| Daily newspaper sales | 241 | 180 | 201 | 82 |
| Restaurant sales in $ | 61 502 | 64 289 | 43 071 | 25 031 |
| Beer, wine, and liquor sales $ | 102 644 | 86 081 | 88 681 | 76 219 |
| Life insurance premiums $ | 60 377 | 66 435 | 57 037 | 27 772 |
| Personal incomes in $ | 4 194 778 | 3 786 898 | 3 010 292 | 2 509 079 |
| Physicians | 1.66 | 1.51 | 1.37 | 0.90 |
| Annual public library circulation | 6 637 | 4 513 | 3 648 | 2 840 |

Source: 1971 Census

191

Some of the big forestry companies operating in British Columbia include MacMillan Bloedel Ltd. (the giant of the province), Crown Zellerbach Ltd, British Columbia Forest Products Ltd, Canadian Forest Products Ltd, Northwood Pulp Ltd, Scott Paper Ltd, Columbia Cellulose Co Ltd, and Weyerhaeuser Canada Ltd.

● 1. (a) Can you devise some way of showing the data in Figure 9-1 so that the comparatively high standard of living in British Columbia shows up clearly?

(b) Can you suggest any reasons for the below average standing of British Columbia in restaurant sales and life insurance premiums?

The indicators in Figure 9-1 show that British Columbians on the average live quite well. They have more cars and telephones per 1000 people than average Canadians have. They buy more newspapers and read more library books; they consume more alcoholic beverages; they have more physicians. And they have higher personal incomes. They also compare very favourably with Atlantic Canadians, though not with Canadians on the whole, in the matter of eating out at restaurants and in the amount of life insurance carried.

In view of the generally high level of these indicators in British Columbia, it is fair to assume that many other things also rank highly there. For example, in November 1976 the Chairman of one of British Columbia's big forestry firms claimed that the province forest workers were "the best paid in the world".

What enables British Columbians to have these high incomes and high standards of living? What geographical factors help to support their life?

## A: THE SUPPORTERS

The environment has been kind to the people of Pacific Canada since before Canada became a nation. One of the oldest customs of the Pacific Indians is the *potlatch*, wherein a tribesman gives as many gifts as he can to all the guests invited to his party. He may finish with nothing; but the more he gives the better it is. When it is his turn to be invited to the parties of others, he acquires wealth in return. Part of the custom of the potlatch has been the element of competition: each tries to outgive the others. It takes an environment of great wealth to support such a custom.

The Indians found their wealth in the forests and waters of British Columbia. Later, other Canadians similarly found wealth in those sectors of the environment, and they have since found additional sources of wealth as well.

BRITISH COLUMBIA'S AREA

FORESTED PORTION

### Forests

Forests cover almost 60% of British Columbia's land. For the most part they occur in three major sections of the province (Figure 9-2). First is the *Coast Forest*, which is located on the offshore islands, especially Queen Charlotte and Vancouver Island, and in most areas of the Coast Mountains. It is the most luxuriant forest in Canada, with many fine tall conifers. The most famous tree is the Douglas fir, which averages 60–70 m in height and about two metres in width. Other important trees include the Sitka spruce, the western red cedar, and western hemlock. Second is the *Columbia Forest,* which ranks next to the Coast Forest in luxuriance. However, the chief trees, notably western red cedar and western hemlock together with some Douglas firs and ponderosa pine, are usually smaller than those in the Coast Forest. Third is the *Northern Forest,* consisting mainly of white spruce. Trees here are smaller than in the other two zones, and towards the extreme north of the province they become quite stunted.

The luxuriance of the Coast Forest is reflected in some of Emily Carr's paintings. Frederick Varley, one of the Group of Seven, was also attracted to the west Coast Forest. The most imposing of all Coast Forest trees is the Douglas fir.

**Figure 9-2 Simplified Distribution of Forest in British Columbia**

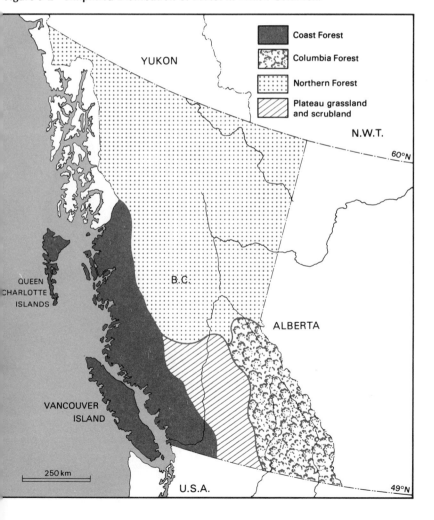

Sustained yield means that a forest can be made to yield a harvest forever. It results from a combination of two things: first, planting one new tree for every tree cut, and second, cutting only that proportion of the forest which is the reciprocal of the growing time of the trees in years. For example, if it takes 50 years for trees to grow to cuttable maturity, then you only cut one-fiftieth of the forest every year; if it takes forty years, then you cut only one-fortieth of the forest, and so on. Clearly it is in the interest of foresters to try to develop faster growing species of trees. Can you think of two or more advantages of faster growing trees?

The British Columbia forests contain more than 50% of the total forest resources of Canada. Altogether it is estimated that British Columbia has at least 7.5 billion cubic metres of marketable timber, including nearly 75% of Canada's softwood timber (Figure 9-6).

Supported by these forests, the various forestry industries form the major economic activity in British Columbia. The annual cut is now well over 55 000 000 m³ (Figure 9-3), almost all of it on a *sustained yield* basis. As the years pass, an increasing proportion of the forest cut comes from the Columbia and Northern Forests, and a diminishing proportion from the Coast Forest. This is a relatively recent trend. Up to 1970 or so the Coast was more important, but during the 1970s the interior forests have become equally important; the trend is for them to gain even greater importance in the future.

The chief products are lumber and plywood, accounting together for about 85% of British Columbia's total forest products. Pulp and

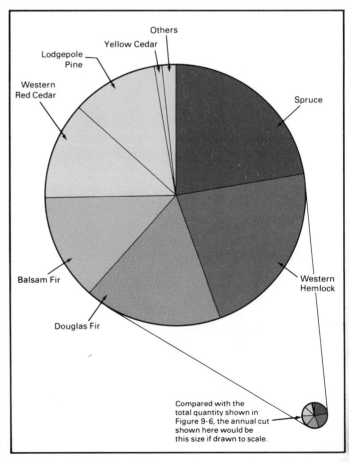

**Figure 9-3   Proportions of British Columbia's Annual Forest Cut**

**Figure 9-4** A paper mill at Gold River on Vancouver Island.

It is not only forest companies that are being driven away from the coast by people who want to use it for other purposes. Until the early 1970s there had been many different industries clustered around the shores of an arm of the sea in Vancouver called False Bay. By the mid 1970s they had all been forced out, their buildings had all been destroyed, and the land was being built over instead with housing and marinas.

paper account for only 13%, while the remaining two percent is accounted for by minor wood products such as poles and posts.

Despite its small percentage of the total, wood pulp is the most rapidly growing sector of the industry, and there are many important pulp and paper mills, as you can see in Figure 9-7. Most mills (16) are in the zone of the Coast Forest, where cheap transportation by water has been a decided advantage. However, the increasing demands by a growing population for a higher priority use of the Pacific coast for housing and recreation are gradually forcing the pulp and paper companies to move their operations into the remote interior. You will notice from Figure 9-7 that the newest mills are located in the interior.

- 2. What do we mean by a "higher priority use" of the coast? What could such higher priority uses be? Does this tell you anything about the beliefs of the majority of British Columbians with regard to their life supporting activities?
- 3. What differences do you notice between Figure 9-6 (volume of marketable timber in British Columbia) and Figure 9-3 (volume of timber actually cut)? Can you find or suggest reasons for these differences?

In the early 1970s a Crown Zellerbach mill at Ocean Falls was scheduled for closing. The mill was old, and the company did not think it worthwhile to spend a lot of new money on refurbishing it; future mills were clearly going to have to be in the interior. However, the closing of the mill would virtually have killed the town of Ocean Falls, so the provincial government decided to take the mill over and operate it as a provincial concern. In effect, the mill was kept alive through the use of taxpayers' money. What would you have done?

New mills in the interior will face very high transportation costs. It will cost a lot of money to transport the logs to the mills, since cheap water transport will not be available, and it will cost a lot to transport the finished pulp or paper to international markets for the same reason. On international markets, the pulp and paper producers have to compete with pulp and paper producers elsewhere. They cannot just raise their prices at will, because customers will then start to buy from competing pulp and paper producers. For this reason, British Columbia's producers need to keep their costs as low as possible. This means that they need to use the most modern and efficient machinery; they need to use as much of the tree as possible, and cut down waste; they need to use the best quality timber; and they need to improve the growing and harvesting of timber in their forests. In November 1976 the Chairman of Crown Zellerbach said that large scale modernization of productive capacity was essential if the British Columbia forest industry was to remain competitive in world markets.

**Figure 9-5**   Is this a high priority use of the coastland?

● 4. How do you think the forest companies are trying to combat the extra costs incurred in doing business in the interior?

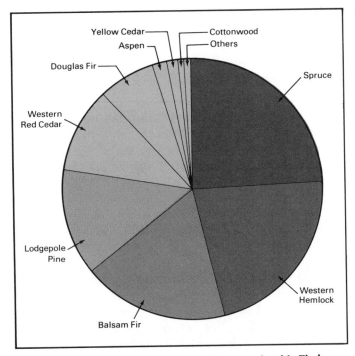

**Figure 9-6   Proportions of British Columbia's Marketable Timber, in Trees at least 18 cm in Diameter**

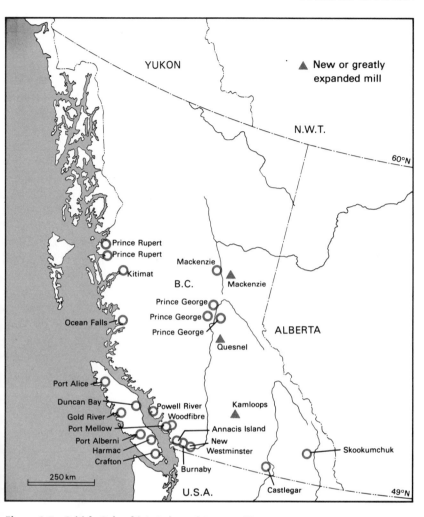

**Figure 9-7 British Columbia's Pulp and Paper Mills**

Most of British Columbia's forest products are exported, mainly to the United States, but also increasingly to Japan. About 75% of the lumber goes abroad, along with 60% of the pulp and 99% of the paper. Altogether nearly 50% of all Canada's forestry export earnings are due to British Columbia's forestry companies. This is the first and most important reason that British Columbians are able to live so well.

## Waters

British Columbia's waters support life in many ways. In addition to fishing, which is the most direct form of support, the waters also provide help to transportation industries, power generation utilities, metal processors, farmers, and recreation enthusiasts. Can you think of any others?

Fishing is important both offshore and in the rivers. By far the most important part (over 80%) of the fishing industry is the salmon catch. Salmon that are spawned in the gravel beds of British Columbia's many rivers swim down to the sea to live. After some years they return to the same rivers to spawn in turn. Every year there are millions of salmon trying to swim upstream to their spawning grounds. Indians used to catch them (some still do) by setting traps or even by just spearing them as they swam upstream, but commercial fishing fleets catch them in large nets as the salmon converge on the mouths of rivers as they come in from the sea. The chief salmon canneries (75% of the catch is canned) are located near the mouths of the main rivers.

Halibut is the second most important fish (eight percent) and cod the third (two percent). They are caught by different fishing crews, with different equipment, and in different places from the salmon. Halibut and cod are both much larger than salmon, and they swim in the deeper waters away from the coast. They are caught by Vancouver and Prince Rupert-based trawlers, which often have to compete on the fishing grounds with trawlers from Japan and the U.S.S.R. Because of the dangers to future stocks if overfishing is practised, the halibut catch is limited according to *season* (April to October only) and *quantity*.

The sea is also useful for helping the transportation industries. We have already noted its value to the Coast forest companies, but we should also include its value to some of the isolated island and

Five species of salmon are important commercially. They are chinook, coho, pink, sockeye, and chum. Sockeye are the most prized, because of their bright red flesh, though chinook and coho are more valuable to sports fishing enthusiasts.

**Figure 9-8** One of the British Columbia ferries, at Victoria.

northern communities as a link with their outside world. Much of the coastal land is so rugged that road and rail links do not yet exist; the sea therefore provides a lifeline. The line may be used by float planes, which are often the only way to reach many of the smaller communities, or by ferries. The British Columbia ferry service is one of the best equipped and best operated in the world.

● 5. What disadvantages do you think the rivers of British Columbia pose for various means of transportation?

Although the rivers of British Columbia may not be ideal as an aid to transportation, they are very suitable for the generation of hydro power. About 30-35% of Canada's flowing waters are in British Columbia's rivers, with the added advantages of fairly regular flow and easily dammed valleys. In quantity of hydro power generated per person, British Columbia ranks equally with Quebec as Canada's leading province. Even so, only about 20% of British Columbia's hydro potential has yet been tapped. There are major expansion possibilities on all the northern rivers, especially the Liard, Peace, and Skeena, as well as on the Thompson in the south. The major unused river, however, is the Fraser, which has as large a potential for hydro power as all the hydro sites already developed in British Columbia.

One of the largest and most imaginative uses of water for power generation is at Kitimat, where it is also allied with a transportation use. Figure 9-9 shows the location of the Kitimat project. You can see that the eastward flowing waters of the Nechako River have been dammed at the Kenney site to form a huge, sprawling lake on the Nechako Plateau. The waters from this lake are led by tunnel westwards through the mountains to a power house at Kemano. Electricity is then sent by a high voltage transmission line overland to Kitimat, located at the head of the Douglas Channel fiord. Kitimat itself is located by the side of deep and sheltered navigable water so that ships full of alumina from Jamaica and Guyana can readily berth at the giant smelter built there. The entire project was designed and is operated by Alcan.

Fishing, transportation, and hydroelectric generation use water, but they do not consume it. They pass the water on immediately, and it is therefore always available for other users. Farming is different, however, in that it consumes water, thereby preventing its immediate use for anything else. Farming in British Columbia uses river water either naturally, as in the moist flood-prone land of the lower Fraser valley, or artificially, as in the pumped irrigation systems of the interior. Farmland is scarce in British Columbia,

Why do you think the flow of British Columbia's rivers is fairly regular? You should find some ideas in Chapter 2. Why do you think the valleys are fairly easy to dam? Have a look in Chapter 4.

Alumina is a partly processed form of bauxite. Shipping bauxite itself would be vastly expensive because of the large quantities that would need to be shipped. The bauxite is therefore partly processed in Jamaica and Guyana, so that a more concentrated form called alumina can be shipped instead. This saves on transportation costs.

In order to make one tonne of aluminum, 20 000 kW.h of electricity are needed. For this reason, aluminum smelters are always located close to areas where plenty of relatively cheap electricity is available.

The flood prone areas of the Fraser delta lands are protected by dykes. Despite the fairly regular flow of the rivers there are still floods. When do you suppose most floods are likely to occur?

The actual figure for farmland is difficult to give. This is because farmland is difficult to define. Can you think of some of the difficulties?

Water used by farming operations eventually gets back into the water cycle, of course. It may get back by transpiration from plants, or it may get back when the moisture trapped in the plants is digested and processed as eventual human waste, or it may get back by direct evaporation from the soil before the plants get a chance to use it, or it may get back by downward percolation through the soil until it becomes part of the flow in a river again. Water is never lost by being used. Indeed there is just as much water now as there ever was, or ever will be. But it may be diverted from one use to another, and it is in this sense that farming consumes it, because it is thereby diverted from immediate alternative uses.

accounting for about three to six percent of the total land area. Most of the best naturally watered land consists of deltaic silts at the mouths of the major rivers, formed where fast moving river waters are forced to slow down in the sheltered waters between the mainland and the islands. Upon slowing down, the rivers deposit much of their load of silt, thereby causing areas of deltaic flat land to grow where once was sea water. Unfortunately, these deltas are so flat that they are exposed to great risks when floods occur. They get some protection when inhabitants dyke the river, but such protection does not entirely eliminate the risks.

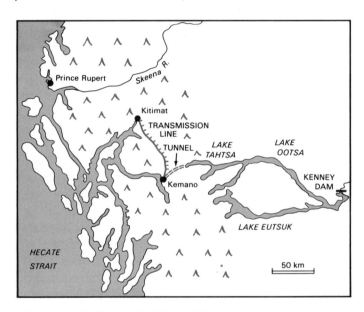

Figure 9-9    Outline of the Kitimat District

The chief farmed delta lands are those of the Fraser, extending from around Chilliwack (Figure 9-11) to just south of Vancouver. Farming on the rich alluvial soils is geared both to the high moisture content of the soil and to the proximity of large urban markets in the Vancouver metropolitan region. Milk and other dairy products, together with vegetables and fruit, are therefore important.

Despite some apparent disadvantages, other valuable farmland in British Columbia is located in some of the interior valleys. Many of the rivers of the interior have entrenched themselves in narrow valleys, which thereby contain very little potential farmland on their floors. Moreover the valley sides are often too steep for agriculture. However, trenching has not occurred just once; in most valleys it has occurred at least twice, as illustrated in Figure 9-12. The not yet eroded remains of former valley floors are called

**Figure 9-10** Fruit orchards on terraces in the Okanagan Valley.

When land is raised up again by earth movements, as may happen when a plateau is formed, the existing rivers start to cut downwards once again. New valleys are eroded inside the remains of the old ones. This process is called *rejuvenation*.

*terraces*. Where they are covered with river deposited alluvium or former lake bed silts they are potentially fertile, if only river water can be pumped up to them. The Okanagan is the major example of such a terraced and farmed valley (Figure 9-13). In the interior, the high sunshine totals and summer warmth promote the growth of valuable crops of apricots, peaches, and grapes. The Okanagan Valley alone contributes about 20% of Canada's fruit crop.

Non-alluvial farmland in British Columbia is potentially vast, encompassing most of the southern interior plateau as well as large tracts in the Rocky Mountain Trench. Soils in these regions are currently unimproved, and precipitation is slight. However, extensive beef cattle ranches already exist, and there are great possibilities for future expansion.

The Okanagan Valley has such a pleasant climate (see Chapter 2) that many people retire there. Land is limited, however. There is not enough for everyone. What do you think is happening to (a) the price of land, (b) the price of fruit, and (c) the use of land?

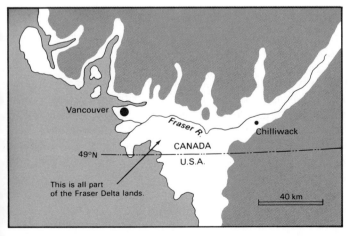

Vancouver

Fraser R.

Chilliwack

CANADA

49°N

U.S.A.

This is all part of the Fraser Delta lands.

40 km

**Figure 9-11   The Fraser Delta Lands**

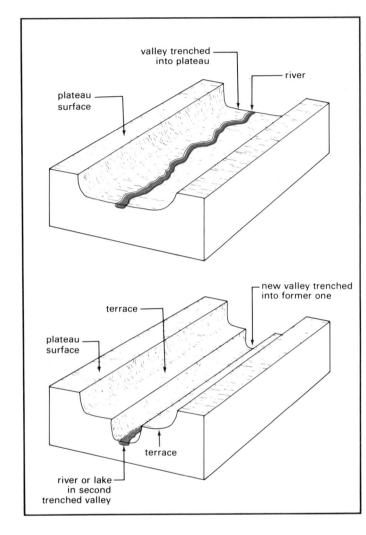

**Figure 9-12 The Successive Trenching of the Valleys in the Interior Plateau of British Columbia**

• 6. Since 1961 the number of farms in British Columbia has de creased by about ten percent and yet the area of land used fo farmland has increased by over 30%. How can you explain this

Why do you suppose British Columbia has such a plentiful supply of water?

Yet another way in which British Columbia's vast wealth in wate helps to support life is its use in recreation. We have already note the recreational demands on the coast (for boating, fishing, beach combing, etc.) But we should not forget the rapidly growing winte sports areas north of Vancouver, which rely on the winter snowfalls Tourism, which is also attracted by the spectacular mountai scenery and is aided by the recently developed roads and camp sites, is now British Columbia's third largest originator of lif supporting jobs (after forestry and mining).

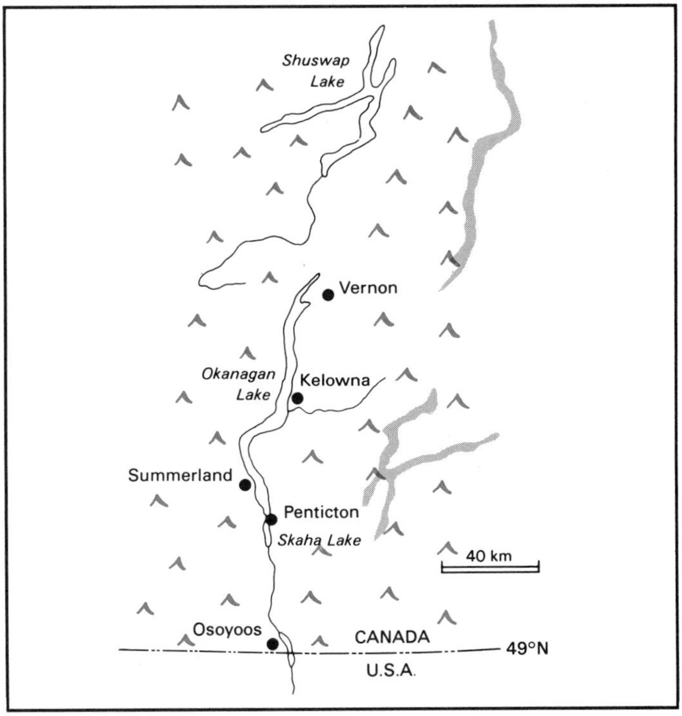

Figure 9-13 The Okanagan Valley

"No other industry in British Columbia has contributed so much to the spread of settlement, the growth of local industry, and the knowledge of the geography and natural resources of the province as the mining industry." Quote from the Eighth British Columbia Natural Resources Conference.

Placer deposits are those found in the beds of rivers. They are washed there from ore bodies up in the hills. Placer deposits are worked very simply by panning.

## Mining

Mining occupies an important place in British Columbia's development, for it was the search for minerals that was largely responsible for opening up the interior. The early finding and exploitation of minerals caused not only the introduction of population but also the origins of forestry (for mine shaft supports) and farming (for food). The first mineral exploited was coal, on Vancouver Island at Suquash in 1835 and Nanaimo in 1850, but it was rapidly displaced in importance after 1856 by gold, which was discovered in *placer* deposits in the interior tributary valleys of the Fraser and Columbia. It was these gold fields that caused people to move in from the coast, even leading to the initial creation of British Columbia as a British colony in 1858. However, placer deposits cannot in their nature be long lasting. They were soon economically exhausted, and attention gradually turned to the underground rocks. Silver was found in 1886 in the Kootenay district of the Columbia Mountains and, together with the coal which was known to exist in the Crow's Nest Pass, acted as the spur for a rail loop connecting Medicine Hat and Vancouver and linking southeastern British Columbia with the recently constructed transcontinental rail line. Mining in British Columbia then started to move away from a dependence on precious metals which could bear the high costs of transportation

In the early days of the gold rush to the Cariboo gold fields, the influx of people caused the growth of Barkerville. In the 1860s Barkerville was the largest Canadian town west of Ontario.

Not all people came to Barkerville from the coast, though this was by far the most common route. In the early 1860s a party actually travelled across the Prairies and the Rockies to reach the Cariboo gold fields. They were called The Overlanders.

*Economically exhausted* is a term applied when it becomes too expensive to continue operations. The mineral exists; it's just that it's not worth mining it any longer. Some people even today still search among the Cariboo gold fields . . . and find gold.

One day in 1886 some prospectors were searching for a runaway horse. In their search they found, quite accidentally, a very rich silver vein. This became the basis for the renowned Silver King mine near what later became the city of Nelson.

The Trail smelter is operated by Cominco, which is a subsidiary of Canadian Pacific.

**Figure 9-14**  Looking for placer gold.

from the interior. Interest began to be taken increasingly in a variety of base metals.

New growth in the mining industry continued with the application of new smelting technology to the mixed silver-lead-zinc ores of the giant Sullivan mine at Kimberley (Figure 9-16), and the consequent opening of one of the world's major smelters at Trail. Exploration was pressed for other minerals also. The 1920s wit-

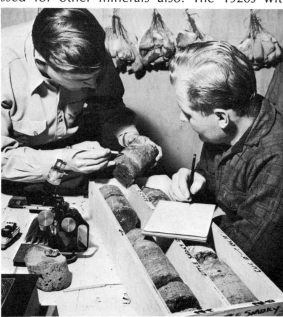

**Figure 9-15**  Searching for traces of oil or gas in core samples.

nessed a major but unsuccessful effort to find oil and gas; so did the early 1940s, during World War II. However, it was not until 1948 that gas was discovered in marketable quantities, in the Peace River District of northeastern British Columbia. The first commercial oil discovery was not made until 1955. Nevertheless, the deposits were large, and many new finds have added to the total supply. Oil now ranks second in value among British Columbia's produced minerals.

Subsequently, asbestos was developed at Cassiar in the far north, and copper near Kamloops. The existence of copper had been

**Figure 9-16   Mines in British Columbia**

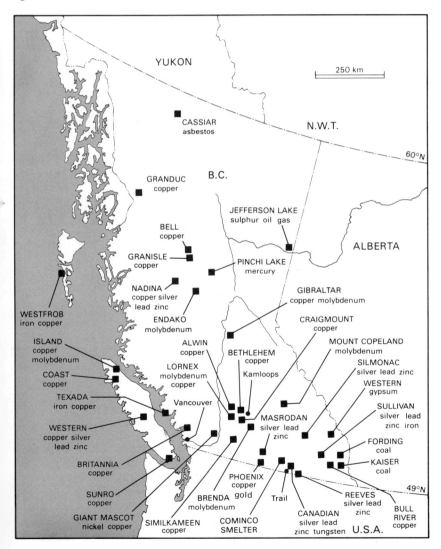

Altogether there have been 16 attempts to start smelters in British Columbia. The most recent failure—indeed it never got beyond the planning stage—was the abandonment in November 1976 of a proposed iron smelter, which was going to be half paid for by Japanese interests.

known for a long time, but the rising world price of copper throughout the 1950s made it worthwhile bringing a number of major copper mines into operation. Today, copper is the top British Columbian mineral by value (Figure 9-17).

Most of the minerals produced in British Columbia are sold as ores and concentrates. Many companies have tried to start smelters, but only the Cominco smelter at Trail survives. The ores and concentrates are sold to smelters in Japan and the United States.

One of the largest mineral sales to Japan is the on-going sale of Crow's Nest coal. The coal field straddles the Alberta-British Columbia border and is linked by a special train to the superport at Roberts Bank, just south of Vancouver.

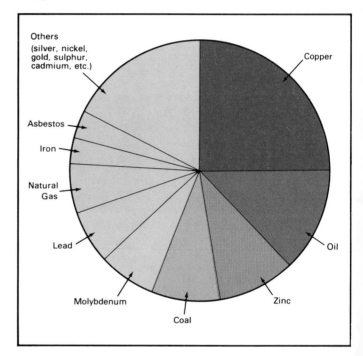

**Figure 9-17   Relative Values of British Columbia's Mineral Products**

## Manufacturing

Manufacturing is mainly connected with the processing and finishing of local raw materials which, as we have noted, are often exported in an only partly processed state. Manufacturing is therefore less important than it could be. The chief manufacturing sector is concerned with wood processing. Lumber, plywood, doors, frames, and similar items account for over 30% of the value of all British Columbia's manufactured shipments. Paper products account for a further 16%. Nearly 50% of the value of all British Columbia's manufactures are therefore related to the forest resources of the province. Food processing (for example, salmon canning and fruit preservation) account for about 17%, while metal fabrication (wire, plate, pipe, etc) accounts for about 12%. Other industries are relatively small, partly because of the emphasis on primary resources and partly because of the lack of a sufficiently large population to permit any economies of large scale production.

### Trade

Figure 9-20 shows the location of British Columbia in relation to Canada and the Pacific Basin. In relation to Canada it is obvious that British Columbia acts as an important, and indeed the only, outlet to the Pacific. Within British Columbia the concentration of transcontinental routes on Vancouver, largely funnelled by the Fraser Valley, has caused Vancouver to become a major transshipment port for trade with Pacific countries. It is thus through Vancouver that Saskatchewan wheat and Manitoba pork reach Japan, and that Japanese cars and Korean textiles reach Ontario. The

Many of the countries of the Pacific rim have large populations. Can you name some? They are also becoming more and more productive, just as Japan did. As time passes, it is likely that the Pacific rim countries will become increasingly involved in trade. Already, Vancouver has become Canada's chief port, having displaced Montreal around the year 1970. Indeed, Vancouver is also the largest port on the entire west coast of North America.

**Figure 9-18** Transcontinental routes to Vancouver are funnelled through the Fraser Valley.

**Figure 9-19** Sulphur exports from Vancouver. The Greek ship is a carrier; it could be taking the sulphur almost anywhere in the world.

growing importance of the Pacific Basin as a trading region cannot be overemphasized. It even has its own trading agreements, negotiated as part of the activities of the Pacific Basin Economic Community (PBEC). British Columbia, and especially Vancouver, is Canada's window on this important part of the world.

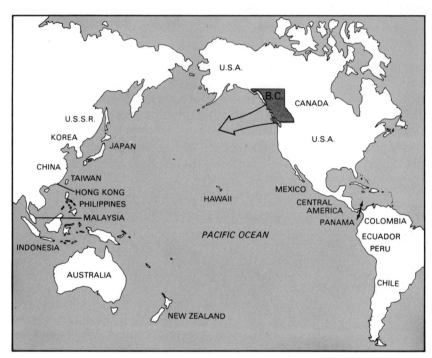

**Figure 9-20    The Position of British Columbia in Relation to Canada and the Pacific Ocean**

● 7. Within British Columbia about 50% of the population lives in and near Vancouver. They do not all farm, nor do they mine or work in the forests or on the fishing boats. What do you suppose they do to earn a living?

● 8. What do you think are some of the problems in British Columbia caused by having about 50% of the population live in the area called the *Lower Mainland,* in and near Vancouver?

● 9. British Columbia is a new area, not long settled. Much of it is still wilderness. What is its future likely to be?

# CHAPTER 10

# ATLANTIC CANADA

## AREAL DIFFERENTIATION

## INTRODUCTION

The four provinces of eastern Canada (can you name them?) are often grouped together for a variety of reasons, particularly by people in central or western Canada. One reason they are often grouped together is that they are regarded collectively as *the Maritimes*. This is wrong. Newfoundland is not one of the Maritime provinces.

Another reason they are often grouped together is that they are believed to be the provinces that first participated in the making of the Canadian nation in 1867. While it is true that Charlottetown in Prince Edward Island was the location of the Confederation Conference, it is not true that the four Atlantic provinces were the prime advocates of Confederation. Indeed the pressure for Confederation came largely from central Canada and from England, and it was resisted by the Atlantic provinces. Eventually, in 1867, only Nova Scotia and New Brunswick joined Confederation. By 1868, however, Nova Scotia was threatening secession, and only astute political manoeuvring by Sir John A. Macdonald kept the confederation together. Desire to avoid financial embarrassment eventually brought Prince Edward Island into the Dominion of Canada in 1873. Meanwhile, Newfoundland kept its independence from Canada. It joined only in 1949, and then for essentially the same reasons as Prince Edward Island.

A further reason for the association of the four provinces into a conceptual unit is the impression many people have of their small sizes and small populations. To some extent this is true. The area of the four provinces together represents only 5.4% of Canada's total, making them collectively about the same size as the Yukon, and smaller than any other single province. Indeed the four provinces together are about half as large as Ontario, and much less than half

A popular song in Newfoundland at the time ran:
*Hurrah for our native isle, Newfoundland!*
*Not a stranger shall hold one inch of its strand!*
*Her face turns to Britain, her back to the Gulf.*
*Come near at your peril, Canadian wolf!*

Newfoundland
            399 834 km$^2$
New Brunswick
            72 586 km$^2$
Nova Scotia
            54 848 km$^2$
Prince Edward Island
            5 591 km$^2$

1976 preliminary
census population
data:
Nova Scotia      812 127
New Brunswick
            664 525
Newfoundland 548 789
Prince Edward Island
            116 251

We say that the unity is imposed upon the Atlantic provinces by the rest of Canada because the Atlantic provinces themselves do not want it. They resist efforts to bring them together; they wish to remain independent from one another. Talk of Atlantic unity gets little support in the Atlantic region itself.

Subsistence means producing enough to keep yourself and your family alive, but not having any surpluses to trade in a market.

the size of Quebec. Moreover, they are the four provinces with the smallest populations. The impression of smallness in size and population is enhanced by their location east of Quebec, which tends to make them remote in the eyes of western and central Canadians — such mental remoteness conferring upon the Atlantic provinces a unity which may not otherwise be warranted. It is also in this impressionist sense that many people in Canada think of South America or Africa as being single regions, which of course they are not.

Yet another cause of the conceptual unity imposed on the Atlantic provinces by the rest of Canada is the concern people think the four provinces have with the sea. There is some truth in this, but there is much error too. Current ocean trade relies much more on land links than on water links, while fishing is now one of the less important economic activities. Indeed the wealth of the provinces arises more from the resources of the land than from those of the sea.

A final reason why the four Atlantic provinces are often regarded as a unitary region is the impression that they are areas of poverty relative to the rest of Canada — indeed, that they form a *problem region,* needing to be helped by the federal government.

Despite the various impressions people have of the unity of the four Atlantic provinces, there are in reality quite large differences between one part and another. There are areas totally unconcerned with the sea; there are areas of high population density mixed in with virtually uninhabited areas; there are areas devoted exclusively to foreign trade and there are areas of subsistence livelihood. Let us examine some of these areal differences, under the traditional geographical headings of landscape, climate, land use, fishing, mining and manufacturing, and population.

## A: LANDSCAPE

The Atlantic provinces represent the frayed and partly submerged northern ends of the Appalachian mountain system. Because of this, there are countless islands and headlands and innumerable gulfs and bays. The larger islands and peninsulas form whole provinces, such as Newfoundland and Prince Edward Island (islands) and Nova Scotia (peninsula). The smaller islands and promontories form a very irregular coastline, and serve to break the entire region even further into relatively isolated pockets of coastal lowland. Some small islands even belong to a different country, and are not part of Canada at all. See if you can find them in Figure 10-1.

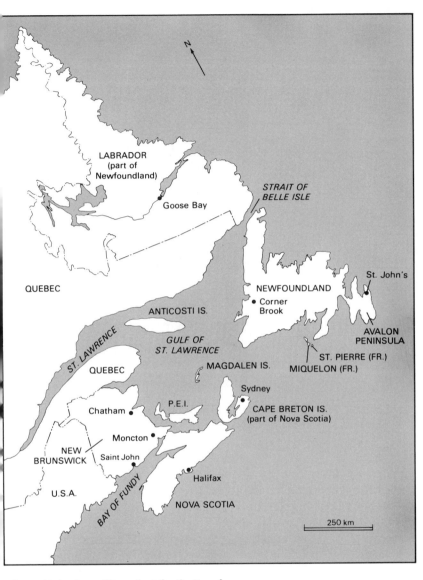

**Figure 10-1  Some Places in Atlantic Canada**

Areal Differentiation is the study of what makes separate areas different from one another. You can look at it on a fairly small scale, such as we are doing with Atlantic Canada, and try to see what makes the separate areas within that region different from one another, or you can look at it on a much larger scale and try to see what makes one country different from another.

Many coasts in the world are of the submerged type. Submergence in the Atlantic provinces was caused by the land being pushed down during the Ice Age (about 1 000 000 years ago) by the weight of ice on its surface, and then after the ice melted and the water returned to the sea the land was unable to return to its former level fast enough to avoid being flooded by the rising sea. The land is still not back to its former level; so it still shows features of submergence.

Partial submergence by the sea has done more than create many islands and peninsulas. It has also made the area much larger than might appear merely from a hectare count. As we have noted, the areas of the provinces are quite small, but that does not take into account the fact that half the region consists of sea. Distances are therefore greater than you might expect, and they are even more time consuming to travel if you take into account the difficulties of

A peninsula is a neck
of land which is
almost an island but
not quite. The word
derives from Latin
*pene,* meaning almost,
and *insula,* meaning
island.

A promontory is a
headland or a cape
or a point.

Some distances
by air:
Halifax to St. John's
                1000 km
St. John's to Montreal
                1600 km
Halifax to Toronto
                1250 km
St. John's to Toronto
                2200 km

There is talk periodic-
ally in Prince Edward
Island of a bridge to
the mainland. A
bridge has never been
built, and the pro-
posals are always
voted down. Why do
you think this is?

**Figure 10-2** Part of the frayed edge of the
Atlantic provinces.

transferring from one mode of transportation to another as you
move from mainland to island or from island to island. Travelling
in the four provinces is not easy, in fact, and this has tended to
promote the isolation and independence of one area from another.

Figure 10-3 shows another aspect of the real size of the Atlantic
provinces. Not only are the distances considerable, as you can see,
but also the sea freezes throughout the winter everywhere north
of a line through Cape Breton Island. This makes transportation
exceedingly difficult, even between Prince Edward Island and the
mainland. There is therefore little mystery why so many communities have developed their own individual identities.

Individuality has also been encouraged by the landscape itself.
There is a great variety of landforms, ranging from the rugged rocky
uplands of the Canadian Shield in Labrador to the gentle alluvial
lowlands of the St. John River in New Brunswick, and there is much
in between as well. Rocky uplands dominate much of the Atlantic
coast and interior of Nova Scotia, especially in Cape Breton Island,

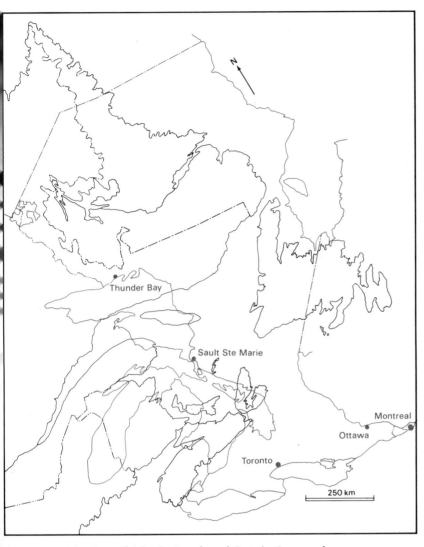

Thunder Bay

Sault Ste Marie

Montreal
Ottawa
Toronto

250 km

**Figure 10-3   The Sizes of Atlantic Canada and Ontario Compared**

One of the best sandy beaches is at Cavendish in northern P.E.I., which was the childhood home of Lucy Maud Montgomery, the author of Anne of Green Gables.

as well as in most of Newfoundland. On the other hand, Prince Edward Island is entirely lowland, with gentle sandy beaches rather than rocky cliffs. Most of eastern New Brunswick is also very flat lowland. And despite the predominance of rocky uplands in Nova Scotia, that province also contains in the Annapolis Valley one of the most fertile areas of lowland in the whole Atlantic provinces. Figure 10-4 gives you a generalized idea of the variety of landforms mentioned.

The Annapolis Valley was the place originally chosen by Champlain as the location of Port Royal, founded in 1604.

**Figure 10-4   Some of the Major Landscape Regions of Atlantic Canada**

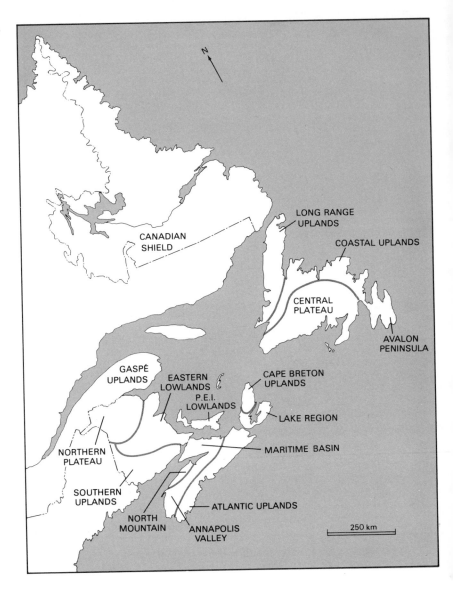

## B: CLIMATE

The concentration in this region of the climatic influences shown in Figure 10-5 almost guarantees great variation, not only from time to time throughout the year but also from place to place within the region. In general terms the meeting of Continental Polar and Tropical Maritime air masses and the frequency of storms along either or both of the major storm channels produces plenty of precipitation and very strong winds over the entire Atlantic prov-

See Chapter 2 for a comparison with the rest of Canada.

inces. As expected, precipitation diminishes fairly rapidly away from the Atlantic coasts (Figure 10-9). The large quantities of water vapour available near the coasts, coupled with the two contrasting ocean currents approaching together, have the effect of inducing high fog frequencies in the area. The approaching of the two ocean currents has an additional effect: it *compresses* the normal latitudinal temperature range. Relatively high temperatures are brought northwards along the east coast of North America by the Gulf Stream, which influences the southernmost parts of the Atlantic

The warm moist air over the Gulf Stream is chilled by contact with the cold waters of the Labrador Current. When it is chilled it cannot hold as much water vapour, which condenses as fog. Winds often blow the fog onshore, so that it becomes impossible to see more than a few metres ahead on the land as well as out at sea. The Atlantic coast of Nova Scotia is one of the foggiest areas in the world.

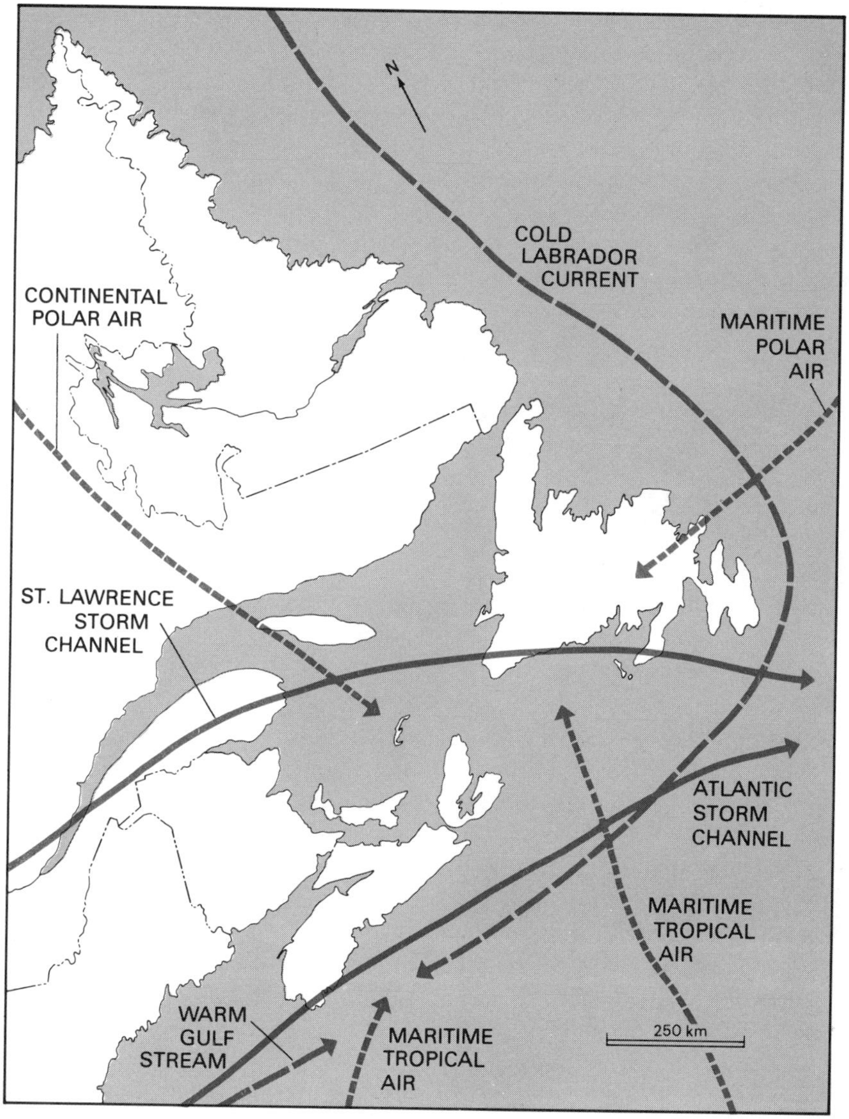

**Figure 10-5   Climatic Influences on Atlantic Canada**

Contrasts in landscape: uplands and low-lands.

**Figure 10-6**  Cape Breton Uplands.

**Figure 10-7**  Southwest Newfoundland.

**Figure 10-8**  Western Prince Edward Island.

provinces. The chief effect, however, is the bringing southwards of unusually low temperatures by the powerful Labrador Current. The eastern shores of Newfoundland are most affected by this, and icebergs are common in summer. The temperature gradient therefore falls very sharply from southwest to northeast throughout the Atlantic provinces, as Figure 10-10 shows.

Why not in winter?

Temperature gradient is a term which refers to the rate at which temperature falls as you move from one place to another. For example, if the temperature at place A is 18°C and at place B it is only 13°C, and the two places are 50 km apart, then the temperature gradient is 1°C per ten kilometres.

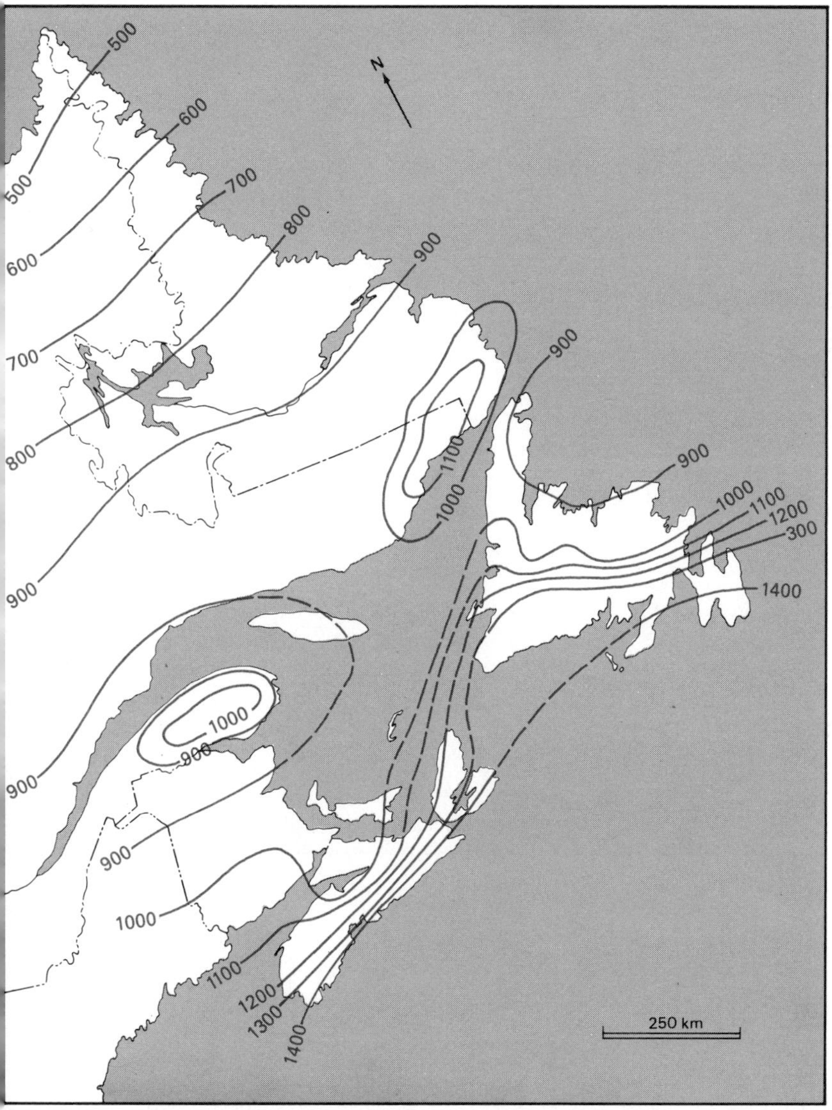

**Figure 10-9    Annual Precipitation, Generalized (in mm)**
    Note: Large differences may occur within small distances because of variations in landscape.

**Figure 10-10  The Summer Temperature Gradient**

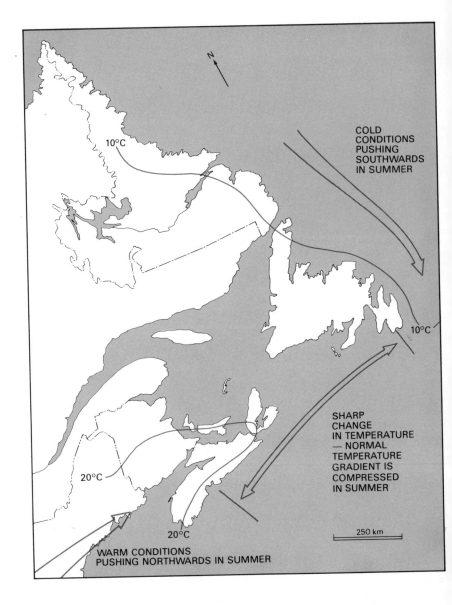

N

10°C

COLD
CONDITIONS
PUSHING
SOUTHWARDS
IN SUMMER

10°C

SHARP
CHANGE
IN TEMPERATURE
— NORMAL
TEMPERATURE
GRADIENT IS
COMPRESSED
IN SUMMER

20°C

250 km

20°C

WARM CONDITIONS
PUSHING NORTHWARDS IN SUMMER

Another aspect of temperatures in the region is that their range increases markedly away from the Atlantic coast. In summer the temperatures experienced in the interior are not very different from those of the Atlantic coast, but in winter there is a great difference. In winter the temperatures may be as low as −15°C in the interior but only −5°C on the Atlantic coast. This is reflected in variations in the amount of snowfall, which is about twice as much in the interior as along the Atlantic coast, despite the generally much higher precipitation totals of the coastal areas. Figure 10-11 gives some climate statistics for four stations in the Atlantic provinces.

| | J | F | M | A | M | J | J | A | S | O | N | D |
|---|---|---|---|---|---|---|---|---|---|---|---|---|
| **Place A** | | | | | | | | | | | | |
| temperature (°C) | −18 | −16 | −9 | −3 | 5 | 10 | 16 | 14 | 10 | 3 | −5 | −13 |
| precip. (mm) | 1.8 | 2.5 | 1.0 | 7.9 | 33.3 | 63.5 | 83.3 | 68.8 | 54.1 | 37.8 | 14.7 | 1.3 |
| **Place B** | | | | | | | | | | | | |
| temperature (°C) | −5 | −6 | −3 | 2 | 6 | 11 | 16 | 16 | 12 | 8 | 3 | −2 |
| precip. (mm) | 61.0 | 61.0 | 69.0 | 79.8 | 93.0 | 79.5 | 79.8 | 100.8 | 94.7 | 119.9 | 132.8 | 87.6 |
| **Place C** | | | | | | | | | | | | |
| temperature (°C) | −11 | −10 | −4 | 3 | 9 | 15 | 19 | 18 | 13 | 7 | 0 | −8 |
| precip. (mm) | 17.5 | 11.2 | 23.4 | 48.5 | 75.2 | 93.5 | 77.0 | 88.7 | 83.8 | 93.0 | 69.9 | 26.2 |
| **Place D** | | | | | | | | | | | | |
| temperature (°C) | −4 | −5 | 0 | 4 | 10 | 15 | 19 | 19 | 15 | 10 | 5 | −2 |
| precip. (mm) | 87.7 | 59.9 | 82.0 | 102.1 | 110.5 | 109.7 | 92.0 | 103.1 | 117.1 | 129.5 | 121.4 | 100.3 |

**Figure 10-11   Climate Statistics of Four Stations in the Atlantic Provinces**

Range of temperature is a term used to denote the difference between the highest and lowest temperatures recorded in a given period. The daily (or *diurnal*) range is the difference between the highest and lowest temperatures within a 24 hour period. The *annual* range is the difference between the average for the hottest month and the average for the coldest month.

Areas remote from the oceans tend to have larger annual ranges of temperature than places next to the oceans. A large range of temperature is therefore often referred to as a *continental* range of temperature, while a small range of temperature may be called a *maritime* range of temperature.

- 1. (a) Construct a hythergraph chart to show the climatic data in Figure 10-11.
  - (b) In the light of the material in section B of this chapter, suggest which name belongs to each set of statistics: Chatham, Goose Bay, Halifax, St. John's.
  - (c) Explain why you suggested a particular name for each set of statistics.

- 2. (a) Which is the coldest part of the Atlantic provinces in winter? In summer?
  - (b) Which is the warmest part of the Atlantic provinces in winter? In summer?
  - (c) Why is the southwest generally warmer than the northeast?
  - (d) Why is snowfall heavier in the interior than along the coast, even though the coast receives much more precipitation?

## C: LAND USE

| | New Brunswick | New-foundland | Nova Scotia | Prince Edward Island | Canada |
|---|---|---|---|---|---|
| Area km $^2$ | 72 856 | 399 834 | 54 848 | 5 591 | 9 861 120 |
| Occupied farmland km$^2$ | 7 247 | 197 | 7 406 | 3 100 | 696 499 |
| Occupied farmland as percent of area | 10.0 | 0.05 | 13.5 | 55.4 | 7.1 |
| Improved land as percent of occupied farmland | 35 | 55 | 26 | 62 | 63 |
| Forest km$^2$ | 59 722 | 224 748 | 39 101 | 2 010 | 4 379 617 |
| Forest as percent of area | 82.2 | 56.2 | 71.3 | 36.0 | 44.4 |
| Percent of forest which is productive | 98 | 38 | 93 | 87 | 56 |
| Other land km$^2$ | 4 344 | 141 251 | 5 721 | 481 | 4 038 093 |
| Other land as percent of area | 6.0 | 35.3 | 10.4 | 8.6 | 40.9 |
| Fresh water km$^2$ | 1 329 | 33 638 | 2 619 | — | 746 422 |
| Fresh water as percent of area | 1.8 | 8.4 | 4.8 | — | 7.6 |

Improved land is cultivated or otherwise cared for. It is land which carries in it a certain amount of the farmer's capital investment.

**Figure 10-12    Selected Land Use Statistics**

An examination of Figure 10-12 reveals some interesting facts. Compare, for instance, the data for farmland as a percentage of provincial area for Newfoundland and Prince Edward Island. In Newfoundland, farmland covers only 0.05% of the area, while in Prince Edward Island it extends over 55.4% of the area. Clearly there can be little similarity between these two provinces in their ways of life. Compare also the percentage of forested land in New Brunswick with that in Prince Edward Island, or even in Newfoundland. Again, there are great differences.

● **3.** How many differences between the various Atlantic provinces can you spot in Figure 10-12?

The reasons for these many differences are rooted in the variations in landscape and climate which we have already examined. Generally, areas of upland and Shield are unsuitable for agriculture, partly because of their thin, stony soils, if soils exist at all, and partly because of their lower temperatures and increased precipitation resulting from their higher elevations. Agriculture is further limited by the prevailing climatic characteristics of the area: the northeast is too cold and has too short a growing season for farming to flourish. This fact, coupled with the generally upland nature of Newfoundland, means that there is about as much farmland (about 200 km²) in the whole of Newfoundland as there would be in a small corner of Prince Edward Island. It is also reflected in the much higher proportion of "other land" in Newfoundland compared with New Brunswick, Nova Scotia, and Prince Edward Island.

Towards the southwest, however, the usually milder climate favours the development of farming wherever the landscape permits it. There are three sizeable areas of lowland in the southwestern half of the region, each widely farmed. They are the Annapolis Valley, the lower St. John Valley, and almost the whole of Prince Edward Island. Within each area, along with all the other scattered lowland pockets, there is considerable attention given to mixed farming, because these areas must supply as many of the various necessities to the local populations as they can. There is, therefore, dairying, vegetable growing, fruit farming, beef production, pig and poultry rearing, and potato cultivation in each area. There is very little grain production, except for some green corn used as fodder for animals, largely because the Atlantic farmers cannot compete with the more efficient grain farmers of the prairies. Nevertheless, each of the three major lowland areas has developed its own specialty with which it can compete to some extent in outside markets. The Annapolis Valley markets apples and juice, while New Brunswick and Prince Edward Island market potatoes.

● 4. What does the fact that two of the three major Atlantic farming areas both market potatoes as a specialty product tell you about:
(a) the actual and potential farming wealth of the region, and
(b) the chances of increased prosperity in the region?

Forestry is far more important than farming in all the Atlantic provinces except Prince Edward Island. The provinces could import all their food, but they could not manage without their forests. The forests are important creators of wealth, not only in the form of jobs and incomes, but also in the form of houses, furniture, boats, and so on. Newfoundland has by far the largest area of forest, used mostly for paper production in two mills, one at Corner Brook and the other at Grand Falls, as well as for linerboard in a mill at Stephenville. As you can see from Figure 10-12, only 38% of Newfoundland's forest is productive. Given attention and careful planting, however, more could be productive, as there is clearly room for expansion. However, there would be problems; because of Newfoundland's low temperatures, the trees tend to be small and take

Two hundred square kilometres is the same as 20 000 ha. A small family farm in Ontario might be about 100 ha; in the prairies a large farm might be 1000 ha. Most Newfoundland farms are small, probably not more than ten hectares.

McCain's is one of the largest food companies in the world, specializing in frozen foods. It has factories in many countries, making it a large multinational company. Its head office is in Florenceville, New Brunswick, where it started as a company making frozen french fries from local potatoes.

The owners of the paper mills are Bowater (Grand Falls) and Price (Corner Brook). Most of the paper is exported to either Britain or the U.S.A. The linerboard mill is owned by the Newfoundland government. It was taken over in order to keep it operating, because it had run into severe financial problems caused by the high costs of bringing in lumber from Labrador. In the mid 1970s the mill was losing $25 000 000 a year. It closed in 1977.

Trees take a long time to grow to a usable size. It is clearly better for the forestry companies if the trees grow quickly, because they can then cut a larger proportion of the existing forest. Slow growth means that foresters can cut only a small proportion of the forest in any one year, because it will take a long time for new trees to replace what has been cut. Forestry companies operating in slow growth areas therefore need much larger timber concessions than those in quick growth areas. This puts up transportation costs, and makes the companies less competitive. In the southern U.S.A. trees grow to a usable size in 25 to 30 years; in British Columbia they take over 50 years; in Newfoundland the trees take closer to 100 years.

a longer time to grow than elsewhere, and the variety of tree types is restricted. These disadvantages mean that Newfoundland is ill suited for timber production in a field other than pulp and paper, and also that its production costs are necessarily higher than those elsewhere.

New Brunswick and Nova Scotia are the two Atlantic provinces with the highest percentage of their areas covered by forest, and both depend greatly on the forest industries. Their timber is more varied than that of Newfoundland, and it is generally more valuable commercially. It supports important saw mills as well as pulp and

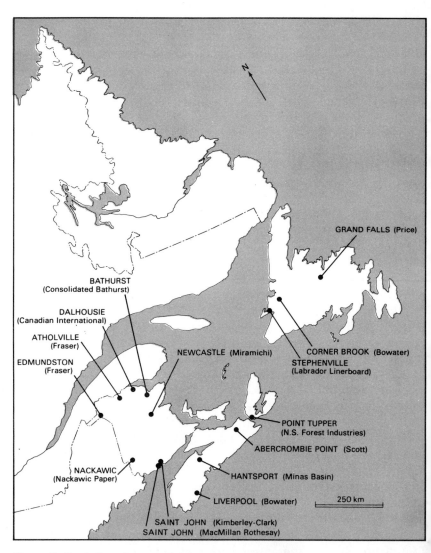

**Figure 10-13   Pulp and Paper Mills in the Atlantic Provinces**

paper mills, for instance, though pulp and paper mills are still the more important. Early development of the Nova Scotia and New Brunswick forests was based on shipbuilding, chiefly in the period before 1850. Before 1850 ships were needed for a variety of purposes, such as trade with England and the Caribbean, fishing, and the transportation of immigrants. In some cases the ships themselves were sold along with the cargo. The forests were rapidly depleted of their best lumberwoods, but in return Canada became the fourth largest shipping nation in the world at that time. After 1850 things began to change. Shipping became mechanized: ships were made of iron, then steel; engines replaced sails. The world's ship-building locations changed from timber areas to coal and iron areas.

A great deal of fishing and trading was done by specially built ships called schooners. When fishing, the schooner would carry several small boats called dories, which would be used for the actual fishing. The catch at the end of the day would be loaded on to the schooner. One of the most famous schooners was the *Bluenose*.

A Nova Scotia man, Samuel Cunard, started the most famous shipping line in the world.

The decline of the lumber trade was therefore gradually balanced by the rise of the pulp and paper trade. This suited the New Brunswick and Nova Scotia forests, which, towards the end of the nineteenth century, were becoming quite cut over. Smaller trees and secondary forests were not, in any event, likely to support a continued shipbuilding industry, but they were ideal for pulping and papermaking. The major mills are shown in Figure 10-13.

● 5. (a) Make a list of some of the useful things provided by forests.
   (b) Make a list of some of the harmful things which happen as a result of the forestry process.
   (c) Is one list more important than the other? Why do you think this is so? What can be done in the future?

## D: FISHING

Fishing is practised in all the Atlantic provinces, but not on an equal scale everywhere. Again, there are great differences from area to area. Some of the differences are summarized in Figure 10-14.

|  | New Brunswick | New-foundland | Nova Scotia | Prince Edward Island | Canada |
|---|---|---|---|---|---|
| Persons employed in fishing | 5 148 | 17 800 | 10 688 | 2 677 | 52 580 |
| Value of fishery products $ | 68 629 000 | 94 943 000 | 127 215 000 | 16 143 000 | 461 833 000 |

**Figure 10-14   Some Fishery Statistics**

● 6. (a) What percentage of Canada's total fishery products' value is produced by the Atlantic provinces?

Newfoundland's fishing techniques were simple largely because of the way in which the fish trade was organized there. Thousands of small boats were used by thousands of fishing families operating from hundreds of small harbours scattered around the southern and eastern coasts of the island.

The techniques were whatever one or two people in a small boat could handle. This meant that *cod jigging* was a favourite practice. Superior fishers used a hooked and baited line, with tens of hooks along the short line. The most superior fishers used a longer boat and a line with hundreds of baited hooks. These were called *longliners*. Newfoundland boatbuilders still build longliners for use in the fishing industry.

One of the things that Prince Edward Island *has* developed in the last few years is sport fishing for tuna. There are several harbours where this is an important source of livelihood, and one of them, North Lake, holds the world record for sport-caught tuna.

The plants are called *phytoplankton*; the tiny organisms which feed on them are called *zooplankton*.

(b) What is the average fishery value per person engaged in the fishing industry in each of the four Atlantic provinces?

Prince Edward Island ranks relatively low both in numbers employed and in value of fishery products. This can be explained by its relatively small size and small population. It also ranks relatively low in value of fishery products per person employed in fishing. How can you explain this?

The provinces with the highest values of fishery product per person employed in fishing are New Brunswick and Nova Scotia. To some extent this is a result of the greater degree of processing which these two provinces put the fish catch through, so that they sell canned or frozen fish rather than dried or salted fish, as Newfoundland has tended to do. It is also a result of their own more efficient catching techniques as well as of their ability to market such higher priced fishery products as lobsters and scallops. Newfoundland is unable to market these products competitively, while Prince Edward Island has not developed them because of its greater dependence and emphasis on farming.

The chief types of fish landed are shown in Figure 10-15. If you calculate the value of the landing per kilogram you can see quite easily that the largest bulk equates with the lowest returns, and that the smallest bulk equates with the highest returns.

| Type | Quantity millions kg | Value millions $ |
| --- | --- | --- |
| Herring and sardines | 420.2 | 13.16 |
| Cod | 204.2 | 25.13 |
| Flounder and sole | 138.8 | 14.88 |
| Redfish | 113.0 | 8.65 |
| Crustaceans and molluscs | 40.2 | 49.85 |

**Figure 10-15   Fishery Landings and Values of the Atlantic Provinces**

One of the reasons for the widespread importance of fishing in the Atlantic provinces, either in bulk or in value, is the coincidence offshore of the existence of shallow water and the meeting together of the cold Labrador Current and the warmer Gulf Stream (see Figure 10-5 again). The shallow water permits sunlight to penetrate to the sea bed, thereby allowing plants to grow. In turn, the plants supply food to countless tiny marine organisms, which then become the chief food source for fish. The contrasting water temperatures of the two ocean currents help by stimulating the breeding of fish. The waters off the south shores of Newfoundland and Nova Scotia are therefore among the major fishing regions of the world. The details and major ports can be seen in Figure 10-16.

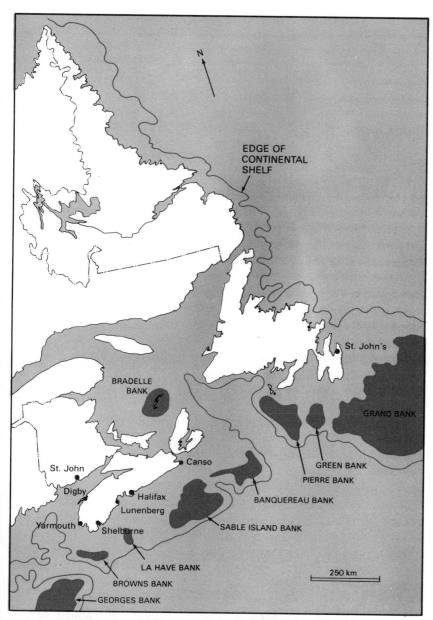

**Figure 10-16   Major Fishing Banks and Ports of the Atlantic Provinces**

Banks such as the La Have Bank are areas of extra shallow water, which, because the sea bed is closer to the surface, support more plant life (phytoplankton) and therefore more zooplankton, and, in turn, fish.

Crustaceans are sea creatures with a jointed and crusted body, such as lobsters and crabs; molluscs are soft and unjointed, but still crusted, such as oysters.

Fishing techniques used to catch bulk quantities include longlines, seine nets, drift nets, and trawl nets. Longlines are long hooked and baited lines. Seine nets are like huge bags in the water; they are put down by a boat which gradually encircles the school of fish, trapping them. Drift nets are nets which hang from floats in the water; the fish swim into them and are trapped by their gills. Trawl nets are huge conical nets pulled along the bed of the sea by ships called trawlers or draggers.

If you were going to have a career in the fishery business, which sector would you want to specialize in?

# E: MINING AND MANUFACTURING

Mining is much more important than fishing in three of the four provinces. In Prince Edward Island there is almost no mining industry, so even the small fishing industry is of greater importance. However, in Newfoundland, New Brunswick, and Nova Scotia mining is quite important, as Figure 10-17 illustrates.

**Figure 10-17   The Relative Importance of Mining**

| | Value of Minerals Mined $ | Value of Fish Landings* $ | Ratio |
|---|---|---|---|
| New Brunswick | 218 733 000 | 14 580 000 | 15:1 |
| Newfoundland | 568 212 000 | 36 078 000 | 16:1 |
| Nova Scotia | 96 688 000 | 55 994 000 | 2:1 |
| Prince Edward Island | 1 500 000 (estimated) | 8 104 000 | 0.2:1 |

\* Note that fish landings are not the same as fish products.
  What is the difference?
  Why do we use fish landings here?

Newfoundland and New Brunswick are the two chief Atlantic provinces for mining, with Newfoundland being the most important. The chief minerals in Newfoundland are, by order of value, iron, copper, asbestos, zinc, and lead. Iron is by far the most important, having twenty times the value of either copper or asbestos. In New Brunswick, zinc, lead, and copper are all very important, but there is no iron. In Nova Scotia there are small quantities of lead and copper, but no iron or zinc. However, Nova Scotia does produce important quantities of gypsum and coal.

The availability of coal and iron in the Atlantic provinces, although in different areas, has nevertheless resulted in the development of a steel industry, from which Nova Scotia has been the chief beneficiary.

Because of the impetus to industrialization given by the development of steel mills, Nova Scotia has become the most important Atlantic province for general manufacturing activity, but its lead over New Brunswick is quite small. There is, however, an enormous gap between these provinces and the other two, Newfoundland and Prince Edward Island having almost no manufacturing activity.

Early industrialization coincided in the period between 1850 and 1875 with the decline of shipbuilding and the rise of interest in railways. For a long time afterwards, the rails for Canada's eventual transcontinental railway lines were made in Nova Scotia; so also was much other railway equipment. Rails, indeed, are still the chief product of the Sydney steel mills. New Brunswick shared in the growth or railway engineering partly because it also had coal but largely because all railway lines to the rest of Canada had to pass through New Brunswick. Moncton became an important railway town because of its location at the junction of three major routes.

With the opening up by the railways of the interior of Canada in the period 1850–1900, trade began to develop. Increasingly, certain major products began to enter world markets on a growing scale. For many years, the most common was wheat, which moved from the prairies to markets in Europe. In response to this movement, a

In Newfoundland, copper, zinc, and lead all come from a large mine in the centre of the island at a place called Buchans. The asbestos comes from a mine in the northeast near Baie Verte. The iron comes from mines in the southeast near St. John's. The iron is now mined in workings which go out for several kilometres under the sea, but it is in serious financial trouble.

The coal in Cape Breton is used with the iron from Newfoundland to form the basis of a steel industry at Sydney. Costs of mining and transportation have always been high, and the Sydney steel industry is barely competitive with other steel industries.

number of different routes developed across eastern Canada, each leading to a wheat transshipment port. In Atlantic Canada, both Halifax and Saint John became important wheat ports, to which they have actively sought to add a larger share of the growing variety of modern world trade. Within recent years they have both developed their container handling facilities in an attempt to capture more of the transatlantic business. Halifax has also developed car assembly plants so that imported parts can be put together for the Canadian market. Halifax and Saint John are the first and second most important manufacturing cities in the Atlantic region, followed by Sydney and Moncton. The range of manufacturing is growing, and all governments in the Atlantic provinces are actively involved in trying to get more factories to locate there. The federal government also promotes Atlantic manufacturing development.

One of the most important requirements for successful industrialization is a plentiful supply of energy. Nova Scotia, New Brunswick, and Prince Edward Island have little. Prince Edward Island is not in a good position to develop any either, unless it uses nuclear power, for there are no coal, oil, or natural gas deposits, and no hydro or tidal possibilities. Nova Scotia and New Brunswick have some coal, but they have also relied a great deal on imported oil. They are planning to use nuclear fuels in the future, and there is the eventual possibility of power from the Fundy tides. The province in the best position for surplus energy is Newfoundland. It possesses, in the Churchill River in Labrador, one of the world's greatest sites for hydroelectric power development. The chief problem is transporting the electricity south to where the labour force, factories, and markets are. At the time of the first development on the Churchill River, at Churchill Falls, it was necessary to transport the generated electricity by land through Quebec. Under this arrangement, as

The main railway through New Brunswick initially came along the east coast, in order to be as far away from the Americans as possible. At Moncton, branches split off to go to Saint John as well as into Nova Scotia.

Containers are standard sized boxes. They can hold almost anything, and they can be loaded and unloaded very simply by means of giant cranes. They can be put on to flat-bed rail cars or on to wheels as part of a road tractor-trailer combination. They are the most important way in which the world's goods are now moved about.

The federal government has a branch called the Department of Regional Economic Expansion (DREE), which tries to attract firms into certain areas by means of tax concessions and grants.

**Figure 10-18** Power is possible from the Fundy tides. Here you can see their great rise and fall reflected in the eroded rocks at Hopewell, N.B.

There has been a great deal of activity in the waters off Atlantic Canada looking for oil and gas. Some oil and gas have been found, but not in the quantities needed to make extraction a commercial proposition.

Imported oil is now very expensive, and the provinces which relied on it are finding their electricity is now very expensive to generate. The nuclear alternative attracts a lot of controversy, but nevertheless New Brunswick is pushing ahead with a nuclear plant at Point Lepreau near Saint John.

Fundy power is technically possible, but it would be very expensive. So far it has not been worth the cost of setting up tidal power generators.

you can see from Figure 10-19, it was not worthwhile trying to get the electricity back into the Atlantic provinces, and in particular, back into Newfoundland — once it had crossed the St. Lawrence. The distance was just too great. The Atlantic provinces, therefore, did not benefit from the Churchill Falls project, other than through the receipt of money from the sale of the electricity. However, electricity transmission technology has improved since the early 1970s, and there are now plans for a direct link on the sea bed across the Strait of Belle Isle. This will permit the construction of a powerful hydroelectric station at Gull Island farther down the Churchill River from Churchill Falls.

**Figure 10-19   Churchill River Power**

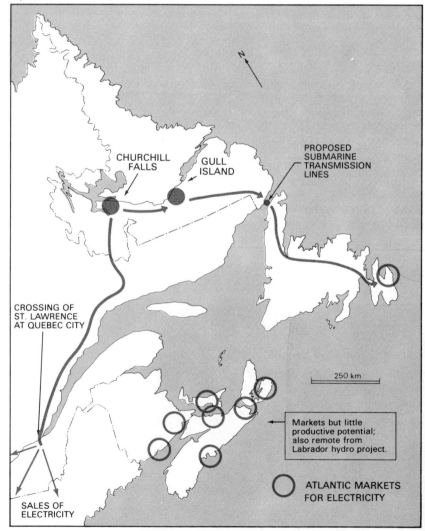

N

CHURCHILL
FALLS

GULL
ISLAND

PROPOSED
SUBMARINE
TRANSMISSION
LINES

CROSSING OF
ST. LAWRENCE
AT QUEBEC CITY

250 km

Markets but little
productive potential;
also remote from
Labrador hydro project.

ATLANTIC MARKETS
FOR ELECTRICITY

SALES OF
ELECTRICITY

## F:  POPULATION

The mixture of peoples that characterizes Canada as a whole also characterizes the Atlantic provinces, but to a lesser degree. The least varied province ethnically is Newfoundland, which is about 95% British in origin, mainly Irish and English. Prince Edward Island is also largely British in origin, although it has a greater Scots element than does Newfoundland. New Brunswick and Nova Scotia are both quite varied ethnically, containing immigrants from many areas. Notable immigrant groups include the Acadians throughout eastern New Brunswick and the upper St. John Valley, the descendants of United Empire Loyalists in southern New Brunswick, the gaelic Scots in Cape Breton Island, and the Caribbean blacks in Halifax. There are many more, often occupying scattered pockets of territory, the Huguenot descendants in Lunenburg and the Acadian descendants along parts of the Cape Breton shoreline as examples.

Many of the immigrant groups have been in the Atlantic provinces for a long time. There has been little new immigration to the area for over 100 years, people preferring to go farther inland to Ontario or the prairies. Even people from the Atlantic provinces have joined in this westward movement; the area has supplied thousands of families to help populate interior Canada. Despite the lack of new immigration and the loss of westward migrating families, however, the Atlantic provinces, with the exception of Prince Edward Island, have steadily continued to increase their own populations. The ability to support these growing populations has been a result of the varied resource base of New Brunswick, Nova Scotia, and Newfoundland. Only Prince Edward Island lacks resource variety; the other three have been able to adapt as new demands have developed.

- ● 7. There are some things that the Atlantic provinces have in common. What are they?

- ● 8. There are many ways in which the Atlantic provinces are different from each other. Usually one or two provinces lack a particular characteristic, while the other two or three possess it. Devise a table to show the variety within the Atlantic provinces.

Newfoundland was under British rule until 1949.

Acadians were the original settlers in Nova Scotia. They were French. In 1755 the British evicted them from their land. Some resettled in unwanted lands in New Brunswick. Many left the area altogether; some even went to Louisiana in the U.S.A.

The United Empire Loyalists were Americans who wished to remain loyal to Britain after the American War of Independence. They came north to Canada. Many settled in southern New Brunswick, which was largely empty. Indeed, they created the province, because it had been a part of Nova Scotia before the Loyalists moved in.

# CHAPTER 11

# FRENCH CANADA

## REGIONALISM

### INTRODUCTION

French Canada is unique within the Canadian nation. Other sections of Canada, such as the Atlantic region, the Northland, the Pacific region, the Prairies, and Ontario, are places with special characteristics of their own. French Canada, however, is more than just a *place*; it is a *state of mind*.

French Canada consists of more than just the province of Quebec. It also contains groups of people scattered throughout Atlantic Canada, especially New Brunswick, as well as in Ontario and the Prairies. There are also French Canadians in British Columbia and the Northland. They are, indeed, in all parts of Canada. Nevertheless, the place *Quebec* lends French Canada a strong locational identity in addition to its characteristic state of mind.

The strength of feeling aroused by this state of mind can be gauged from the responses illustrated below, which are letters to the editor of the Toronto *Star* debating the issue of bilingualism. Note that none of the letters is from a French Canadian; but the intensity of feeling is still apparent.

**Quebec makes Canada different**

Given no other choice I would choose a bilingual Ontario, where all government services are offered and available in both official languages, over the separation of Quebec.

In my opinion the existence of Quebec and French Canadians in Canada is one of the few differences between our country and the United States.

With the removal of Quebec from Canada we lose what is possibly the only distinctive feature that separates us from the Americans.

I have lived my entire adult life in Toronto, and I have yet to have French "rammed down my throat." What are these people talking about?

Albert Strauss

## Separation of Quebec would end Canada

I personally feel if Quebec separated from the rest of Canada it would be the end of Canada and we would be part of the United States of America in a short time.

Mrs. K. Collins

## Canada can't afford this province

With the concessions granted Quebec and the high cost of bilingualism the rest of Canada cannot afford this province.

Walter Chambers

## They don't care about rest of Canada

I have just moved here from Quebec. I was born in Montreal and spent my life there up until about six weeks ago. I feel now like a new person.

I have lived with these people all my life and believe me the only thing they are concerned with is having a unilingual Quebec (French).

They do not care about the rest of Canada, and as far as they are concerned, they live in the nation of Quebec.

I get a great kick out of these bleeding hearts in Ontario, and other parts of Canada, who are always wanting to give the poor French an even break. Believe me they want everything for themselves and nobody else.

Janice Cohen

## Quebec makes Canada distinct

If Quebec separates, there will be no more Canada.

We will revert to being Britain's North American colony, or become nine more states in the United States of America.

Quebec is the only entity that gives Canadians a distinct personality.

Marilyn Browning

Letters to the Editor, the Toronto *Star*, October 11, 1976

- 1. What are some of the feelings that the non-French Canadians have about Quebec? How do *you* feel?

Two of the letters talk of Quebec in terms of its giving Canada a distinct personality. Just what is this special quality that Quebec possesses? And that French Canadians as a whole possess?

## A: THE FRENCH FACT

In December 1976 the Quebec government decided that as of 1978 vehicle licence plates in Quebec would read *Je Me Souviens* (I remember) instead of *La Belle Province* (The Beautiful Province). The decision highlighted two of the major aspects of the French Fact: history and language.

The ties of history are very strong among French Canadians, and they are rendered personally significant by the use of *Je* (I) rather than of *Nous* (We). Each person shares individually in the common heritage. There is great personal pride in the achievements and tribulations of the past.

The first achievement in the development of this prized heritage occurred in the mid 1530s, when Jacques Cartier explored and

Many Europeans were at this time trying to find a way across the Atlantic to China. It is for this reason that the rapids in the St. Lawrence River which prevented Cartier from sailing any farther westwards are called the *Lachine* Rapids.

**Figure 11-1** The St. Lawrence estuary, as Jacques Cartier might have seen it.

The St. Lawrence trading charter was granted in 1608. It followed a similar, but abandoned, charter which was awarded in 1604 to de Monts to trade in the Bay of Fundy area.

claimed for France the lands of the Gulf of St. Lawrence and the valley below Montreal, as shown in Figure 1-3. The subsequent European fashion craze for beaver hats led eventually to the granting of a charter to the Sieur de Monts to trade in the St. Lawrence. In order to develop the trade in what came to be called *New*

Quebec City was founded in 1608. It was not the first French settlement in Canada, but it was the first *permanent* settlement, the earlier ones being abandoned.

**Figure 11-2** Quebec City occupies a strategic location on the St. Lawrence River. It is on high ground overlooking the river approaching from the Gulf. This is a view looking down the river.

*France,* de Monts sent Samuel de Champlain to build a fort and trading post at a strategic location on the river.

Champlain thus chose the site of Quebec, which became the first permanent settlement of modern Canada. At the time of its founding, however, Quebec was but a tiny foothold on the edge of a vast and largely unknown continent. It functioned chiefly as a fortified trading post for many years, relying upon furs brought in by Indians. However, in attempting to trade with the Indians, Champlain found that the French were expected to become involved in local Indian wars. Because most of the furs were traded from the remote reaches of rivers on the northern side of the St. Lawrence River, it was therefore to the Indians of the northern areas — the Hurons and Algonquins — that the French gave their allegiance. This produced hostility from the Indians to the south, namely the Iroquois.

Gradually French trading and missionary efforts spread further inland than Quebec itself. An additional post was established at Trois Rivières in 1634, and a further one at Ville Marie in 1642. In order to feed the missionary and trading elements, a few small farms were permitted to develop on cleared land along the banks of the St. Lawrence. New France was growing.

However, Champlain's death in 1635, coupled with the resurgence of the Dutch-backed Iroquois tribes, boded ill for the French. The French lost a far-sighted administrator; the Iroquois gained new strength. From the 1640s onwards the Iroquois began to cross the St. Lawrence, attacking the northern tribes and trading their furs southwards through New Amsterdam rather than through Quebec. The Hurons and French began to have an extremely difficult time: hundreds were killed; isolated farming and missionary settlements were wiped out; fur traders were ambushed; and the life of New France came close to extinction.

By 1663 conditions in the colony were so bad that the King of France took direct control. He sent a regiment of 1000 soldiers to build forts and keep the colony alive. The Iroquois were beaten back, and the French survived. In 1665 the King sent over as *Intendant* one of France's most able administrators, Jean Talon, with instructions for him to clear land for cultivation, promote local industries, and encourage colonization. Talon's target was the creation of a sturdy colony that would survive on its own. His initial surveys revealed a population of about 3000 and a cultivated area of several hundred hectares. Talon sought to settle retired soldiers onto much of the newly cleared land, thereby guaranteeing a degree of self-reliant security to the riverside farmers. Additionally he recruited new settlers from France by offers of free passage and

Quebec City. Quebec is now the name of the province; but in the early days, Quebec referred only to the city. The larger territory used to be called New France, and then Lower Canada.

The settlement at Ville Marie was founded by Maisonneuve. The new town was built next to the heights of Mount Royal (Montreal), and the full name of the town was Ville Marie de Montréal. It displaced an original Indian settlement called Hochelaga.

New Amsterdam is now called New York City.

Montreal itself was saved from destruction by the bravery of a group of defenders led by Dollard, in memory of whom there is now a special holiday throughout Quebec.

This was Louis XIV, who was one of the most famous French kings.

*Intendant* was the name given to the person who superintended the operations of New France.

In order to remedy the shortage of girls and young women in the St. Lawrence area, Talon set out specially to recruit them in France. He sought recruits among orphaned girls and girls from poor families. By these means, a more balanced population was obtained for New France. Since there has been relatively little new immigration to Canada from France it is largely to the work of Talon that modern French Canadians owe their existence.

The *seigneur* was the landowner. After receiving his land grant, or seigneury, from the King of France, the seigneur had to swear loyalty to the King, and guarantee to undertake the various obligations of a seigneur.

The *habitants* were the tenants. In return for the right to occupy a farm lot within a seigneury, they undertook to pay taxes to the seigneur, to cultivate the land they were allotted, to permit right of way to neighbours, and to work for the seigneur for a few days in each year.

The river frontage was important because it provided access. In the days of early settlement there were no roads, and so rivers provided the main means of transportation. The river was like the main street.

free land. In order to encourage population growth, the government instituted a system of marriage gifts and family tax rebates. The Catholic Church, which was active in the affairs of the colony, supported these aims. Within a few years, the population had grown from about 3000 (in 1666) to about 8000 (by 1676). The colony was thus kept alive; the Iroquois crisis had been met and resisted.

These early events, leading to the founding and eventual survival of New France, are a source of great pride to all French Canadians. There is pride in being the first settlers, in being successful in surviving the unexpectedly severe winters, and in resisting the attacks from the Iroquois. And there is great pride in being the originators of a unique New World culture. There is also pride in the culture which developed after the survival of New France had been assured. This culture is rooted in both the *seigneurial system* and in the *fur trade*.

The seigneurial system was a system of land tenure designed to help create a self-reliant yet cooperative group of settlers. The seigneur was a person of some standing who was granted land in return for sworn fidelity to France. The seigneur's duties included the renting of land to *habitants,* the building and operating of a flour mill, and the support of a priest and church. The seigneuries fronted the St. Lawrence and ran back from it in a relatively narrow strip. The homes of the *habitants* followed a similar pattern in miniature, being strung out along the river frontage, each with a narrow strip of land running back from the river (Figure 11-3). The strips of land farmed by each *habitant* were generally sufficient to support a small family on a subsistence basis; but they were not large enough to support large families in anything but poverty. There was therefore some poverty attached to the seigneurial system, but there was also a strong incentive to colonize new areas. Under the pressure of the population growth started by Jean Talon, colonization gradually spread along both banks of the St. Lawrence between Quebec and Montreal, and eventually along the major tributaries. The character of French Canada as a rural, self-reliant, subsistence culture was thereby established.

But it was not enough for everyone. Many of the people who had helped to colonize New France were adventurers rather than farmers; they wanted something other than the life of a *habitant*. The fur trade provided it.

The Huron Indian fur trading network had been destroyed by the Iroquois in the 1640s and 1650s. If the French wanted furs in the 1660s and later, then they had to go out themselves and trade. The trader adventurers who fanned out northwards and westwards from the St. Lawrence trading posts were called *voyageurs* and

**Figure 11-3** French Canadian settlements and field patterns along the Yamaska River in Quebec. Notice the farm houses strung along both banks, and the narrow fields running back from the river.

A small family would be one with three to five children; a large family would have six or more children. Subsistence means that the people get enough to eat to keep them well, but there is no surplus for sale.

There has not been much immigration from France since the time of Talon.

Quebec was the first trading post, but as the traders moved into the western interior the French began to build western trading posts. Trois Rivières succeeded Quebec, and was then in turn succeeded by Montreal. For the early French traders, Montreal represented a trading post on the edge of the interior wilderness; it succeeded only because of its location at the junction of the Ottawa River with the St. Lawrence River.

This arm of the sea would be Hudson Bay.

At this time, France was sending out Jean Talon to build up New France.

*coureurs de bois.* The search for beaver pelts took these fur traders far into the northern and western wildernesses. Two of the earliest traders were Radisson and Grosseilliers, who made several journeys to the northwest during the 1650s and 1660s. From their contact and friendship with Indians north of Lake Superior they learned of an arm of the sea to the north. One of their problems in getting furs back to the St. Lawrence was the risk of Iroquois raids; to avoid this risk it was necessary to use the Hudson Bay route to Europe, so they went to France to seek help in setting it up. They were rebuffed. France at this time was investing much effort in establishing the St. Lawrence Valley settlements, and it did not want to see them bypassed in favour of a remote northerly route. France instead organized the seigneurial system and made sure that the St. Lawrence colony would survive.

Prince Rupert was the cousin of King Charles II of England.

The trading rights were granted for an area of land that was largely unknown, and one of the major tasks of the new Hudson's Bay Company came to be exploration of the area granted to them.

Can you name the five Great Lakes?

Within the New World area of New France, which stretched in loose form from the Gulf of St. Lawrence to the mouth of the Mississippi, and from the east coast of the Maritimes to the Rockies, the area of the St. Lawrence Valley was called Canada.

Americans who came to Canada after the American War of Independence were called the United Empire Loyalists. They were the people who really started the English settlements in Canada.

The first time was during the Iroquois raids of the 1650s and 1660s.

In doing so it lost the chance of developing the Hudson Bay route, for Radisson and Grosseilliers, rebuffed in France, went to England instead. There they were warmly welcomed, initially by Prince Rupert. A successful first voyage by the *Nonsuch* in 1669 resulted in the creation of the Hudson's Bay Company in 1670. The company was given a trading monopoly over all the lands whose rivers flowed into Hudson Bay. The stage was therefore set for the ultimate conflict between French and English interests, and the eventual reduction of direct French influence in the New World.

In the meantime, however, the French continued to explore and trade westwards. They passed the Great Lakes, crossed the Mississippi and Red Rivers, ascended the prairie rivers, and reached the Rockies, all before the loss of their empire at the Battle of the Plains of Abraham in 1759.

The English took charge of a French area of influence comprising a settled core of about 100 parishes in the St. Lawrence seigneuries, a few small trading towns such as Quebec and Montreal, and a vast but loose network of fur trading links established by the voyageurs. The English found that the French in the St. Lawrence region called themselves *Canadiens*. A large part of the pride that today's French Canadians take in their ancestry is, indeed, attributable to the fact that the early French settlers had developed a unique Canadian culture during the 150 years prior to the British takeover.

The British did not set out to destroy or alter the *Canadien* culture; they merely became its new administrative rulers. The French administrators and military personnel either returned to France or retired to lands in the St. Lawrence Valley. Their place was taken by British equivalents; ordinary life continued generally undisturbed. The Catholic Church still bound the settlers in a uniform system of beliefs and actions; the fur traders still operated throughout the west. Indeed, the fur trade prospered, and the voyageurs eventually pushed their way down the Mackenzie to the Arctic Ocean (1789) and across the Rockies to the Pacific (1793).

The next survival crisis faced by the *Canadiens* was the ending of the American War of Independence, and the consequent migration into Canada of thousands of Americans who wished to remain loyal to Britain. These loyalists were granted land along the southern edges of the St. Lawrence Valley, especially in the area shown in Figure 11-4. These British settlements, together with the more westerly ones along the northern short of Lake Ontario, began to alter the ethnic balance of Canada: the predominantly French character of Canada began to diminish, and for the second time since 1608 the *Canadiens* feared for their ethnic survival.

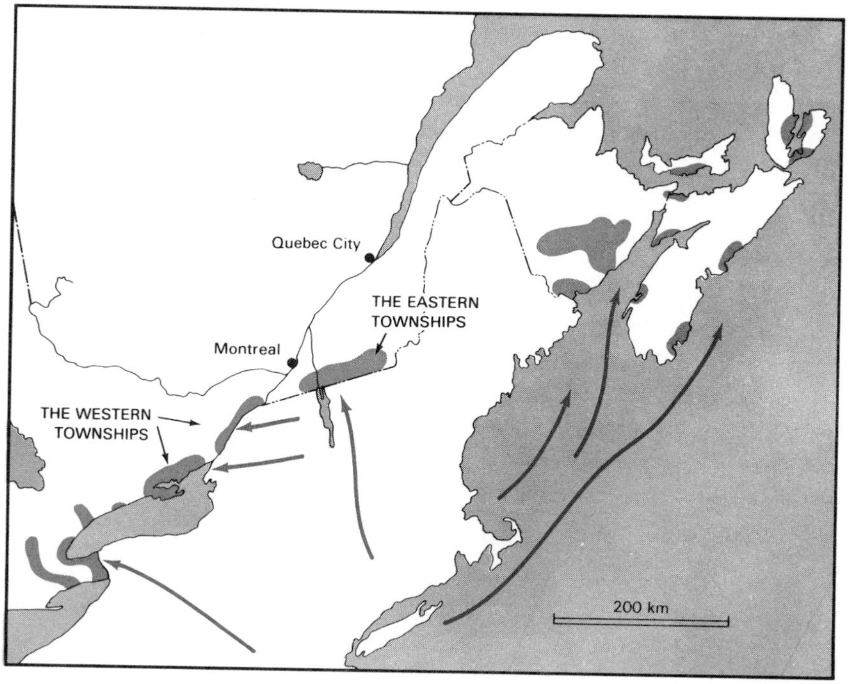

**Figure 11-4 Lines of Movement and Major Settlement Areas for the United Empire Loyalists**

The loyalist settlements in the southern parts of the St. Lawrence Valley were called the Eastern Townships, to distinguish them from the Western Townships along the shores of Lake Ontario. The name Eastern Townships still survives.

Their continued existence was assured, however, by what later came to be called the "power of the cradle". A continued high birth rate kept the *Canadien* population growing vigorously, so much so that during the nineteenth century the St. Lawrence Valley eventually proved unable to support all the *Canadiens*. In order to maintain their rural farming tradition, the *Canadiens* pushed their seigneurial pattern of settlements into all available land. The high value attached to a section of river frontage meant that tributaries of the St. Lawrence were settled immediately the St. Lawrence itself had become fully used. Second, and subsequently third, rows of settlements were then opened up in lines parallel to the first, as shown in Figure 11-5. In this manner the alignment of a river was repeated in parallel fashion in lines of settlements which were quite remote from the river. This pattern of rural settlements is unique to the *Canadiens,* and as a result of it their countryside has a different appearance from all others.

With the eventual filling of all available land with the rang pattern, the *Canadiens* began to settle increasingly in the English areas of the Eastern Townships. The British element was thus gradually submerged, although not eliminated. Meanwhile, the *Canadien*

The rows of settlements are called *rangs*. The row next to the river is called the first rang, the next farthest away is called the second rang, and so on.

Turn to Topographic Map #4 in Chapter 3 and see if you can identify the different rangs.

Topographic Map #4 in Chapter 3 contains evidence of former British settlement, and of its submergence by the more numerous French population. Can you suggest what this evidence might be?

**Figure 11-5    The Rang Pattern of Settlements in the St. Lawrence Valley**

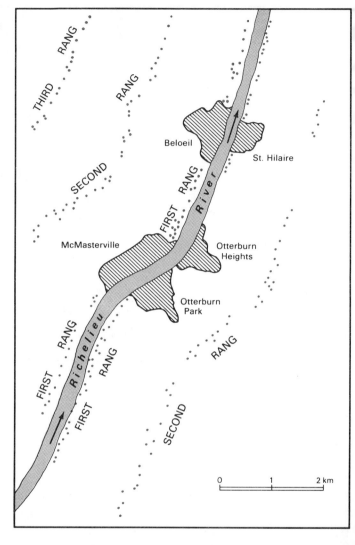

population continued to grow, forcing French speaking groups eventually to migrate out of the province of Quebec altogether. Many moved up the Ottawa Valley into Northern Ontario; others moved down the St. Lawrence into the Gaspé peninsula and across into northern New Brunswick; still others left eastern Canada entirely, moving either westwards into the prairies or southwards into the northeastern U.S.A.

At the time of Confederation the British administrators of Quebec province were able to persuade the *Canadiens* to become part of the new state of Canada only under the agreed conditions that the *Canadiens* would be allowed to retain their own unique culture.

The Canadian Constitution is called the *British North America Act,* or *BNA* for short.

The preservation of the "French Fact" was thus enshrined in the new Canadian constitution.

The growth of the *Canadien* population did not slow down, however. Pressure on available St. Lawrence farmland thus became considerable, resulting in continued out-migration, the beginning of a drift to the major cities, and the development of pockets of real rural poverty. By the early years of the twentieth century the provincial and religious authorities had become seriously concerned over these changes. Out-migration was seen by them as leading ultimately to the removal of *Canadiens* from their heritage in the St. Lawrence homeland. The drift to the cities was regarded in the same way, because the continuity of rural occupancy was thus being destroyed. By the 1920s the authorities were forced into action: they organized colonization projects and sponsored the opening up of new areas in some of the marginal lands on the Canadian Shield, notably the Lac St. Jean basin of the Saguenay and the Quebec portion of the Clay Belt (see Figure 11-7 and compare it with Figure 6-3).

Don't forget that the size of a rang farm was such that only small families could be fed adequately; large families meant hunger.

Marginal lands are lands that people do not think are worth using, or that they think are only just worth using. Given a choice, people will use these lands last and abandon them first.

**Figure 11-6**  Downtown Montreal, from Mount Royal.

Farming conditions in these marginal areas were not ideal, however, for supporting large numbers of subsistence farmers. After the first enthusiasm had worn off, many farmers abandoned their holdings and returned to the St. Lawrence Valley, where the only places they could find livelihoods were usually big city factories.

Increasingly, therefore, the population became urbanized, and Montreal, as the largest city, came to dominate the life of the province. In 1867, about 20% of the population was urban; by 1901 it

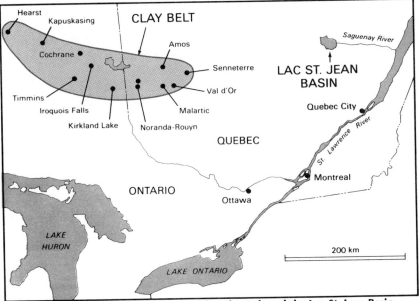

**Figure 11-7   The Colonization Areas of the Clay Belt and the Lac St. Jean Basin**

One of the ironies of the situation is that the area of the St. Lawrence where the *Canadien* lifestyle developed became the first to lose it, while the remote marginal areas, where it still survives, were the last to acquire it. It is even more ironic that the strongest support for the *Canadien* lifestyle comes now from the urbanized areas of the St. Lawrence, where the people have mostly never experienced it.

The *Canadien* culture has largely lost two of its major mainstays, rural lifestyle and Roman Catholic religion. Will the third major mainstay, language, survive?

was up to 40%; by 1975 it was about 80%. Traditional lifestyles have not entirely died out; they may still be seen in areas remote from the St. Lawrence heartland. Nevertheless, for most *Canadiens* the traditions are now just history. Yet it is a history of which they are immensely proud, and even though the rural way of life has largely gone, the French language still survives. Logically, the efforts of the *Canadiens* are now directed towards preserving their language as a major key to the preservation of their culture.

● 2. Describe the things that you think the French Canadians take pride in.

● 3. Suggest and explain some of the causes that may have led to the loss of the traditional *Canadien* rural way of life.

## B: QUEBEC

*Québécois* are the French speaking people of Quebec.

Quebec is the homeland of the *Canadiens*; it is also a political unit within Canada. Accordingly the efforts of *Québécois* have a political as well as a cultural orientation. These efforts are directed towards more independence for the province of Quebec. Some *Québécois* even want full independence, with Quebec leaving Canada and becoming a separate country of its own. Others, however, together with the non-French elements in the population (Figure 11-8), wish to see Quebec remain in the Canadian confederation.

The *Parti Québécois* is the political party which supports separatism. It does not call it separatism. It calls it *independence*.

The separatists (those who seek full independence) justify their beliefs on the grounds of their feelings of *Canadien* nationhood.

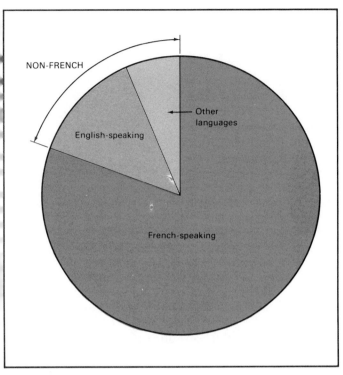

NON-FRENCH

English-speaking

Other
languages

French-speaking

**Figure 11-8   Major Ethnic Proportions in
Quebec**

They point to their longstanding occupancy of the St. Lawrence Valley and to their productive use of the Quebec environment. They refer to their history of trial and survival and to their unique cultural development. They look at their patterns of settlement and at their ties of kinship and common purpose. They see that these factors give them a distinct identity, sufficient to justify their existence as a separate country. They also see that many of the seats of economic power are occupied by non-Québécois, and this has created a considerable degee of resentment. Accordingly they have used the expression *Maitres Chez Nous* to combine their feelings for control as well as independence.

The separatists argue that Quebec could survive quite easily on its own. Even without the non-Québécois element in the population, Quebec still contains over 5 000 000 people, thus approximately ranking in numbers with Denmark, Norway, and Finland, albeit in a much larger territory. Agriculture is also fairly productive, although there is still a living tradition of pioneer self-sufficiency on the farms in some places remote from the St. Lawrence heartland. However, in the heartland, farming is now highly productive and market oriented, and there is generally sufficient food produced to feed the province. Forestry is also a major source of jobs and wealth, especially along the north side of the St. Lawrence Valley

Masters in our own house.

In 1976 the total population of Quebec was 6 300 000. Francophones, or French-speaking people, numbered about 5 000 000. Other languages, mostly English, accounted for the remaining 1 300 000 people.

**Figure 11-9**  The St. Lawrence North Shore and its forestry industry.

Most of Quebec's pulp and paper is exported to the United States, England, and Japan.

Most of the unused potential is in Quebec's northern rivers, which presents the problem of Indian rights for land which might otherwise be submerged by reservoirs.

Rapid industrialization has in turn promoted rapid urbanization and the equally rapid loss of the traditional rural life style. These changes in Quebec have been called the *Quiet Revolution,* because they have occurred with little fanfare, at least until after they had happened.

and the *north shore* of the St. Lawrence estuary. The timber is suited to both pulp and lumber production, but pulp and paper are the chief products by virtue of the demands of the export markets. Given proper management, the forests of Quebec form a source of wealth capable of lasting indefinitely. Mining is another major source of jobs and incomes, with important mines at Noranda-Rouyn (copper, zinc), Matagami (copper, zinc), Chibougamou (copper, silver, gold), Murdochville (copper, silver), Amos (asbestos), Thetford Mines (asbestos), Black Lake (asbestos), Asbestos (asbestos), and Gagnon (iron) (Figure 11-10).

One of Quebec's greatest resources, however, is hydro power. Quebec produces more hydroelectricity than any other province (Figure 11-11) and could well produce even more. It has been partly the abundance of cheap hydro power that has caused the rapid industrialization of Quebec during this century. As a result of industrialization, Quebec is now a greatly different place from that of 75 or 100 years ago. No longer is it mainly a rural and farming area; instead it has modern cities and industries, much trade, and a highly developed service sector. The changes are not without some problems, however, for there is a high level of unemployment. To some extent this could possibly be remedied by the construction of more factories, especially those of medium size, which seem to be scarce at present. Many of Quebec's industries are either quite small (such as textiles and leather) or internationally large (such as paper and aluminum). More of the intermediate size are probably needed for a balanced industrial structure.

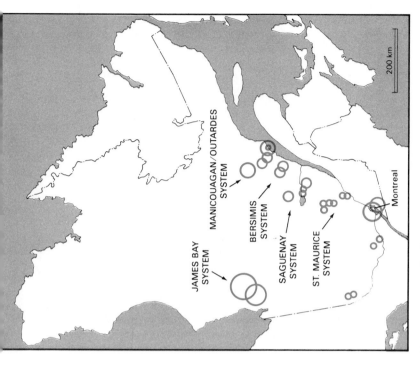

Figure 11-11  Hydroelectric Generating Capacity and Chief Locations

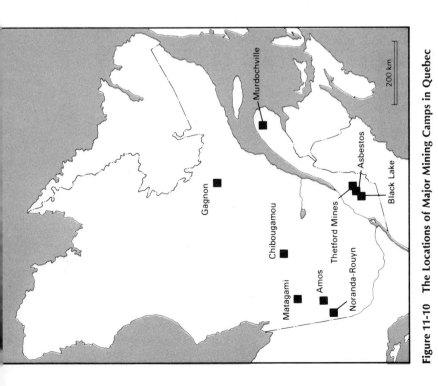

Figure 11-10  The Locations of Major Mining Camps in Quebec

**Figure 11-12** Modern industries in Montreal: the oil refinery in east Montreal.

Federalism is the idea that all the provinces and territories of Canada stay and work together. It is the idea in favour of confederation, as supported by Prime Minister Trudeau in his speech in Chapter 1.

By no means do all Québécois agree on the question of separation. Many oppose it, preferring *federalism*. They argue that the withdrawal of Quebec from Canada could destroy Canada itself. Canada would become split into two areas, separated by about 500 km of foreign territory. They further argue that Atlantic Canada would feel even more remote from the rest of Canada than it does

**Figure 11-13** The port of Montreal: would it decline with independence?

now, and that it might seek to become part of the United States. They also assert that once separatism is accepted for Quebec, then some of the western provinces such as British Columbia and Alberta might also want to become independent. They point also to the possibility that Ontario might turn more and more to the use of New York City as a port, replacing Montreal, and that since many of Ontario's economic ties are with the U.S.A. then it would be only a matter of time before Ontario became a state of the union.

4. What do you think about the issue of independence for Quebec?

5. Many of Canada's largest enterprises are headquartered in Montreal, such as Bell Canada, Canadian Pacific, Canadian National, Air Canada, Royal Bank, Alcan Aluminum, CBC, and Dominion Bridge. The port of Montreal also serves the needs of areas of the country right across to the Pacific (for example, the prairie grain trade). It is also the world's largest French speaking city outside France. In what ways is Montreal
   (a) a Canadian city, and
   (b) a Quebec city?

6. The following article is taken from the Toronto *Star*. Read it and then answer the following questions:
   (a) Why do you think that the birth rate in Quebec has dropped so sharply in recent years?
   (b) If Quebec remains part of Canada, what do you think some of the effects of a low birth rate in Quebec might be, bearing in mind that most immigrant groups learn English rather than French not only in Quebec but also all across Canada?
   (c) What can the Québécois do to protect themselves against this latest threat to their survival?

It should be noted that Montreal has a poor reputation for strikes, and that the port has to make great and expensive efforts to remain open during the harsh St. Lawrence winters, whereas New York remains ice free, as well having worldwide connections and larger dock accommodation.

If Quebec were to separate from Canada then there is little doubt that Montreal would be severely hurt. It would lose a great deal of the trade which currently passes through it, and it would lose many of the jobs which are currently provided by Canadian firms whose headquarters are there.

# Quebec's Shrinking Share of Population is a Political Time-Bomb

By Robert McKenzie

QUEBEC

A study of population trends in Canada over the next 30 years released by Statistics Canada in June is shaping up as a political time-bomb in Quebec.

The study indicates Quebec's share of Canada's total population could, according to one plausible hypothesis, shrink from the present 28 per cent to 22.6 per cent.

The report passed almost unnoticed here when it was

first made public but, in the last few weeks, a number of population experts and newspaper editorialists have pointed to its disturbing implications for Quebec's future within Canada.

With only 22.6 per cent of Canada's population, Quebec's number of seats in the House of Commons would drop to 60 out of 264 in the year 2001 compared with its present 74 seats.

According to the same population projections, Alberta and British Columbia combined would have as many Commons seats as Quebec, and Ontario would have twice as many.

What this would do to Quebec's influence within the Canadian federal structure—and consequently to the survival of a distinct, French-speaking way of life in North America—is easy to imagine.

With only 60 Quebec MPs in Ottawa, it would be much easier than it is today to form a majority government without Quebec. The bargaining position of Quebec MPs and cabinet ministers in Ottawa would be seriously weakened as, of course, would the Quebec government in its dealings with the federal government and the rest of the country.

The chances of conserving special constitutional privileges for Quebec, as the home of French culture in Canada, would probably be diminished.

Certainly, the policy of official federal bilingualism across Canada instituted by Prime Minister Pierre Trudeau's Liberal government would rest on increasingly shaky foundations as the French population became proportionally smaller.

Statistics Canada examined population trends in the light of a number of different hypotheses of birth, death and migration rates and made several different projections—not predictions, the federal experts emphasize.

According to the strongest hypothesis, Canada's population would increase by 13 million by the year 2001—but only 1.4 million of these people, slightly more than 10 per cent, would be in Quebec.

Taking the weakest figures, the national increase would be 6.8 million by 2001 with Quebec's accounting for only 356 000, about 5 per cent, of that total.

Between these two extremes, a "medium hypothesis" produced a figure of 9.1 million more Canadians, of whom less than 900 000 would be in Quebec.

Contrasting with Quebec's feeble growth, Ontario's population would jump by 7 million, 4.8 million or a minimum 3.5 million depending on which set of figures is used.

But what has struck Quebec observers most forcibly is that British Columbia, whose population in 1971 was only one-third of Quebec's, would mark up larger gains than Quebec according to all three calculations. Even Alberta, which has only one-quarter of Quebec's present population, would gain more than the province in two out of three cases.

With the strongest figures, Quebec would fall from 28 per cent to 24.9 per cent of the Canadian population by 2001. With the weakest figures Quebec would be at 22.5 per cent. The proportion is just a shade higher, 22.6 per cent, according to the medium figures.

T h e Statistics Canada projections add a new dimension to the already bitter debate over the diminution of the proportion of French-speaking Quebeckers within Quebec itself.

The 1971 census indicates that just under 81 per cent of Quebec's population is of French mother tongue and uses French as its first language, but everything points to a steady drop in this proportion.

More than 40 per cent of the foreign immigrants entering Quebec in recent years had English as their mother tongue and more than 90 per cent of those who speak neither English nor French on arrival become absorbed in the English Quebec community.

A less well-known factor which contributes to the Anglicization of Quebec is inter - provincial migration —Quebeckers leaving for other provinces and Canadians from elsewhere entering Quebec.

The reason is that a large majority of the Quebeckers who leave the province are French-speaking and are thus a loss to the French-speaking population here. On the contrary, almost all of those who come to Quebec from other provinces are English-speaking.

In a series of articles and editorials in the influential Montreal daily Le Devoir recently, Ottawa correspondent Claude Lemelin expressed amazement that the federal government appears to have no clear population policy.

Describing the issue as potentially "one of the most explosive" in Canada today, Lemelin pointed out that it is not only dynamite in the hands of the separatist Parti Quebecois in Quebec, but could also mean trouble in other areas, such as the Atlantic provinces, faced with "demographic stagnation."

Several groups testifying before the Quebec parliamentary committee examining the province's controversial language act recently warned Montreal could become "another Londonderry" if the French population, as seems possible, loses its present majority status.

Although it dismisses such predictions as alarmist, Premier Robert Bourassa's Liberal government is moving in directions which indicate it is aware of the future threat of a drop in the French population in Quebec and in the rest of Canada.

The avowed intention of the language act—although many Quebec nationalists claim the effect will be the opposite—is to shore up French against the threat of encroaching Anglicization.

Bourassa's proclaimed policy of "cultural sovereignty," however weakly he has defended it so far in negotiations with Ottawa, is also aimed at protecting French life in Quebec as the o v e r a l l percentage of French in Canada drops.

Bourassa is seeking veto power over the type of immigrants who enter Quebec, presumably with a mind to encouraging French-speaking and potentially French-speaking immigration. At the same time, he has indicated he will seek guarantees in a revised Canadian constitution for some degree of Quebec control over radio and television broadcasting in the province and a Quebec takeover of the field of culture.

How vigorously Bourassa will fight for this type of constitutional guarantee and his chances of obtaining it are, of course, another matter.

But he may be forced into action by the Parti Quebecois, now the official opposition in Quebec.

While t h e separatists fought the last Quebec election, in October, 1973, on the dollars-and-cents question of whether Quebec independence would be viable, there are signs that the Parti Quebecois is returning to the more emotional "gut" issues of language and the survival of French in North America.

from the Toronto *Star*, September 6, 1974

## C: OTHER FRENCH-CANADIAN AREAS

Francophones formed 26% of Canada's population.

Francophones formed 80% of Quebec's population.

In the mid 1970s there were nearly 6 000 000 francophones (French-speaking persons) in Canada. Only 5 000 000 or so lived in Quebec. The other 1 000 000 were scattered throughout the other provinces and both northern territories, as shown in Figure 11-15.

The most significant group of French Canadians outside Quebec is in New Brunswick, with associated sub-groups in Nova Scotia and Prince Edward Island. These Maritime French are not all called *Canadiens;* they are mainly called *Acadians,* and they are descendants of settlers from the early 1600s. The Acadians were actually the first French to settle in Canada, coming over in 1604 under the

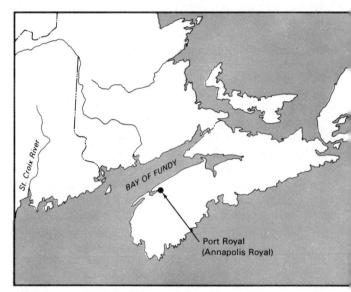

**Figure 11-14    Initial Settlement Locations**

leadership of the Sieur de Monts and Samuel de Champlain. They spent their first winter on an island at the mouth of the St. Croix River in the Bay of Fundy, but they were too exposed to storms, so in 1605 they moved across the Bay of Fundy to a new settlement at Port Royal, now Annapolis Royal in Nova Scotia (Figure 11-14). When de Monts returned to France in 1605 the small new colony was left in the care of Champlain, who founded The Order of Good Cheer in order to keep up the morale. However, in 1607, intrigues in France caused de Monts to move the whole colony back to France. Port Royal was abandoned, and the following year de Monts and Champlain transferred their interest to the St. Lawrence Valley. Although Port Royal was the first French settlement in Canada, it was not the first permanent settlement, for it was abandoned in 1607.

| | Number | Percentage of Individual Provincial Population |
|---|---|---|
| Quebec | 4 867 250 | 80.7 |
| Ontario | 482 042 | 6.3 |
| New Brunswick | 215 727 | 34.0 |
| Manitoba | 60 547 | 6.1 |
| Alberta | 46 498 | 2.9 |
| Nova Scotia | 39 333 | 5.0 |
| British Columbia | 38 034 | 1.7 |
| Saskatchewan | 31 605 | 3.4 |
| Prince Edward Island | 7 363 | 6.6 |
| Newfoundland | 3 639 | 0.7 |
| Northwest Territories | 1 162 | 3.3 |
| Yukon | 450 | 2.4 |

**Figure 11-15   Numerical and Percentage Distribution of Francophones, 1971 census**

In 1610, however, other French settlers came back to Port Royal. They survived until 1613, when the colony was destroyed by English attackers from the American colonies. English interests gradually began to vie with French for control of the Maritimes. In 1621 James I of England granted all of Acadia to a Scotsman, who renamed the area Nova Scotia. The first English settlement occurred in 1628, but it did not survive. In 1632 the whole area was ceded back to France, and French colonization began in earnest. Early settlements developed along both sides of the Bay of Fundy, but just as soon as a unified administration had developed, the English captured Acadia again, in 1654. The English did not at this time favour immigration, however, and so the French settlements continued to grow without any competition. In 1668 the area became French again, although it continued to remain isolated from the main French developments in the St. Lawrence Valley. Its French population was 400.

King James granted land which many would say was not his to grant. Nevertheless it was the custom of the times for European rulers to act as if they owned large parts of the non-European world; eventually, however, their claims had to be supported by military force.

In 1690 the English again invaded, and Port Royal was destroyed. In 1697 it was once more returned to France, but English raids thereafter became more frequent. In 1713 the French finally gave up all rights to Acadia, which they defined as the land south of a line through the Bay of Fundy, Northumberland Strait, and Canso Strait. After 1713 some Acadians left this area rather than be subject to British rule. They migrated to the Isle Royale (now Cape Breton Island) and to the Isle St. Jean (now Prince Edward Island). The British meanwhile began to move settlers in along the Atlantic shore, away from those Acadians who remained along the Fundy shore. Many of the new British settlers were of German origin, because England had just acquired a German monarchy (the House of Hanover, 1714 onwards).

Nova Scotia was the only name used for the area of the Maritimes. The names of New Brunswick and Prince Edward Island followed later.

Lunenburg is one of the most famous of the German settlements along the Atlantic shore.

On Isle Royale (now called Cape Breton Island), *Louisbourg* was begun in 1719 to act as a great fort protecting the sea routes in and out of the Gulf of St. Lawrence. It was captured by the British in 1745 after a six-week battle. The captors came mainly from the American colonies, and when England ceded Louisbourg back to the French in 1748 the American colonists felt that they had been betrayed. In compensation, and to prevent French ships sailing south to attack the American colonists, the British started to build a great fort at Halifax in 1749. This was the origin of Halifax.

The war which eventually occurred was called the Seven Years' War. It lasted from 1756 to 1763.

When the Acadians were split and scattered it was not unusual for members of the same family to be separated and sent to different places.

By 1755 the British had become very concerned about the continued existence of the Acadians and, foreseeing a war between England and France, they began to deport the Acadians from their long-held lands. Since the purpose was largely to gain military security, the Acadians were split and scattered throughout the known areas of eastern North America. Many went to the mouth of the Mississippi, into Louisiana, where they came to be called the *Cajuns*. Others went into Georgia and the Carolinas; a few went to Isle Royale and Isle St. Jean; but most went to eastern New Bruns

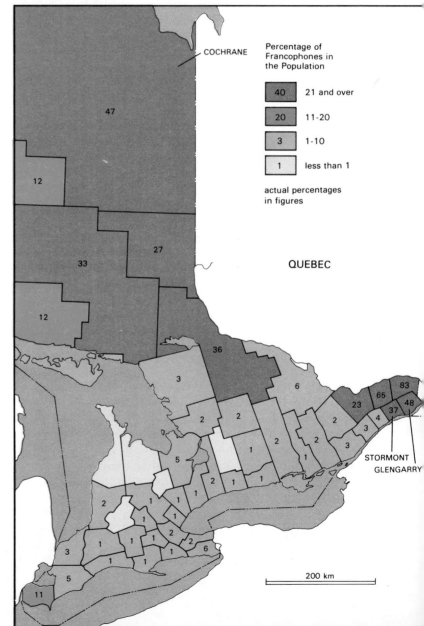

COCHRANE

Percentage of Francophones in the Population

| | |
|---|---|
| 40 | 21 and over |
| 20 | 11-20 |
| 3 | 1-10 |
| 1 | less than 1 |

actual percentages in figures

QUEBEC

STORMONT
GLENGARRY

200 km

**Figure 11-16   Percentage of Francophones in the Population of Ontario Counties** (Based on data in the Atlas of Canada)

wick, where their descendants now form the main bulk of the present day Acadians. Apart from the French language, they have nothing in common with the Québécois: their history has been totally different.

The New Brunswick Acadians do not have much in common, either, with the Québécois overspill which exists in the upper St. John Valley and around the shores of Chaleur Bay. Nevertheless, the two groups of francophones in New Brunswick combine to give New Brunswick the second largest percentage of French-speaking people in Canada.

Despite this, there are more francophones in Ontario than in New Brunswick, as Figure 11-15 shows. There are even traces of the St. Lawrence style of rang settlement pattern in southwestern Ontario, along the banks of the Detroit river. The main distribution of Franco-Ontarians, however, is along the eastern borders of the province, all the way from the St. Lawrence counties of Glengarry and Stormont to the most northerly one of Cochrane (Figure 11-16).

There are also pockets of French Canadians scattered across the prairies, as the following article describes.

There are many thousands of francophones in Toronto, even though they amount to about only one percent of the city's total population.

# French is Alive and Well in the Prairies

By Nicolaas Van Rijn
ST. VINCENT, Alta.—It's noon, and in the prosperous mixed-farming belt surrounding this hamlet 120 miles[1] east of Edmonton the Dargis boys are converging on brother John's farm for dinner.

The scene is common enough on any Prairie farm, but on this one there's a difference: All the talk is in French.

The Dargis family is not experimenting with bilingualism. They and hundreds of other French-Canadian families in this northern Alberta district have been living the fact of it all their lives.

[1] 192 km

They don't feel especially isolated from Quebec, for many have never been there. And they don't feel out of place on the Prairies because they know of dozens of other French-Canadian communities scattered throughout Alberta, Saskatchewan and Manitoba.

**French TV**
French-language television and radio programs are available to them and they have access, likely as not, to a French-language weekly newspaper.

The young children don't yet have the fluent bilingualism of their elders. While they're growing up, before they go to school, most can

speak only one language — French. Within months of starting school they've picked up English as if they've been speaking it all of their lives.

French-Canadian settlers came to the Prairies in the 1890s and the early 1900s, along with Ukrainians, Germans, Czechoslovakians, Hungarians, Dutch and Anglo-Saxons. Their children grew up speaking little or no English until they were well along in school— and then they acquired a tortured, heavily accented English that would be with them for the rest of their lives.

That generation decided their own children wouldn't

have that language difficulty. So they saw to it that their children spoke only English at home.

There were exceptions— parents who insisted that their children grow up speaking both languages and aware of their full heritage. But it wasn't until the largely unilingual generation started bringing up families in the 1950s and early 1960s that they realized they'd been "shortchanged" culturally. Parents began insisting that their children do what they couldn't — grow up speaking two languages.

Where French wasn't taught in school, the children were sent to private classes to learn the language of their grandparents. Cultural organizations, by then the preserves of the old, were revived and invigorated by the injection of youth. New ones were founded.

At the Dargis family's dinner table, the animated conversation would be in French but for the presence of a visitor who doesn't speak the language. They're all fluently bilingual; the switch to English is made smoothly and effortlessly.

"If the French people don't keep up their own language it's their own fault," says 51-year-old Jacques, a fiercely independent farmer / businessman who opposes the federal bilingualism policy.

Jacques' children speak English and French fluently. "We speak French at home, and they still pick up the English without any problem," he said.

His mother, Annette, who brought up her children in northern Alberta speaking both English and French, wonders whether it isn't more difficult now to keep the children speaking both languages.

"They watch English television so much, and the radio stations they listen to are all in English," she says. "The parents don't have to teach English at home. Radio and television takes care of that now."

Jacques says the money that the government now spends on bilingualism is b e i n g misspent. That money, he says, "can be better used to truly educate the people.

"It should be used, for example, to improve Canadian television and radio programming . . . the kind of programming that would boost this country, start a dialogue.

"Who are we? What kind of country is this? Where are we going? Television is the greatest tool there is for teaching, for education — and look what we're doing with it."

### Can't Force

The family is agreed on one basic point: You just can't force someone to learn another language.

John says: "You can encourage him to think that it's to his benefit to become bilingual, but you can't force him. That's how you build up the backlash."

Simon: "One man knowing two languages is worth that much more. Why have a battle over it?"

Jacques: "I've told my dad that it's pure luck that we've settled into an English area, because we now know Canada and what it is. In Quebec they know nothing of Canada.

"You can build love for your neighbor or you can build hate. There, they've built hate."

The question of Quebec separatism doesn't often crop up among the French-Canadians on the Prairies. And when it does, there's not much sympathy for the Quebeckers cause.

"Quebec," Jacques says, "has been using its French identity and threat of separatism as a lever to get concessions out of the federal government. That's wrong.

"That's no way to build a country and that's no way to build a province. If you can't stand on your own two feet, that's too bad. Don't force someone else to do for you what you yourself should be doing."

"Alberta," Simon says, "has been developing for 50 years, and look where we are. Quebec has been developing for the past 300 years, and look where it is."

". . . If they don't get their way, they threaten to separate. It's all a big bluff. Like a kid who threatens to run away from home if he doesn't get his way."

Less than 20 miles[2] away, on his farm near St. Paul, 39-year-old Thomas Lamontagne sits at his kitchen table and says: "It's important to me that my children speak both French and English well. Canada is a country of two languages, and it's our culture."

Beside him, his 12-year-old son Charles is working on Grade 7 homework assignments — in French. At Racette School in St. Paul, Charles receives about half of his instruction in the French language.

Lamontagne was 13 when his father moved from near Dorchester, Que., to start farming near St. Paul in 1952. He spoke no English when he started school at St. Paul, and at that time most of the instruction was in English.

Yet his wife Helen, who grew up in the St. Paul district, spoke only French while she was attending a small country school in the area.

Lamontagne says there are people in the district whose name is French, but who don't know a word of the language.

"They blame their parents now," he says. "They say they should have been forced to learn French. Now they realize that it wouldn't have been any harder to learn both languages."

As for Quebec and separatism, Lamontagne says: "They're fools if they want to separate, because for all their complaining they've got it good in this country.

**Canadians First**
"We're Canadians first then French Canadians. And that's how they should feel over there, too . . . Quebec would certainly be the loser if it goes."

In St. Isidore de Bellevue, 70 miles[3] northeast of Saskatoon, they talk of visitors who think they've taken a wrong turn at a country junction and have ended up deep in rural Quebec, instead of in "just another Saskatchewan town."

Bellevue is six miles[4] from the battlegrounds of the Riel Rebellion, and some of its French-Canadian settlers were there before 1885 when federal troops placed Louis Riel in custody for the last time.

Mederic Gareau's ancestors were in Bellevue in 1884, and Gareau, now 60, remembers growing up in a totally French environment. "We spoke French at home. We didn't know any English. All our neighbors were French, and everything at school was French," he says. "Things didn't change much for a long time."

His 35-year-old son, Germain, remembers a time in Grade 6 when the teacher decided the class was going to speak only English.

"We had always played in French, and talked it among ourselves," he says. "One day the teacher gave each of us 15 markers, and each time someone heard us speaking French we had to turn over one of our markers to him. When we had no more markers, well, we got the strap."

Unlike other French-Canadian areas in Saskatchewan, Bellevue has remained culturally unadulterated. It is the last holdout against the ethnic mix of newcomers that has reduced the French population of other towns in the area to a minority.

"And it will happen here too," Gareau says.

"But we will still keep up the language like we've always done, because we want to — it is part of our heritage, part of ourselves."

For many years, Gareau says, isolation was the only reason the French communities on the Prairies stayed French.

[2] 32 km
[3] 112 km
[4] 9.6 km

Things changed with the introduction of television and of regional schools, with children from different backgrounds being bused in from a wide surrounding area.

As the regional schools became established in the 1960s, provincial education departments started designating some of them as French. In non-designated schools, French is offered only as a language option and instruction is limited to 30 or 40 minutes a day.

In designated schools, up to 50 per cent of the curriculum may now be taught in French, and in a few special cases, all instruction is in French and it's English that's taken as a language course.

**Designated Schools**

Manitoba, with a proportionately higher French-Canadian population than either Saskatchewan or Alberta, already has 28 designated French schools, 11 of them in Winnipeg.

"It wasn't so long ago," recalls Roger Boucette of Winnipeg, "that it was actually illegal to teach French in Manitoba schools.

"If we want our children to speak another language," Boucette s a y s, "we've learned that we've got to do it ourselves. The government can't do it, the com-

munity can no longer do it, so it's up to the family. And, with a bit of help from the schools — which we're now getting — I'm optimistic that we will continue to be aware of our heritage.

"At least, out here, there's no discrimination against us because we want our kids to know French. The Germans want their children to speak German, the Ukrainians want their children to speak Ukrainian, and when we all get together we can speak English with each other.

"That's very Canadian isn't it?"

from the Toronto *Star,* December 4, 1976

● 7. Suggest various ways in which French Canadians in one area differ from those in other areas.

● 8. Why do you think French Canadians outside Quebec feel differently from the Québécois about being Canadian?

● 9. From the evidence presented in the last article, can you say what the various means are by which a group can maintain its individual identity?

● 10. In the introduction to this chapter, we noted some of the feelings expressed about separatism.
    (a) What do you *now* feel about the issue of separatism?
    (b) What do you feel about the preservation of the French language?

# CHAPTER 12

# ARCTIC CANADA

## CHANGE

## INTRODUCTION

Why is the old Eskimo not overwhelmed by an Arctic weather station? Is it because he is able to predict the next day's weather by sitting on a bench and watching the sky? Why does one of the most successful Eskimo carvers of soapstone take his family away from Rankin Inlet to live off the land for a month every year? He says that it is good for the children to see the old way of life.

Eskimos like these are but two of the approximately 20 000 Canadian Eskimos who today can know two lifestyles, both the modern and the old. The middle aged and old remember a life of hunting, fishing, and living in igloos and skin tents, but the young are increasingly weekend or holiday hunters. They are growing up in Eskimo communities of prefabricated wooden homes and going to school. Their parents are involved in producing handicrafts such as sculpture and parkas or in marketing Arctic gourmet foods. Some have government jobs, while most of the rest are on welfare. Very few can support their families entirely on hunting. In 1971 the first Eskimo medical doctor graduated from the University of Manitoba. In that year also the first Eskimo helicopter pilots completed their training.

Thus, the Arctic today is different from the Arctic of yesterday. The reasons for the change are complex, of course, and are not just the result of the imposition of white rule. The Eskimos themselves were attracted to the advantages of trading with a more economically developed people. However, it has meant, on the one hand, that the animal population has been depleted through overhunting, while, on the other hand, the Eskimo population in recent years has increased due to improved medical facilities. Now the Arctic could not actually support the Eskimo population of today if they were to live off the land.

The name *Eskimo* was given by the Indians to the northern peoples. It means *Eaters of Raw Meat*. Inuit is the name the Eskimos call themselves, meaning people.

There are 33 Eskimo communities in the Northwest Territories. These are principally of government origin, set up to bring the Eskimos together where it would be easier to prevent starvation.

Arctic char, a variety of trout, is a luxury fish in southern Canada and sells well, frozen or canned, in gourmet shops.

255

## A: THE PAST

What exactly was it like before? After all, these people first wan-dered along the shores of Canada's Arctic looking for a peaceful home, perhaps as long as 5000 years ago. They came from Siberia across the Bering Strait (Figure 12-2). Indeed, there are about 2000 Eskimos still in Russia and 20 000 in Alaska. No other race has ever tackled the polar region without aid from the rest of the world and survived. While it is true that there are a few physical differences between the Eskimos and other peoples, these differences are not really enough to make survival easy, although they may make it a little more possible. For example, their arms are shorter, their hands and feet are smaller, and their nose cavities are tinier than those of other peoples. Why do you think these differences might be an

The only other group of Eskimos in the world are 30 000 or so in Greenland, making a world total of about 70 000.

**Figure 12-1    Place Name Map of the Arctic**

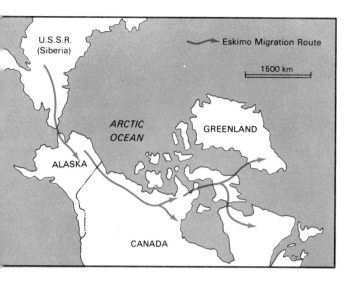

**Figure 12-2   The Arrival of the Eskimos**

advantage for survival in the Arctic? And which came first: did the characteristics develop because of the cold, or did survival require people with these characteristics?

The Eskimos were undoubtedly tough, but it took more than toughness to live in their formidable land (Figure 12-1). It also required great ingenuity and adaptability. They had to build their homes of snow and skins because there was no wood in this barren land. They learned to skim over the ice and snow in sleds in order to hunt during the long winters. They used bone bows and arrows to stalk caribou, and bone harpoons to kill whales, seals, and walruses. The Eskimo kayak, a skin-covered boat, was sufficiently manoeuvrable to allow them to spear caribou as these animals swam rivers and lakes. When a whale was sighted at sea it required groups to encircle, harass, and direct it into shallower water until the water was too shallow for the whale to survive. This was a risky adventure, but for those who succeeded and survived it meant food for months.

Life was always very hard. Life expectancy was, at most, about 20 years. Yet the Eskimos are a happy and extremely tolerant people. Do you think this might be because, during the long, cold, and dark winters, they were virtually confined, often up to 18 hours a day, day after day, in the extremely cramped quarters of an igloo, with only their families and an occasional visitor?

Early contact with the Europeans was made, first, in a limited way, through explorers, and then later with whaling fleets. The results of this contact were manifold and permanent. The whalers brought death in the form of disease, and took away with them the whales themselves, thereby depriving the Eskimos of a major source of

The Eskimos eat mostly meat. Seal liver provided the nutrients we receive from vegetables so they escaped the ravages of scurvy that others suffered when deprived of fresh fruits and vegetables.

Igloos do melt and if too many people are crowded into one its water will drip on your head.

*Before the arrival of white people, the white fox was not part of the Eskimo hunt. The meat was not fat enough and the pelt was not strong and durable enough.*

*Aklavik in Eskimo means The Place of the Brown Bear.*

food. But in the nineteenth and early twentieth centuries the white fox became an important item of trade, and Eskimos thus were introduced to flour (bannock), along with tea, sweets, and tobacco. In return the Eskimos traded away not only white fox furs but also their independence. In the Mackenzie delta the muskrat also became a valuable trading fur, and in the 1920s southern Canadians built the town of Aklavik in the delta in order to supervise and manage muskrat trading during the most prosperous trapping period. Aklavik subsequently became known as the "million dollar fur capital of the North".

However, fur prices vary from year to year, and so they are not a reliable source of income. Why do you think fur prices vary in this manner? Another problem was that during the off-season for trapping there was always great difficulty in finding food. Moreover, as medical facilities began to improve, the population began to increase, and this made the problem even more serious. In 1929, for instance, when shortage of food became very serious in the Mackenzie delta, the federal government purchased a herd of reindeer and had it driven across Alaska into the delta. The herd is still there but the venture has never been a success. The Eskimos did not take kindly to herding domestic animals; they greatly preferred the thrills of a hunt.

**Figure 12-3**   Part of the Mackenzie Delta reindeer herd.

- 1. If life was so hard, why do you think the Eskimos stayed in the Arctic?

- 2. In what ways did white people first cause changes in the lives of the Eskimos?

# B: RECENT CHANGE

## The Islands

Gradually, with the realization that the Eskimo's life as a hunter was ending and that life as a trapper was unreliable and insecure, the federal government began to exercise a little more control over the lives of the Eskimos. This ensured their survival, but often it curtailed their independence even more than previous contacts had done.

Some of the changes made had their origins in another development. Back in the early 1900s Canada was concerned when a Norwegian named Otto Sverdrup explored and claimed on behalf of Norway about 250 000 km² of northern Arctic islands. In 1930 Canada paid Sverdrup $67 000 and Norway thereby relinquished its claim. Nevertheless, Canada remained uneasy. Three RCMP posts were established in the islands during the 1920s, and they occasionally housed an Eskimo family. There were no permanent groups, however, and so the government gradually decided to move some Eskimo families into the north. Eskimos were persuaded to leave areas where game was scarce and becoming depleted and to move into permanent settlements in the high Arctic, where hunting was likely to be successful. Grise Fiord (Figure 12-4) is an example of this type of resettlement program; it is on the southern tip of Ellesmere Island. Today, there is a population of about 100 people who live in government built, three-bedroom homes, each with a modern kitchen. The community even has its own school. Nearly all the men hunt and trap. But although there is plenty to eat, there is still a lack of cash around: fur prices still vary, there is a quota on polar bear skins, and sales of sealskins are limited because of the outcry against the hunting of baby seals off the Labrador coast. However, life is more secure than in the past.

With the development of transpolar flights to Europe came another development. A series of Arctic weather stations was built. Indeed, Canada's most northerly permanent outpost is the weather station at Alert. It is located on the northern shores of Ellesmere Island, at 83°N, and is manned by Eskimos living in an experimental, artificial climate within a group of huts to make life comfortable away from the intense cold and severe blizzards.

During World War II the United States and Canada jointly built an air field at Frobisher Bay, to provide a staging post en route to the European war. Many Eskimos were hired to work in its construction and maintenance, and modern technology became a part of their lives. After the war, Canada bought out the Americans, and maintained the base as an operational air field. Subsequently the

In 1949 the market for white fox collapsed; from $30.00 a pelt in 1949 the price dropped to $5.00 in 1950.

The National Film Board has made a film entitled *In One Day*. It depicts the weather of Canada and the opening scene shows the weather station at Eureka.

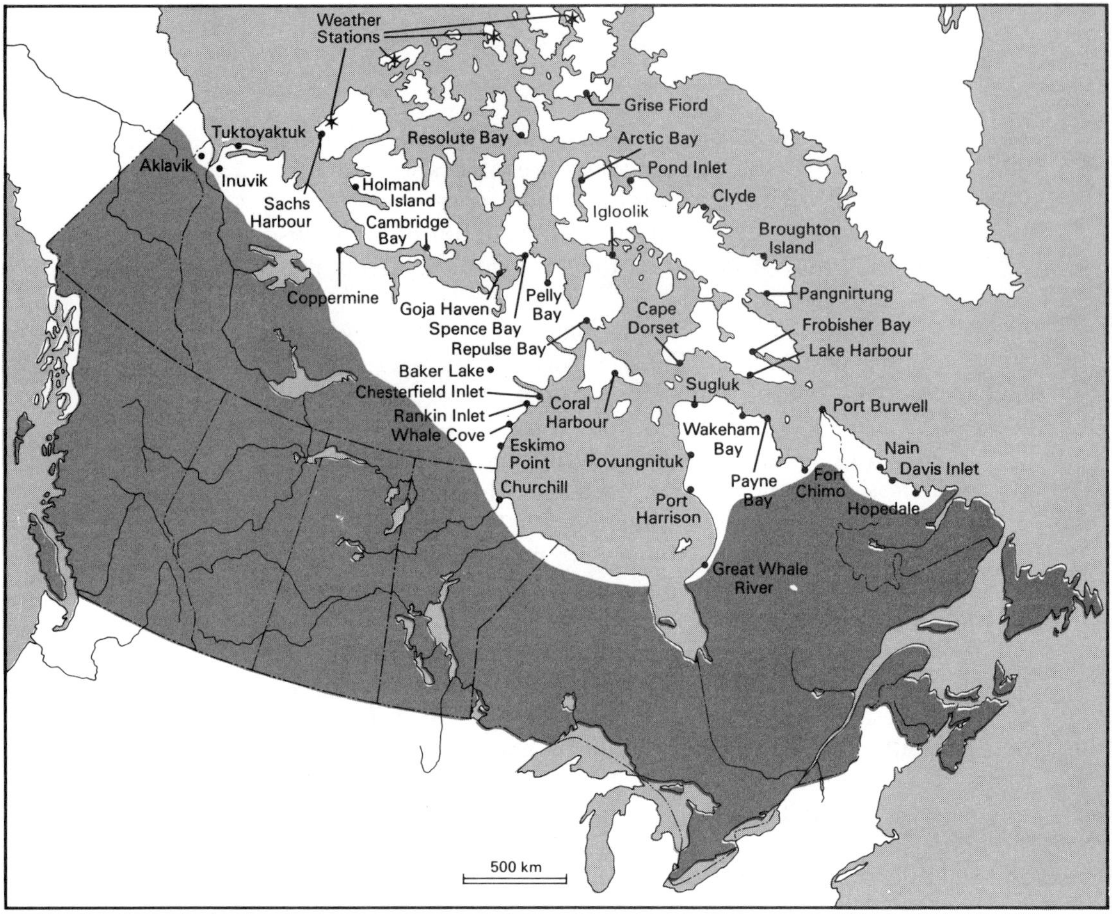

**Figure 12-4  Canada's Arctic Settlements**

U.S. Strategic Air Command established a refuelling base there during the period between 1959 and 1963. This was because the Arctic had gained in strategic importance with the introduction of long range bombers and the growth of hostility between the U.S. and the U.S.S.R. It was no longer an isolated and out-of-the-way land. The Russians and Americans faced each other across it, indeed, in a "cold" war. At the time, long range bombers flying the shortest distance between the two countries were considered to be the main strike weapon. Examine a globe to see just why the Arctic was involved. As part of NORAD (North American Air Defence) the Americans contracted with the Canadians to build a series of radar stations across northern Canada to form what became known as the DEW (Distant Early Warning) line to give warning of approaching bombers. Later, as Intercontinental Ballistic Missiles (ICBMs) were developed, a second series of stations called BMEWS (Ballistic Missile Early Warning Stations) became necessary. Much of the labour required in the building and maintenance of these warning systems came from southern Canada, but there was some Eskimo labour as well.

## Northern Quebec

In northern Quebec, where the caribou population had dropped alarmingly by the 1950s and where there was little other wild game to provide a mainstay for existence, more and more Eskimos were coming to depend for longer periods of time on government relief. Any communities that existed were not Eskimo ones: they were outposts of the Hudson's Bay Company, of missionaries, and of the police. The Eskimos were nomads. In an attempt to provide more means of livelihood in the area the government did open up a few new possibilities, some of which have been quite successful. Fort Chimo became the local administrative centre and Eskimos were hired to work there full time as civil servants. In Port Burwell a co-operative was formed to sell seal and fox pelts. This improved marketing procedure gave the Eskimos a share of the profits as well as creating new work for them. Food for the village is largely provided by a few hunters who share the meat of the caribou with everyone, retaining only the skins for their own use. In the hunt, dogs have now been replaced by snowmobiles. What do you think are the advantages and disadvantages of such a change? For cash the Port Burwell Eskimos fish for Arctic char, a species of trout. Boats are provided by the government. Although cod fishing has been organized by the government, it is considered too easy and not very exciting; it is therefore not popular. The Eskimos seem to prefer to hunt seal even though they are more unreliable. In another community, George River, a musk-ox farm has been established as well as a tourist lodge to cater to wealthy people interested in fishing. The Eskimos make good guides and possibly this area of activity will become more significant as more people are able to afford holidays in the Arctic.

## The Western Arctic

By the 1950s, on the western side of the Arctic, the largest community, Aklavik, had grown to its maximum size. Only low lying land susceptible to serious flooding remained to be built on. The Mackenzie delta area, meanwhile, needed additional educational and medical facilities. Accordingly a site for a new town to be called Inuvik was found on the eastern side of the delta, on higher ground

In Canada the caribou population declined from about 600 000 to 175 000 between 1945 and 1950.

The Hudson's Bay Company was founded as a fur trading company in 1670. Today it stands as the only fur trading company operating in the Arctic other than the small cooperatives that have been established locally in some communities. The Hudson's Bay Company today also operates the urban department stores referred to as *The Bay*.

The undercoat of the musk-ox provides a beautiful fine wool for knitting. It is a protected species and survives today in Greenland and northern Canada.

Package tours into the Arctic are now available. You may go for the night or for two or three weeks. You may visit the port of Churchill, abandoned mines, or the art communities of Cape Dorset and Pangnirtung. It is even possible to travel by barge down the Mackenzie to Inuvik.

*Inuvik* is an Inuit term that means *Place of Man*.

Permafrost is ground which is permanently frozen, at least below the active layer — that is the top 25 cm or so which melts in the summer.

with good drainage. Construction began in 1955. The major construction problem for this modern planned town was to prevent the melting of the permafrost, especially as a number of large buildings were included in the plan. Frozen water in the ground provides a solid building foundation as long as it is not allowed to melt; but if it melts then any structure built on it may slump, or even slide away altogether. Heated buildings constructed either directly on or a level below the ground will transfer their heat to the earth, creating a quagmire as the ice melts. There are different methods of dealing with this problem. Sometimes, as in Alaska, the basements of very large buildings may be kept permanently at a temperature below freezing. In Inuvik most buildings are raised above the ground on piles, which are sunk deep into the permafrost. Roads and airport runways in the Arctic must be constructed to rest on beds of gravel. Pipes cannot be laid underground. In Inuvik all waterlines, sewage pipes, and pipes containing water for heating are contained in *utilidors* which wind their way through the town, a metre or so above the ground.

Today 90% of all school age children in the Northwest Territories are attending school regularly.

Today, Inuvik is the key administrative, educational, medical, and communications centre in the Mackenzie delta. Aklavik, which was initially slated to be abandoned, has, however, remained, because it is closer to the muskrat trapping grounds. Inuvik has a population of about 5000, which is predominantly white. There are 1100 students attending school there, about 50% white, 30% Eskimo, and 20% Indian. The high proportion of students to the total population of the town is due to the fact that the secondary school is a collector school for this part of the Arctic, and that students come here and live in hostels during the school year. The sparse and scattered population of the Arctic requires that students move away from home. Complaints of dislocation and severe homesickness have now resulted in the establishment of elementary schools in many of the smaller communities, like Grise Fiord, but high school students must still move to centres such as Inuvik, Yellowknife, or Frobisher Bay. All students at Inuvik speak a dialect of English called *Deltanese*. At the moment there are not many jobs for successful graduates. Most of the jobs in Inuvik, especially in education, are already taken by the more educated whites. This means welfare, for at least part of the year, for most Eskimo and Indian townsfolk.

The town of Inuvik is well provided for. There is a large well equipped hospital, a hotel, a theatre, taxis, and a research station for visiting scientists.

• 3. In what ways has the government of Canada attempted to reorganize the lives of the Eskimos in a systematic manner?

Scenes of Inuvik.

**Figure 12-5** The airport.

**Figure 12-6** Government houses for Eskimos and Indians.

**Figure 12-7** An Anglican hostel for Eskimo students.

## C: COMMUNICATIONS

One of the problems in the Arctic has always been that of isolation and distance. But this is changing as well. Television came to the Arctic in 1972 with the launching of the world's first domestic communications satellite, *Anik One*, from Cape Canaveral (then called Cape Kennedy). It is now permanently in place over the Equator at 114°W. Nowadays, *Anik Two* provides an additional operational back-up service. Ground stations at places such as Inuvik, Frobisher Bay, and Resolute pick up signals from the satellite and the clear dustless air allows excellent reception within the range of the ground receiving stations. Indeed, some of the most recent receiver developments permit direct reception from the satellite without the need to have ground relays. There is, of course, only one channel, the CBC. The first CBC northern service radio station was established back in 1958 in Whitehorse, thus bringing professional broadcasting to the north. Expansion has been continuous, and there are now about 30 stations. They broadcast national network programs as well as local ones in English, French, Eskimo, and Indian. The following article tells how one Eskimo became a radio announcer and how he copes with two cultures.

**Figure 12-8** A ground receiving station at Inuvik for signals from the *Anik* satellites.

# How 'Jonah E7262 Eskimo' Learns to Adjust to a White Man's World

By Harry Goldhar

FROBISHER BAY — For most of every weekday, Jonah Kelly is a radio announcer who spins records and reads newscasts for CFFB, the CBC's small radio station here, only a little less than three degrees south of the Arctic Circle.

Then he goes home to eat raw meat or hunt seals and cariboo on the weekend.

He has, he says, "two lives, absolutely two lives." He finds it hard sometimes to mix those two lives.

He is an Eskimo, one of the leading members of the community of 1350 Eskimos who live here.

As a radio announcer, a member of the community council and other civic groups and a regular worshipper at the Anglican church, he mixes freely with the 700 whites of Frobisher Bay, most of whom are temporary residents.

But he doesn't mix easily. "I feel sort of strange with white people," he said one morning when we were alone in the radio station, the only one in the Baffin Island district. "I say to myself I don't speak enough English.

"I can speak about my hunting, but I don't know much about the moon shot. But I have to live with the white people. I have to work with them."

Jonah Kelly is 23 and one of the better educated of all Canada's 16 000 Eskimos, and has one of the best jobs. He is respected in both white and Eskimo societies and he is an example of the type of Eskimo the government of Canada hopes all the others will become — the kind who can move freely between two cultures.

Most other Eskimos cannot. They have more than a feeling of strangeness in white society. They haven't yet learned to cope with liquor or school, with the white man's clock or his compulsion for work.

**Arctic is a 'Foreign' Land**

To the rest of the population of this country the Canadian Arctic is a foreign land in which Eskimos live in igloos and eat raw meat and fish. They have a vague picture of a great waste of snow and ice, peopled by nomadic hunters.

Until 1953 that was roughly the way it was.

But 17 years ago, after the Eskimos had been ignored by the rest of the country and had been dying off quickly because of starvation and white man's diseases, the government decided to do something.

They developed a plan to give the Eskimos a white man's education and to develop the North. Their hope is to make every Eskimo able to choose between his own way of life and the white man's and to be able to take advantage of both cultures, either in the south or in an industrialized North.

There have been complaints that the government is imposing the white man's culture on the Eskimos, but the civil servants in the Department of Indian Affairs and Northern Development in Ottawa defend their plans by saying there is no alternative.

"Once civilization touches you, there's no turning back," said Alex Stevenson, chief of the Northern Services Division of the Northern Economic Development Branch of the department.

"I've got a thousand books on the Arctic, but the critics don't say what else we can do.

"The only answer is to educate the Eskimos so the choice will be theirs to do what they want within Canadian society. Our role is to ease the transition, not to dictate it, but there is no simple answer."

Eskimos like Jonah also approve of the coming of the white man's civilization. He would like to live the Eskimo way "for my holidays, yes, but not for permanent."

And so the North has changed.

The Canadian government has assembled 2401 prefabricated homes for them since 1959, and plans to erect another 232 within the next year.

All are placed in settlements, which has ended the nomadic life. You can't move a house as easily as a tent, but a house is warmer and the Eskimos choose the house and the settlements where there is electricity and other services.

When I first moved in with Jonah he lived in a three-bedroom house that looked like a southern Ontario summer cottage.

Within the house were his wife Lizzie, his adopted 14 - month - old daughter Pudloo, his mother and father, his 6-year-old brother Jolly, and his 19-year-old sister, Rosie.

### They Share Accommodation

I slept on the couch in the living room, but I wasn't the only guest. For a couple of days a year-old boy who had just been released from hospital after treatment for stomach disorders shared the living room, and a young woman who had recently given birth slept in Rosie's room.

It's an old Eskimo custom to have an open door for anyone who needs help and the hospital here, the only well-equipped one in the Baffin area, sometimes sends out-of-town outpatients to the Kelly house for short stays.

Food is expensive. Frobisher Bay is on the 63rd parallel, north of the tree line where there is little soil or summertime to grow food. Most of it is brought in by Nordair, which has one or two flights a day from Montreal.

### Food Costs are High

Five years ago there were only two flights a week in the winter and fresh fruits and vegetables were a rare delicacy.

Today a dozen eggs cost $1.25. A dozen oranges cost about $2 and hamburger 98 cents a pound.[1] The family often buys canned fruit and vegetables and they eat a lot of stew. Occasionally they'll have pork chops.

The family also eats raw meat and fish because they like it and because hunting keeps the cost of food down.

[1] approximately 45¢/kg

Jonah has now moved into a newer two-bedroom house with his wife and daughter, but will still help with the expenses of his father's household and hunt for them.

He paid all the expenses before out of his $9000-a-year salary. The others saved most of their income.

Jonah was able to save about $300 a month, but that didn't last long because he bought such things as a snowmobile, a stereo, a freighter canoe, an outboard motor boat, a rifle and an encyclopedia (which he now admits was likely a mistake).

Four and a half years ago he applied for a job at CFFB and got it.

Shortly afterwards he became famous throughout Canada when he complained on the air that he was known officially as Jonah E7262 Eskimo, and because of an administrative mistake he was getting bills for Jonah E6262 Eskimo, who also lived in Frobisher Bay.

The practice of giving a number to Eskimos was started by the government in Ottawa so it could identify them when it sent out family allowance cheques.

Eskimo names at that time changed at the whim of each individual and there was no difference between names for males or females.

The Northwest Territories government, which has

now been given legislative authority over the area, has embarked on a campaign to give all Eskimos family names and assigned the job to Abe Okpik, the first Eskimo appointed to the NWT council.

Jonah is now the longest employed announcer at CFFB and Bob Stanley, the station manager sent up from Ottawa by the CBC, says he'd like to have 10 like him.

**Adjusting to White World**
But sometimes, says Stanley, when Jonah wants to go hunting he has to point out that he can't unless he gets his work done ahead, or someone takes his shift.

Eskimos are considered by the white men to be intelligent, good workers and adaptable, but to most Eskimos the white man's clock means very little. In past centuries the only time that was important was how long you could survive between successful hunts.

When Jonah isn't busy with civic chores or hunting, he'll sometimes go to a movie. Some Eskimos gamble with cards, a game called pudik, which Jonah describes as "just one of those kill-times.

**Keep Old Culture**
Jonah would also like to see something done to keep alive the old culture that is slowly disappearing in Frobisher Bay.

As part of his radio work

Jonah spends a lot of time taping music and old folk songs of the Eskimos.

He was elected to the community council last November and hopes that through it he will also be able to help his people. The council, following a plebiscite, has asked for hamlet status from the NWT government in Yellowknife. That will give it control over budget expenditures and other civic matters. It will also give men like Jonah a lot more power than an Eskimo has ever had in Frobisher Bay.

Frobisher Bay was a small trading post until 1942 when the U.S. Air Force built a Strategic Air Command station here. The RCAF followed, and so did the Canadian government.

By the time the Americans left in 1963 hundreds of Eskimos had been attracted by the jobs and had learned to live with civilization.

By then the usefulness of Frobisher Bay as a military site and as a refuelling stop for pre-jet aircraft was over, but the Eskimos had no desire to go back to their former life.

And so Frobisher Bay is today mainly an administrative centre.

**A Beautiful Setting**
It is an ugly sprawling town with bleak, treeless streets and dusty gravel roads in

the springtime. The dominant color is brown, except for the white of the snow on the mountains and the bay that create a strikingly beautiful setting.

This is an unusual place in the Arctic. Its Eskimo population is almost one-tenth of the total in Canada. It is the only urban centre a formerly nomadic people have. Yellowknife, the capital of the NWT, is mostly white.

If Ottawa is successful in its plan to attract enough industry to balance the economy of the Northwest Territories and educate the Eskimos to as high a level as in southern Canada, Eskimos like Jonah Kelly will run Frobisher Bay.

Meanwhile, it's still a white-run town, and Jonah happily puts on his crash helmet each morning, gets on his motorcycle or snowmobile depending on the weather, and arrives at the radio station every morning before 9, where he gets ready to read the news, introduce hit records and read announcements, all in Eskimo.

"The government has done very well," he said that morning in the studio. "You don't expect everyone to do a perfect job every time. You have to make mistakes, sometimes bad ones, but there's been more good than bad."

from the Toronto *Star*, June 20, 1970

The Arctic is a long way from southern Canada. But even in the Arctic itself distances are vast. It is another 2100 km from Frobisher Bay to Alert, and 2900 km from Frobisher Bay to Inuvik. For comparison it is 1800 km from Montreal to Winnipeg.

The first jet plane landed in the Arctic in 1968. Now you can fly by jet to Frobisher Bay for the weekend. It is a long way to go for the weekend, over 2000 km, but the service is there. There is also a whole network of regularly scheduled jet flights by three regional airlines (Figure 12-9). There are problems flying jets into the Arctic, however. Since it is uneconomical to build many concrete runways where the Arctic permafrost and large temperature ranges would necessitate constant repairs, most runways are of gravel. For propeller driven planes this produces no problems, but for jets certain modifications are required to keep the gravel away from the engine intakes. Pilots must also deal with very cold temperatures, sometimes so cold that engines are never shut down for fear they would freeze solid. High winds, blizzards, and darkness are other hazards. And if there are no high winds the airfields are probably blanketed by fog. Jets have the big advantage, however, of cheaper operation

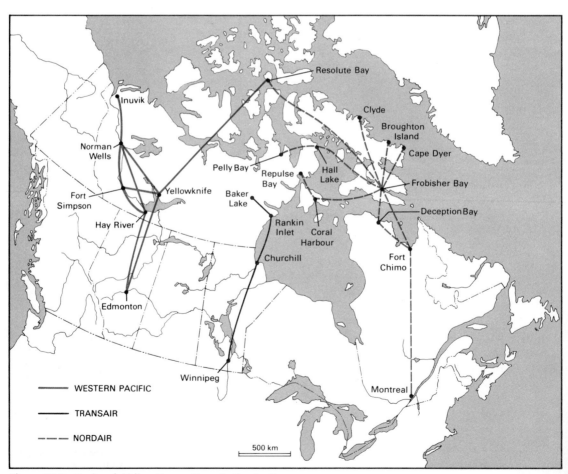

**Figure 12-9   Regional Airline Connections in the Arctic**

per seat-kilometre. Of course, traditional propeller driven float planes and courageous bush pilots still fly between scattered outposts, providing connecting links with the scheduled airlines. You will still hear of heroic rescues and of downed pilots and passengers. The Canadian Armed Forces operate an air search team, which provides the backbone of many rescue attempts.

The ancient dream of using the Northwest Passage through the Arctic Islands as a shipping route surfaced again in 1969 when the American oil tanker *Manhattan* attempted to make the Passage. With the help of Canadian icebreakers, it eventually succeeded. However, to the relief of many Canadians who feared new American claims in the Arctic, the Passage provided an expensive solution to the problem of transporting oil from Alaska, and the idea was accordingly shelved in favour of the Alaska pipeline.

In order to get around in some of the dense fogs of the Arctic, poles topped with different coloured flags were set into the ground along paths between buildings so that foot traffic could find its way.

## D: NORTHERN SOURCES OF ENERGY

The Arctic is receiving much press coverage for its possible role as a provider of energy for the energy deficient south. Searches are going on in the north, especially in the Mackenzie delta and Beaufort Sea areas, to discover enough oil and natural gas to justify a pipeline up the Mackenzie Valley and into Alberta to link with the southern distribution system. At present there has been enough natural gas discovered, but not enough oil. Many questions have developed into a heated controversy. For example, should only a natural gas pipeline be built? If we do not need all the gas, should

**Figure 12-10**  The search for oil and gas in the Arctic is neither easy nor cheap.

we sell the excess to the United States? Should a Canadian gas pipeline have a connection to Alaska's North Slope in order to carry American gas to the U.S.? What would be the effects of the building of a pipeline on the permafrost, on the surrounding flora and fauna, and on the native inhabitants of the areas? Years of research to collect volumes of data have already taken up large amounts of government workers' and oil company representatives' time. Some decisions have been made. Mr. Justice Berger, who was appointed by the federal government to investigate the desirability of a northern pipeline through Canada, recommended delaying construction of a pipeline until 1987, as he felt that the Arctic was not ready for the changes that would be brought by this development. In the meantime, Indian and Eskimo land claims could be settled. The National Energy Board in 1977 indicated that it preferred the route which would carry U.S. gas from the Alaska North Slope (Prudhoe Bay) along the already existing Alaska Highway route, the route that would least disturb the environment. This choice is conditional to the building of a connecting link between Dawson City and Inuvik to tap Canadian gas as well. The article on the following page will help to explain some of the problems.

**Figure 12-11　Arctic Pipelines Existing and Proposed**

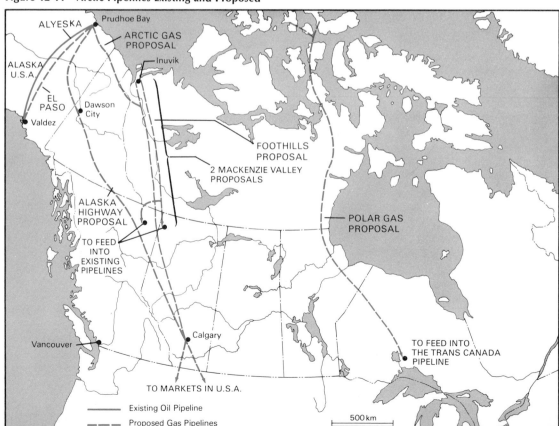

# While Piles of Pipe Lie on the Arctic Tundra...

By Fred Bruemmer

Unlike oil, which has to be pumped hot (140 to 180 degrees F.[1]) because otherwise it would congeal in the pipe, gas will be chilled (to below 32 degrees F.[2]) and kept chilled as it travels south in a 48-inch[3] pipe buried at least 10 feet[4] deep in the North's permanently frozen soil. Thermokarst, heat erosion of permafrost, soil slumping and subsequent severe environmental degradation, will thus be totally avoided, say the pipeliners. There will be a compressor station every 50 miles[5] along the pipeline, to keep the gas cold and moving. These stations are extremely noisy, and Canadian Arctic Gas has employed teams of biologists to find out how this will affect wildlife. If and where necessary, Canadian Arctic Gas is willing to muffle its noisy compressors.

The social objection is twofold. The pipeline will create a maximum of 8000 temporary and 400 permanent jobs. During three winter seasons, about 8000 men will be required to build the pipeline; thereafter 400 people will be needed to look after it. Northerners, and particularly the natives, dread the social impact and dislocation that may result from such a drastic influx of outside labor. Apart from this, Indian land claims could halt the project entirely. The Indians and Eskimos understandably feel that if the mineral wealth of their ancestral land is to be sold south, they want, at least, some say in the matter, plus a healthy slice of the financial pie. The United States, they point out, in its 1971 Alaska Native Claims Settlement, provided $1 billion and 40 000 acres[6] to the Eskimos, Aleuts and Indians.

[1] 60°C to 80°C
[2] 0° C
[3] 122 cm
[4] 3 m
[5] 80 km
[6] 16 200 ha

Adapted from the *Weekend Magazine*, September 29, 1973

A search for oil and gas is taking place in the Arctic islands, and some gas discoveries have been made in those areas that are underlain by sedimentary rock basins. However, any tapping of these resources must be considered in the light of severe weather conditions (much more severe than in the Mackenzie delta), the remoteness of the area, and the engineering problems of constructing a pipeline across frozen seas as well as frozen lands. A considerable increase in the price of gas and oil is necessary before this will become an economically viable enterprise.

## E:  AIR, SEA, AND LAND

As you fly over the Arctic, it will look for hundreds of kilometres just as it has for thousands of years, since the ice caps disappeared. But then, as you descend to land on a modern airstrip, you will see a row or two of box-like prefabricated houses. The airstrip and the

What does come to
mind, in fact?

houses are part of the picture of the new Arctic superimposed on
a backdrop of the Arctic which has not yet changed. The Arctic
that is not changing is the Arctic that comes first to mind when we
say "Arctic". The statisics in Figure 12-12 give you some comparisons with southern Canada.

- 4. (a) Using the data in Figure 12-12 calculate the average annual
    temperature for each station.
  - (b) Calculate the temperature range for each station.
  - (c) How many months is the average monthly temperature
    below 10°C for each of the five stations? Where all 12
    months of the year are below 10°C, trees have great diffi-
    culty growing. The land is said to be beyond the *tree line*,
    and tundra vegetation occurs instead. Where would you put
    Aklavik in relation to the tree line? (refer to Figures 12-4
    and 12-13).
  - (d) From the calculations made above, compare the Arctic with
    southern Canada.

| | Mean Monthly Temperatures (°C) | | | | | | | | | | | |
|---|---|---|---|---|---|---|---|---|---|---|---|---|
| | J | F | M | A | M | J | J | A | S | O | N | D |
| Alert | −32 | −33 | −33 | −25 | −11 | −1 | 4 | 1 | −10 | −20 | −26 | −30 |
| Aklavik | −29 | −27 | −22 | −13 | 0 | 10 | 14 | 11 | 3 | −7 | −20 | −27 |
| Frobisher Bay | −26 | −25 | −22 | −14 | −3 | 4 | 8 | 7 | 2 | −5 | −12 | −20 |
| Toronto | −4 | −4 | 0 | 7 | 13 | 19 | 22 | 21 | 17 | 11 | 4 | −2 |
| Vancouver | 3 | 4 | 6 | 9 | 13 | 16 | 18 | 18 | 14 | 10 | 6 | 4 |

**Figure 12-12  Selected Temperature Statistics**

There has been a proposal to build a dam across the 50 km of
Bering Strait between Alaska and Siberia. Cold Arctic water would
be pumped into the Pacific through the dam, and not allowed back.
Meanwhile, warm Gulf Stream water would be drawn into the
Arctic, as now, past northern Norway (Figure 12-13). The increasing
warmth of the Arctic Ocean would thereby melt much of the
Arctic's sea ice, permitting improved shipping and fishing. If the
Greenland icecap were to melt as well, it would cause the world
sea level to rise, and no one knows by just how much. This *could*
be disastrous to the rest of the world. For instance, a rise of ten
metres would drown all European coastal cities, along with New
York and Tokyo. Thus temperatures in the Arctic are permitted to
remain cool.

Partly because of these low temperatures trees are stunted. Most
of the Arctic is covered with grass, moss, lichen, and flowering
plants, collectively called Arctic *tundra*. Sometimes there is no
vegetation at all. Indeed the true Arctic is usually taken as that area

*Tundra* is a Finnish
word meaning *barren*
*or waste ground.*

north of the tree line, which lies approximately along the 10°C July mean isotherm (Figure 12-14).

There is another reason for the absence of trees in the Arctic. Trees usually develop extensive root systems, but in areas where the average annual temperature is below 0°C the ground remains frozen all year at depths a few centimetres below the surface. Where the average annual temperature is well below 0°C, as at Resolute on Cornwallis Island, the ground is frozen to depths of more than 400 m. Below that the interior heat of the earth prevents freezing. The areas of Canada which experience what we refer to as *permafrost* actually include almost half the country.

**Figure 12-13   The Arctic Ocean, Bering Straits and Gulf Stream**

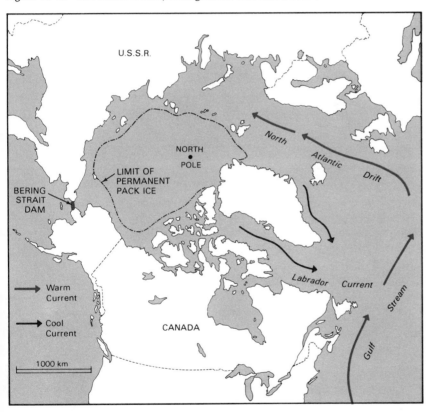

But because it is cold does not mean that precipitation levels are high. Statistics gathered at Arctic weather stations have established *very low* precipitation totals, despite the image in our minds of lots of snow and ice. Just why, then, do we have that image of high precipitation? After all, very cold air is unable to hold much water vapour, and therefore can release very little (Figure 12-15).

There are several major weather stations in the Arctic. Four of them, strung out between Banks Island and Ellesmere Island, can be seen in Figure 12-4.

**Figure 12-14 The Southern Edges of the Arctic**

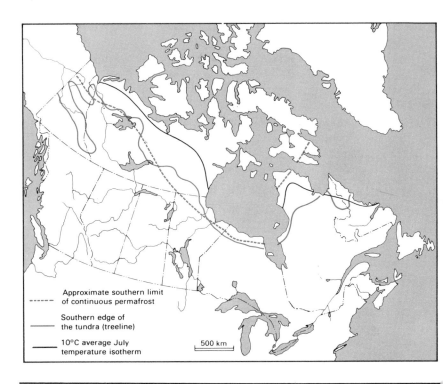

- - - - - Approximate southern limit of continuous permafrost

——— Southern edge of the tundra (treeline)

——— 10°C average July temperature isotherm

500 km

| | **Total Monthly Precipitation (mm)** | | | | | | | | | | | |
|---|---|---|---|---|---|---|---|---|---|---|---|---|
| | **J** | **F** | **M** | **A** | **M** | **J** | **J** | **A** | **S** | **O** | **N** | **D** |
| Alert | 8 | 5 | 7 | 7 | 11 | 14 | 18 | 27 | 28 | 16 | 8 | 8 |
| Aklavik | 12 | 11 | 11 | 8 | 8 | 18 | 34 | 36 | 20 | 32 | 21 | 24 |
| Frobisher Bay | 24 | 28 | 21 | 22 | 23 | 38 | 53 | 58 | 43 | 42 | 37 | 26 |
| Toronto | 66 | 59 | 67 | 66 | 70 | 63 | 74 | 61 | 65 | 60 | 63 | 61 |
| Vancouver | 140 | 120 | 96 | 58 | 49 | 47 | 26 | 35 | 54 | 117 | 138 | 164 |

**Figure 12-15 Selected Precipitation Statistics**

● 5. Write a few lines to explain the contrast between precipitation totals in the Arctic and those in southern Canada.

Perhaps you have been thinking as you read this section not only of cold but also of darkness. It is true that north of the Arctic Circle, at 66°30′N, all places have at least one day of 24 hours of darkness, increasing to six months at the North Pole itself. However, this is balanced by the existence of at least one day with 24 hours of daylight, increasing to six months daylight at the North Pole. Throughout the year as a whole, there is as much daylight as there is darkness; it is the distribution that is unusual, with long periods of darkness in winter and long periods of daylight in summer. Experiments in growing vegetables, even strawberries, in Inuvik have succeeded by taking advantage of so much continuous sunlight during the summer period.

## F: A FEELING FOR CHANGE

What of Eskimo attitudes amidst this change? We are starting to hear. Their recently acquired education and their now frequent contact with southern Canadians has made them less reticent about speaking out on their own behalf.

Early in 1976, the Inuit Tapirisat, a group representing the Canadian Eskimos, laid claim to about 650 000 km² of land. They demanded hunting, fishing, and trapping rights, as well as a three percent royalty from natural resource revenue gained over an additional 1 300 000 km². This entire area was to be called *Nunavut* (Our Land) and would eventually attain provincial status. The proposal has now been withdrawn partly because it became obvious to the Eskimos that it would be unworkable and partly because of internal difficulties among the members of Inuit Tapirisat. Nevertheless, the Eskimos are still interested in gaining much more control over their own affairs, and the Nunavut proposal must be interpreted as an important step along that way.

The Eskimo language, called *Inuktitut*, is now taught in many schools in the Arctic. One of the main problems is getting teachers.

The Indians are also looking for self-determination in the Northwest Territories. The National Indian Brotherhood, when testifying in 1976 before the National Energy Board's hearings into pipeline construction in the Mackenzie Valley, said that the native people, called the *Dene*, wanted self-determination throughout an area encompassing most of the Northwest Territories. They want a decision before the pipeline is built, in order to give them some direct control in its construction; at present, they say, that means no pipeline.

On the other hand, other Eskimos and Indians are happy to forget their former life of hardship, starvation, and death, and are not so worried about the advance of white civilization into northern Canada.

In 1965 the federal government approved a five-year rental housing program. The aim was to provide suitable living accommodation to all Eskimos living in the north. This program has resulted in the construction of over 2200 modern housing units, usually rented fully serviced and with a clause allowing for part of the rent to be applied to the purchase price. Eskimo tenant associations manage these rental projects. This has brought more families out of their scattered camps and into nucleated communities where the old trading post has become the general store. This has produced a much more sedentary way of life, although not all are able to adapt to it easily. The life and society in an established town or village, together with the need to comply with certain work regulations, do not sit well with those Eskimos who crave for the open spaces. Security holds them; lost thrills sadden them. Some have not yet even come to the settlements, preferring to hold onto the old ways as long as they can. In 1975, for instance, there were about 1000 Eskimo families spread over a vast area hunting and trapping by choice.

In most settlements jobs require a specific skill and some competence in written and spoken English. These attributes are not yet common, and many Eskimos are therefore unemployed. The unemployed may generally be divided into two groups. One group consists of the middle aged and older trappers who want to trap but can barely subsist on their trapping incomes. Few have any other skills to make them employable during the non-trapping months, and so they have to depend on welfare. The second group comprises the young who have not yet made a complete adjustment to settlement life. They have enough schooling to see no future on the trap line, but not enough to provide them with an occupational skill. Their background does not make it easy for them to adapt to a regular routine either.

The development of the north requires skilled technical labour. Just the same, the jobs for which such skills are needed are still largely in the future. The problem lies in providing jobs now, while at the same time training for the future.

James Houston wrote a book entitled *The White Dawn*. It was made into a screenplay of the same name about the Arctic.

There is a film available called *Kenojuak* which depicts the artist at work. She is now an old woman but she still works in Pangnirtung.

In one part of the Arctic a quiet success story has been created. Back in 1951 James Houston and his wife established an art community at Cape Dorset on Baffin Island. Pangnirtung, Povungnituk, and Inoucdjouac followed. They have all succeeded in selling carvings and woodcut prints throughout the world. Kenojuak, one of the artists, is well known among international buyers of primitive art. Next time you get a chance, take a careful look at the Eskimo art displays in numerous shops and stores across southern Canada.

● 6. What would you do in order to balance the needs of southern Canada with those of northern Canada?

# CHAPTER 13

# FORESTRY

## INTRODUCTION

"The nature of forest cutting has changed rapidly in the last 50 years. The days of Joe Montferrand, the legendary powerful axeman of the forests of the Ottawa Valley and the teams of horses dragging the logs on sleighs have slipped into the folklore of Eastern Canada. The river drivers who, in the spring break-up, drove the pulpwood down the tributaries of the St. Lawrence to the mills are also among the memories of the past, as are the agile and fearless lumberjacks and the two moustached British Columbia loggers captured in many photographs while resting on their axes after chopping at the base of one of the province's immense Douglas fir trees."[1]

In the old days of the river drive, one of the hardest tasks was to stand upright on a rolling log. Skills of logrolling are now seen only in contests and exhibitions.

Forests have always been a feature of the Canadian landscape. Today they are also part of an efficient mechanized industry. Whereas pioneers cut trees not only to use but also to clear the land for agriculture and settlement, Canada today is in the business to use and conserve its forests.

## A: FOREST GROWTH

Thirty-five percent of Canada's total land area is forested. The forest is located in many parts of the country, but much of it forms the great *Boreal* forest that sweeps in a great arc across Canada from the Alberta foothills, north of the Prairies to Quebec, and east to Newfoundland (Figure 13-3). This is a coniferous forest, meaning that the trees are cone bearing. Usually these trees do not shed their leaves (needles) in winter and thus are referred to as evergreens. The thin needles (the trees are also referred to as needle-leafed trees) reduce the exposure surface from which transpiration

[1] Canadian Imperial Bank of Commerce, *Newsletter*, June 1971

**Figure 13-1** The Boreal forest, seemingly endless.

Transpiration refers to a plant's release of moisture, especially from its leaves.

can take place and the waxy surface also limits the release of moisture so that the trees can survive a long winter. The summer of the Boreal forest is too short for trees to grow leaves and carry out the other normal growth processes as well. Coniferous trees are also known as softwoods since the wood of most coniferous species is soft. The most common species in the Boreal forest is *spruce*, but *pine* and *fir* are also common. Since in Canada 85% of all pulp is from spruce, Canada's Boreal forest provides much of the raw material for its pulp and paper industry.

Pulp is the raw material from which paper is made.

A second major forest of Canada is the *Coast* forest of British Columbia. Again, the trees are conifers but here the mild, humid climate allows for rapid tree growth. The resulting tall, straight trunks provide excellent construction timbers. The principal species are *red cedar, hemlock,* and *Douglas fir.*

The *Interior* forests of British Columbia (also principally conifers) vary in size and density. The warmer areas (at low elevations) that receive plentiful rainfall from facing the winds blowing inland from the Pacific Ocean (Figure 2-15) produce the taller and denser stands of trees.

In Eastern Canada the *Acadian* forest of the Maritimes once covered all these provinces but now is restricted to north and

**Figure 13-2** The Interior forest of British Columbia. Notice how the trees do not reach up to the higher slopes on the far mountains, which are still snow covered in May.

central New Brunswick and the interior of Nova Scotia, since the rest of the area has been cleared. The trees are mostly coniferous with spruce being the dominant species. Hence, pulp and paper becomes a more important product than construction timber.

Southern Ontario and the St. Lawrence Lowlands form an area of *Mixed* forest characterized not only by coniferous species such as pine and hemlock but also by deciduous species. This mixed forest gives way to a *Deciduous* forest of almost entirely deciduous trees in southwestern Ontario. The most characteristic deciduous types of both forests are *maple, oak* and *elm* but many other varieties also exist. Elm trees have suffered recently from Dutch Elm disease and have been gradually disappearing from the landscape. And, except in the Algonquin Park and Muskoka regions, most of these forests have disappeared to allow for agricultural and urban development. Many deciduous trees are also called hardwoods because their wood is usually hard. They may, as well, be referred to as broad-leafed trees because of the leaf shape. In pioneer times maple and oak along with *black walnut* and *cherry* provided timber for hundreds of furniture factories. Today *oak, ash,* and *hickory* provide wood for hockey sticks and baseball bats. Many of the furniture factories have disappeared and those that remain produce furniture containing a hardwood veneer over a softwood interior rather than producing solid hardwood furniture. Why do you think solid hardwood furniture has gone out of style?

Deciduous trees are those which *do* shed their leaves in the winter.

Veneer is a thin layer of wood.

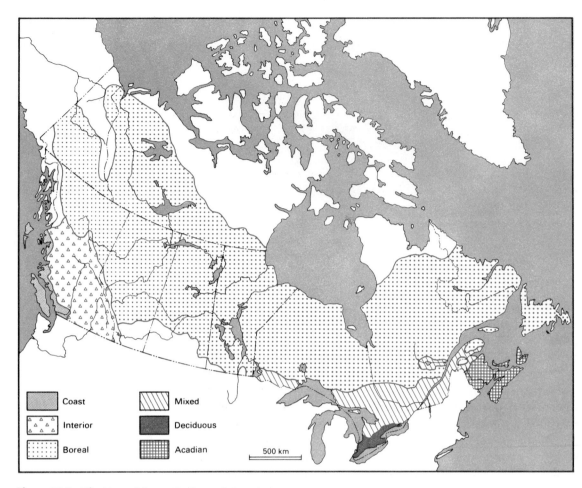

**Figure 13-3   The Natural Forest Regions of Canada**

- 1. Compare the map entitled *Natural Forest Regions of Canada* (Figure 13-3) with the map of *Climate Regions of Canada* (Figure 2-4), and answer the following questions:
  - (a) What climate region does much of Canada's Boreal forest lie within?
  - (b) In which climate region is Canada's only area of deciduous forest?
  - (c) Name two climate regions that contain little forest, if any.

- 2. The Coast forest is the location of Canada's tallest trees. Refer to Figure 2-15 and explain the reason for this.

- 3. Using what you have learned in this section, state the differences between coniferous and deciduous trees.

## B: THE FOREST INDUSTRY

The value of the forest industry varies from province to province. The reason for this variation is not just the presence or absence of trees. In areas where the winters are very long and cold or where precipitation is sparse, trees often do not grow to a commercially productive size. A thin soil cover over the bedrock will also limit their growth. This is a typical feature of both the Canadian Shield and all areas with steep mountain slopes. In Northern Ontario, for instance, forests cover 75% of the total land area, but only a little over 50% of this area is considered to be productive. Great areas of the north are also isolated and it would be too expensive to transport the logs to market. In the mountains many areas are inaccessible.

Bedrock is the solid rock immediately below the soil.

Much of our forest land is Crown land, that is land owned by the government. Pulp and timber companies lease the rights for the use of timber on a long term basis. Today much of the cutting of timber is done by mechanized tree harvesters, cranes and booms, winches, cables, and tractors. The objective is to recover every useful part of the tree. The power saw now allows cutting the tree within a few centimetres of the ground. Skidders then gather the logs or tree lengths by the roadsides and trucks carry the logs to water, railway, or directly to the mills. This sort of operation is most typical of British Columbia. In British Columbia, also, logs may be gathered from inlets along the coast onto self-unloading barges to be dropped into storage ponds beside the mills. In the east, a few of the largest rivers are still used for the spring drive, where the logs, piled on the ice during the winter, journey down swollen rivers to the mills.

Timber cutting goes on all year except (a) during the deepest snows of winter, (b) the spring thaws when the roads may be too

Figure 13-4 Loading logs onto a truck in British Columbia.

muddy, and (c) in late summer droughts when the threat of forest fires is greatest. In spite of mechanization the work is still hard and dangerous. The lumberjacks will often work 18 hours a day for several weeks if they are encamped in the wilderness. However they are well paid and many of the jobs (that of a crane operator, for instance) carry considerable prestige.

If Canada's forests are to continue to be useful to us, time and energy must be spent on preservation and reforestation. In British Columbia it takes 60 years for a tree to reach a size which is profitable to cut. In the east where the winter is longer, the growing season shorter, and the rainfall less, growth is slower and it takes 100 years to produce a tree which is profitable to cut. Thus, if *sustained yield* forest management is to exist — that is if a forest is to continue to provide timber forever — then only 1/60 of the usable forest in British Columbia and 1/100 of the usable forest in the east can be cut every year. This is not yet being done everywhere. That is to say, more than the above fractions are being cut and our usable forests are slowly being depleted.

Clear cutting is prefeferred because selective cutting often produces high losses from windfall when surrounding trees are removed, especially of shallow-rooted species like black spruce.

Cutting is done by two methods, one called *clear cutting,* the other *selective cutting.* Perhaps from the terms used you can guess how one method differs from the other. Clear cutting is the most common method used everywhere, although selective cutting is occasionally practised in the east. In clear cutting everything is cut but very young trees and seedlings. The next year the area to be logged is chosen some distance from that of the previous year. In selective cutting only the largest trees are cut leaving the smaller trees to mature further.

Silviculture is a branch of forestry dealing with the development and care of forests.

Reforestation can be done by natural reseeding but most often it is done by hand planting trees. Clear cutting makes this easier. The common practice is to wait for two or three years, then, if necessary, plant two-year-old trees at approximately a rate of 1000 trees per hectare. When planted the trees are about 30 cm high and are planted at about three metre intervals. This allows the seedlings sufficient soil nutrients and sunshine to grow healthily and vigorously.

A forest fire could develop from sunrays concentrated through a bit of broken bottle glass.

Fire is a major hazard and the provincial governments provide a constant air patrol in search of fires. Although carelessness with campfires, matches, and cigarettes is often a cause of forest fires near civilized areas, the most serious danger is lightning because it can strike in very isolated areas where patrolling is limited and access for firefighting is difficult. Today special planes which can scoop up water from lakes and drop it on the flames are used.

A method of increasing our logging without decreasing the strength of our forests is to produce *super trees* — trees which grow faster than normal and thus will be ready for harvesting earlier. Much of the research involving the growing of these trees is going on in southeastern United States. High branches of those trees that have grown naturally taller and faster than others are grafted to stems of seedlings. Then these seedlings are cross-pollinated. Superior seeds are produced.

The southeastern United States is a new and important forest area because land there is relatively cheap and the climate is warm. Trees can therefore be planted easily, to mature quickly to harvest time.

4. Define what you think is meant by the following terms:
   sustained yield
   clear cutting
   selective cutting
   super trees

5. Give four reasons why the value of forests in Canada varies from place to place across the country.

6. Examine Figure 13-5, which shows data for volume of wood cut in 1970. Rank the provinces from high to low according to the volume for each province; include the volume beside the name of each province. Then answer the following questions:
   (a) Why is British Columbia so high on the list?
   (b) Why are the Yukon and the Northwest Territories so low?

7. Examine Figure 13-5 and calculate the volume of wood cut per capita per province. Rank your answers from high to low and include the name of the province beside each answer. What do your answers mean?

8. Using all the information in this section, state in what ways the forestry industry can provide for our needs and still remain a continuing resource.

| Province or Territory | Volume of Wood Cut (thousand cubic metres) | Population (thousands) |
| --- | --- | --- |
| Newfoundland | 2 849 | 517 |
| Prince Edward Island | 245 | 110 |
| Nova Scotia | 3 224 | 782 |
| New Brunswick | 6 815 | 627 |
| Quebec | 28 899 | 6 013 |
| Ontario | 16 800 | 7 551 |
| Manitoba | 1 260 | 983 |
| Saskatchewan | 2 375 | 941 |
| Alberta | 4 143 | 1 595 |
| British Columbia | 54 726 | 2 128 |
| Yukon and Northwest Territories | 83 | 50 |

Figure 13-5   Volume of Wood Cut by Province and Population by Province, 1970

## C: FOREST PRODUCTS

All wood is cut as logs. But some will go to a sawmill to be turned into a multitude of wood products and others will go to a pulp mill to be turned eventually into paper.

Large logs relatively free from knots are usually assessed for lumber or plywood as these are the most valuable uses of high quality wood. About two-thirds of Canada's sawn lumber is used for residential construction, half in Canada itself and half in the United States, Great Britain, and Western Europe. Plywood which consists of cross-layered sheets of veneer glued together is widely used today in domestic house construction for roofs, sub-flooring, counter tops and many other purposes. Now, however, the use of plywood is being challenged by particle board, which is made from wood chips and sawdust fused together using glue and heat. Non-residential uses of lumber include railroad ties, scaffolding and frames, and boxes and crates.

Thin layers of wood called veneer are peeled from logs in lathes which rotate the logs against razor-sharp blades. The peeling process leaves a wood core of about ten centimetres in diameter and this too is put to use, often as fence posts.

Any species of tree can be used for pulp, but softwoods are preferred because the longer fibres produce a stronger pulp. Wood is composed partly of cellulose fibres and partly of lignin, a binder that holds the fibres together. The making of pulp consists of separating these cellulose fibres, either mechanically or chemically. *Groundwood* or *mechanical pulp* is made by grinding blocks of wood or sawdust into fine fibres by forcing them against a revolving grindstone. A variation of this method was introduced at Powell River in British Columbia in 1975 with some success. It involves steaming wood chips until the fibres swell and loosen before they are mechanically ground. This is called thermo-mechanical pulping. Groundwood pulp is the chief ingredient of newsprint, but because the pulp is not very strong it is mixed with chemical pulp, generally at the ratio of four to one.

Paper entirely made from mechanical pulp becomes brittle with age.

*Chemical pulp* is made by reducing the wood to chips and then cooking the chips in chemicals so that the non-celluloid components are dissolved and the useful wood fibres are recovered. There are two main processes which differ mainly because they use different compounds of sulphur. One result, *sulphate (kraft) pulp,* which is by far the most common type produced in Canada, is a very durable and strong pulp; as well as being used to strengthen newsprint, it is used for making paper bags, corrugated paper, folding boxes, envelopes, and writing papers. The other, *sulphite pulp*, is the most suitable process when hardwoods are being made into pulp, but because of the shorter fibres it is not as strong. It is used in both inexpensive papers and the higher grades of writing paper. It may be further processed to be used in the manufacture of photofilm, plastics, synthetic fibres, cellophane, explosives, and artificial sponges and leathers.

*Kraft* is a German word meaning *strength*.

Kraft pulp makes up 45% of the total production, sulphite 12%.

Pulp becomes paper because wood fibres, when wet, will adhere one to the other as the water is removed. In pulp and paper mills machines, often as long as a football field, produce a continuous ribbon of paper at speeds exceeding one kilometre per minute. At one end, a thin mixture of pulp and water flows onto a wire screen. As it moves along most of the water drains away and the pulp forms a continuous sheet. As it moves through press rolls, more water is removed and the pulp becomes more consolidated. It then passes over steam-heated cylinders which act as dryers and then through a stack of steel cylinders which effectively iron the paper and give it a smooth finish. On a high-speed machine it may take only ten seconds from the time it enters the machine as pulp to its exit as finished paper. Paperboard may be made by pressing together a number of thin layers of wet pulp. Some papers may be waxed and waterproofed and still others passed through rollers stamped with an embossed design.

Port Alberni (population 30 000) on Vancouver Island's west coast is an example of a city whose chief function is that of a forest industry city. The major employer in Port Alberni is the big, integrated complex of MacMillan Bloedel, employing over 6000 people — over 80% of the city's labour force. Logging did not actually thrive in this area until the beginning of this century but

The first mill in Canada to manufacture paper from wood began production in 1864 at Windsor Mills in Quebec. Before that, cotton and linen rags beaten and dissolved to a pulp were used. Even today, the highest grades of writing paper are made with rags.

Canada's newsprint making machines are capable of producing every hour, day and night, the equivalent of a two-metre width ribbon of paper stretching from Halifax to Vancouver and back.

Paperboard serves many purposes. It forms the heavy cases that carry everything from canned goods to refrigerators. In lighter varieties it packages thousands of products from toothpaste to phonograph records. Boxboard, linerboard, and corrugated board are also durable and versatile packaging materials.

**Figure 13-6** Port Alberni, Vancouver Island.

A complex is referred to as *integrated* when one company operates close together various combinations of logging operations, sawmills, and plants making pulp and paper, plywood, and other specialty wood products.

today the Alberni valley is the source of the raw material for the local plants. The logs destined for Port Alberni come largely from two nearby sustained yield units, called *Tree Farm Licences*. A Tree Farm Licence holder accepts many obligations, including full utilization of the wood harvested and proper management of the resource. The licensee assumes for the entire area all responsibility for renewing the forest and for fire prevention and firefighting. This policy gives considerably more operational responsibility to the forest companies than is typical in the other provinces of Canada. The logging operation employs about 2000 people. The usual method is to clear cut about a 40 to 80 ha area. Logs are cut to standard lengths and then sorted into categories by species, grade, and size so that each type of mill can be supplied with the wood it is best able to use to full advantage.

The pulp and paper plant produces pulp, kraft paper, and newsprint. The kraft paper is then shipped to other plants for conversion into corrugated cartons. Nearby sawmills produce lumber and plywood. To obtain the best and fullest use of each tree logged, residues of one mill become the raw material for another. For example, trimmings, edges, and sawdust from the lumber mill become pulp, and bark from the logs is used as fuel to provide the power to run the mills.

In Port Alberni, MacMillan Bloedel is located along the waterfront of one of the finest deep sea, inland water harbours on the North American continent. The harbour is located 40 km inland from the Pacific Ocean at the end of a kilometre-wide, deep water fiord. Forest products from the plants can thus be shipped directly all over the world. Port Alberni has the advantage of being not only next to the forest itself but next to an excellent transportation system as well.

But this double advantage is not always the case. Thus pulp and paper mills and sawmills are not necessarily located near the forest resources. For example, several paper mills are located in southern Ontario and southern Quebec. Transportation is easy on the lakes and the St. Lawrence River, hydroelectricity is available, and, unfortunately, the water is there is be used for dumping chemical wastes. The huge pulp and paper mills at Thorold in the Niagara Peninsula are examples of plants which get their pulp logs from a considerable distance. Sawmills also sometimes find it more advantageous to be closer to labour and markets than to the actual resources. For instance, the Vancouver area contains the greatest concentration of sawmills in Canada. A plentiful labour force, as well as a market, is always available.

Canada contains 22% of the world's softwood or coniferous forests. From these forests Canada produced, in 1970, 38% of the world's newsprint. Canada also produced far more sawn timber than it could absorb within itself. Thus the forest forms one of Canada's major sources of exports. The divided circle graph (Figure 13-7), compares Canadian newsprint production to the other major countries involved. But Canada cannot be complacent about its leading position because it must compete with countries which can grow trees at a much faster rate than Canada can.

Of the total production of newsprint less than ten percent is used in Canada. The remainder is exported all over the world, but mainly to the U.S.A., making Canada the world's leading producer and exporter of newsprint.

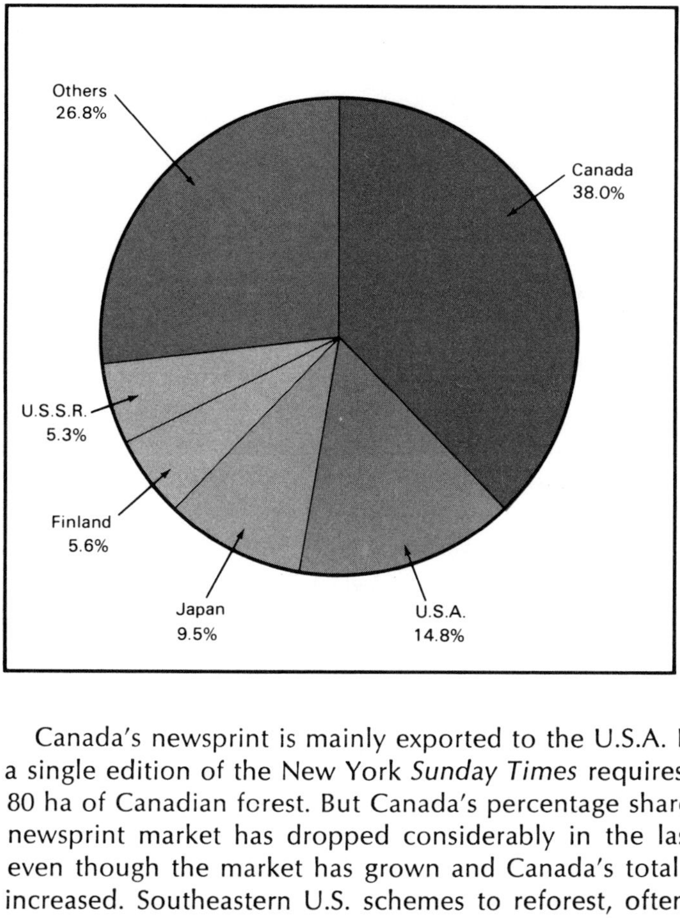

Others 26.8%
Canada 38.0%
U.S.S.R. 5.3%
Finland 5.6%
Japan 9.5%
U.S.A. 14.8%

Figure 13-7   World Newsprint Production

Canada's newsprint is mainly exported to the U.S.A. For instance, a single edition of the New York *Sunday Times* requires wood from 80 ha of Canadian forest. But Canada's percentage share of the U.S. newsprint market has dropped considerably in the last ten years, even though the market has grown and Canada's total volume has increased. Southeastern U.S. schemes to reforest, often with super trees and vast tracts of land, have meant that the United States has been able to capture some of its own market. The area of the southeastern United States has the great advantage of a much milder climate and thus a much faster maturing time. For this reason there is now a Brazilian company which is 51% owned by Canada's Mac-Millan Bloedel, developing an area on the south Brazilian coast where eucalyptus trees can be cut at six to seven years old and pine trees can be used for pulp in 12 years. Quite a contrast with Canada where 60 years on the British Columbia coast is the minimum maturing time.

● 9. Draw a divided circle graph to illustrate the data in Figure 13-8 of this lesson. Figure 13-7 shows you what a divided circle graph looks like. When you have finished the graph, colour the section entitled *Wood and Wood Products* one solid colour in order to emphasize the significance of wood among Canada's exports.

| Canada's Exports | Percentage of Total Exports |
|---|---|
| Food, Feed, Beverages and Tobacco | 12 |
| Raw Materials (minerals and inedible agricultural products) | 18 |
| Chemicals | 4 |
| Refined Metals | 10 |
| Machinery | 6 |
| Motor Vehicles | 23 |
| Other Consumer Products | 7 |
| **Wood and Wood Products (including pulp and paper)** | **18** |
| Others | 2 |
| | 100% |

Figure 13-8    Canada's Exports

● 10. Make a list of all the forest products you can think of. Do it in three columns, one headed lumber products, another pulp and paper products, and the third other products.

## D: OTHER FOREST USES

Forest land, besides supplying raw material for industry, protects soil and water, supports wildlife, provides recreation, and in some stands furnishes pasturage for livestock. As population rises and the economy develops, the demands on forest land increase and change. Even in Canada today where there are still vast spaces of uninhabited land, especially when compared with many other countries of the world, there is nevertheless arising the need to establish a rational policy for the multiple use of our land. This is particularly true for areas like Algonquin Park in Ontario which is so close to the densely populated areas of Southern Ontario. Already groups with special interests are attempting to influence the government to establish a policy in their favour. It should be possible (even if difficult) to satisfy all but the very purist conservationist who wants the forest to remain in its absolute natural state. But in that state only the hardiest of us would ever be able to enjoy that kind of wilderness. The article on the following page offers a view of one who feels the forest can be used for recreation, wildlife, and forestry.

Multiple use means that a resource is used for more than a single purpose at a time. What uses do you think fit together in a forest?

**Figure 13-9**    Forests support wildlife.

# Forest Management Aids Wildlife

Proper forest management can increase the wildlife in the area dramatically, Robert Loughlan, manager of the Ontario Forest Industries Association told the Lincoln County Game and Fish Protective Association at a recent meeting in St. Catharines.

By clearcutting in a suitable pattern and providing plenty of young browse and forest e d g e conditions, moose population in an area can be boosted substantially, he said. Prior to man's influence, Algonquin Park had few deer. When logging and fires opened up the solid canopy of mature trees and allowed young growth to flourish, so did the deer.

"Of course, bears love blueberries, and blueberries flourish in recent cutovers or burns," said Mr. Loughlan.

"When I was living in the north most frequently when I've seen moose they were in or near clearings, either natural or man-made. The best fishing I've experienced was on a log jam in the river or near log storage areas in lakes. The best partridge hunting was along old logging roads or work trails. And in a tent camp, don't trust bears or skunks to leave your food alone when you're gone."

from *The Forest Scene*, December 1976

- 11. Why do you think conservation is a concern today but was not so in the past?

- 12. How do you feel about a multiple use policy being established by the government for our forests?

# CHAPTER 14

# ENERGY

## CHOICE

## INTRODUCTION

### Story A

As they climbed slowly up the last flight of stairs to their workplace, Rob looked at Petra and then at the permanently closed doors along the side of the central hallway. He often wondered whether they would ever open. He had heard tales passed down by oldtimers that at one time people could wait before these doors and the doors would open to admit the people to a car which would whisk them up or down to their destination. "They used to call them elevators," Rob said aloud to himself.

Petra knew what he was talking about, for Rob was often curious about what things had been like. The signs were all about them, signs of a previous civilization quite different from theirs. And yet at the same time, not all that different; the same fields were still tended and the same buildings still occupied, just as they had been two hundred years before in 1980. What did it matter if people no longer lived and worked above the tenth storey? What did it matter if most people had to walk or bicycle to work? What did it matter if they had rationed fuel supplies only for cooking and heating at home?

Rob and Petra both worked on the ninth floor of a 60-storey building. There were some younger people on the tenth floor, but almost no one ever walked up all those floors. It was three years since Petra had one day decided to explore above the tenth floor; she had found the remains of some temporary occupation on the 11th and 12th floors, and not much more than dusty furniture and papers on the other six floors she had wandered through. She had found strangely wired typewriters that did not work, calculating machines without levers, clocks that all stopped at the same time, 11:30. She had been pleased to get back to her brightly candlelit office on the ninth floor.

Rob meanwhile continued to muse about the strangeness of the past: how sprawling the towns had been, for instance. Had people really travelled in on the cars and buses he had seen in the museum? Had they enjoyed living such a long way out? Was it true that they had visited from continent to continent in only a matter of hours? And brought in goods for themselves from around the world? It must have been so, he thought: all the oldtimers he had ever known said the same things. They had talked of energy as though it had been cheap and plentiful. He almost disbelieved them, and yet there were all these strange features he did not fully understand: the tall buildings, the sprawling towns, the many machines; all of them presumably requiring lots of energy to make them work.

## Story B

Nick had almost landed when the buzzer sounded in his earset, so he stepped up the pressure immediately and headed back to base. He had just been on a routine check of the pipelines, and had covered merely 450 km in his gyrocopter; everything had been well. However, the buzzer was an emergency signal for all flying line crew to head back to base. The buzzer would also bring back the other field workers. It was important.

As he neared base an hour later he could see the service landing field almost covered with evacuation and repair equipment. He put his 'copter down very carefully in between a giant stress machine and a couple of churning cement trucks. His earset had told him that there had been a major blowout in a gas well and that this had fractured a nearby oil pipe. A serious fire was raging and there was a risk of explosions in the underground gas reservoirs. People were being moved out of the area with superb efficiency: all cars and aircraft, all buses and trucks, and all trains and aircushion vehicles had been pressed into service.

Nick's job was to be part of the emergency traffic control, to direct ground traffic by the quickest routes. This meant getting the evacuation vehicles out and the repair vehicles in without wasting any time in unnecessary diversions and yet without permitting any jams to develop. It was a massive operation, but it all went smoothly. Within 15 hours everything was back to normal; it was as if nothing had happened.

Nick was proud to be part of the energy network, especially when the next day he saw on his video monitor that the large industrial complexes and residential areas had not experienced even the slightest break in service. That's the way things ought to be, he thought to himself. Energy should be readily available to all the people all the time; they should be able to take it for granted. He thought of the motto of the Energy Service, "Energy for the Good Life".

● 1. The two stories represent two views of the future: energy scarcity and energy abundance. In not more than about a page, say why you think *one* of them is more realistic than the other.

● 2. Story A outlines some of the possible future results of a scarcity of energy. What others can you suggest?

# A: THE USES OF ENERGY

We were given some ideas in the introductory stories of the uses of energy: power for elevators, transport systems, machines, factories, and residences.

Canada is a large user of energy in comparison with other countries in the world. For instance, on a *per person* basis, Canada uses

What uses of energy have *you* made today?

The United Nations produces statistics on a *coal equivalent* basis for the reason that it makes comparisons between different countries much easier. If one country uses a great deal of oil compared to another, while other countries use relatively large quantities of coal or hydroelectricity, then it becomes difficult to make comparisons unless everything is standardized into the same units. The United Nations therefore converts the power produced by all countries into its equivalent in units of coal, just for statistical comparisons like the one here.

the coal equivalent of 10 757 kg/year (latest U.N. statistics) compared with:

| | |
|---|---|
| U.S.A. | 11 611  kg/year |
| Sweden | 5 739  kg/year |
| Britain | 5 398  kg/year |
| West  Germany | 5 396  kg/year |
| U.S.S.R. | 4 767  kg/year |
| Japan | 3 251  kg/year |

Indeed *only the U.S.A.* uses more energy *per person* than Canada, all other countries use much less, often *very* much less. For example, the average for Asia is 481 kg/year, for Africa it is 363 kg/year, for South America 759 kg/year, and for Europe 4000 kg/year

**Figure 14-1**   What are the uses of energy that you can see or imagine in this photograph of downtown Toronto?

There has been much talk in Canada in recent years of cutting back on the use of energy. Do you think this is possible? Do you think it is desirable? Do you think it is necessary?

There are four main reasons for Canada's high use of energy. First is the fact that Canada is predominantly a *northern* country with long, cold winters and a great need for heating. Second is the fact that Canada is a *big* country with a widely scattered population and a great need for efficient transportation. Third is the fact that Canada is economically a very *advanced* country with a great need for industrial power. Fourth is the fact that Canada's population has a *high* standard of living; it has many appliances as well as heated and air-conditioned homes and therefore a great need for residential energy. Figure 14-2 gives information on the major uses of all types of energy consumed in Canada.

|  |  | Percent |
|---|---|---|
| Industrial Uses |  | 43 |
| Transportation Uses |  | 19 |
| Road | 14 |  |
| Rail | 2 |  |
| Air | 2 |  |
| Ship | 1 |  |
| Commercial Uses |  | 15 |
| Residential Uses |  | 19 |
| Farm Uses |  | 4 |
| **Total** |  | **100** |

**Figure 14-2   Distribution of Energy Uses in Canada**

● 3. Examine Figure 14-2. Construct a ranked vertical bar graph to illustrate the data. Do not forget to divide the transportation bar to show the sub-users.

● 4. In not more than a page explain *how* and *why* you think the distribution of energy uses would change if the future as shown in Story A began to come true. In other words, what do you think the most essential uses of energy are in Canada?

## B: THE PRESENT SOURCES OF CANADA'S ENERGY

There are two main classes of energy: (i) primary energy and (ii) secondary energy. *Primary energy* is that which is obtained directly from nature, such as from windpower, oil, natural gas, coal, solar power, tidal power, timber, the force of falling water, and the splitting of atoms. Ultimately all energy comes from one or other of these primary sources. However, the power available from these sources is not always in the most convenient form for people to use. Coal, for example, is bulky and dirty; oil emits bad odours; natural gas is potentially dangerous. In consequence, people have developed over the years a variety of techniques for converting these awkward primary energy sources into a more easily usable form, namely electricity.

*Secondary energy* is the term used to describe electricity produced by burning coal, oil, or natural gas. It is also called *thermal electricity* to distinguish it from *hydroelectricity,* which is a primary source since it is made directly from the force of falling water. Secondary energy is not new energy; it is converted energy, and when it is produced some primary energy is used up. Only primary

We use the word *new* to indicate that the energy is new to human use. It is not new in the sense of geophysics, where even solar energy is the product of a nuclear fusion process. Thus the tides represent a conversion of energy from the gravitational attraction of both the sun and the moon for the large bodies of water on the earth; in the geophysical sense, their energy is derived from another source. Nevertheless, from the human standpoint, tidal energy is new in that some other human resource does not have to be used to create it.

Oil has long been used in one form or another for fuel. Oil lamps, using combustible vegetable oils, have been in use in the Old World for centuries, while similar lamps based on combustible fish and animal oils have had widespread use in Eskimo lands. However the widespread availability of oil from rocks in the last hundred years or so has almost totally replaced the use of oils from vegetable and animal matter. The first major breakthrough occurred in Nova Scotia, when a local scientist invented kerosene, using rock oil (= petroleum) as his raw material. Almost immediately this saved the whales of the Arctic. Can you think how? It also meant a rapid exploration for new sources of rock oil. The next major breakthrough in the use of rock oil came with the invention of the internal combustion engine around the turn of the century; cars became popular, and the use and exploration for rock oil became quite frenzied. As people have found out more about rock oil, so its uses have widened; it is now important, for example, in the manufacture of fertilizers and plastics, as well as in thousands of other things.

energy is new energy. Figure 14-3 summarizes the situation, as well as indicating the percentage contribution of each energy source to Canada's total supply.

**Figure 14-3    Composition of Canada's Energy Supply**

|  |  | Percent (primary only) | Percent (total, including secondary) |
|---|---|---|---|
| * Fossil | Oil | 44.5 | 41.5 |
| Fuels | Natural Gas | 20.0 | 19.3 |
|  | Coal | 8.8 | 5.0 |
| Hydroelectricity |  | 26.0 | 26.0 |
| Nuclear Electricity |  | 0.7 | 0.7 |
| **Total Primary** |  | **100.00** |  |
| **Thermal Electricity |  |  | 7.5 |
| **Total, Including Secondary** |  |  | **100.0** |

\* *Fossil Fuels* are fuels derived from the remains (fossils) of once-living matter.
\*\* Thermal electricity is a secondary power source, generated by converting fossil fuels into electricity.

You can see that oil is the largest source of energy for Canada. It supplies 44.5% of primary energy, with about three percent of this going to help generate thermal electricity in oil burning power stations, as at Lennox on the northeast side of Lake Ontario. Most of the oil Canada produces comes from Alberta (75%), with smaller quantities from Saskatchewan (18%) and British Columbia (five percent). Some of this oil is exported to the United States, especially to those areas near Alberta. To balance this, Canada buys oil from Venezuela and other countries, shipping it into the Maritimes and

**Figure 14-4**    Canada now imports more oil than it exports. This is Point Tupper on the Canso Strait in Nova Scotia.

Quebec, which are far from Alberta. Canada currently imports more oil than it exports.

Within Alberta the chief oil fields lie scattered in the sedimentary rocks and Devonian reefs just east of the foothills of the Rockies (see Chapter 3). The largest ones are near Edmonton, which therefore claims to be one of the oil capitals of Canada. Calgary claims to be the other oil capital because most of the oil companies' offices are there. There are other producing oil fields in southern Saskatchewan, which is Canada's second oil province. Figure 14-5 shows the locations of the major oil fields.

Natural gas is only about half as important as oil (Figure 14-3). Nevertheless it is still tremendously important because it provides about 50% of all the power used by industry as well as about 35% of all the residential and commercial power. It is even used to generate thermal electricity, as at the Hearn power plant in Toronto. It is found in the same general areas as oil, with Alberta again being

The oil drilled in Alberta costs a lot more to produce than the oil drilled in Venezuela and the Middle East. The reason is in the nature of the geological structures, and in the depths and concentrations of oil within those structures. The effect is to make Alberta oil more expensive than Middle East and Venezuelan oil *at the well-head*. The well-head cost is not a large part of the final selling price, because different levels of government levy large royalties and taxes on top of the well-head price. Nevertheless, the difference in well-head costs between Alberta and overseas suppliers is sufficiently great for it not to be worthwhile transporting Alberta crude all the way across Canada to the east coast.

**Figure 14-5   Locations of Canada's Major Producing Oil Fields**

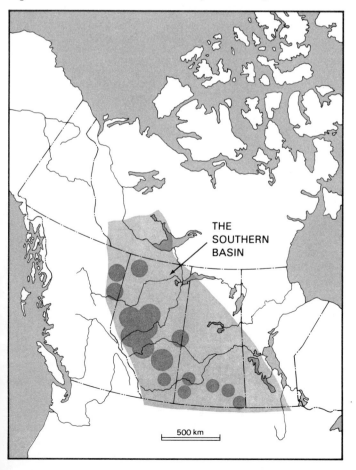

THE
SOUTHERN
BASIN

500 km

**Figure 14-6**  Natural gas processing plant at Pincher Creek, Alberta.

**Figure 14-7**  An oil refinery in Edmonton.

the most important province (83%) followed by British Columbia (14%) and Saskatchewan (three percent).

Coal is the least important major fuel in Canada, accounting for less than ten percent of primary energy. Its chief use is in thermal power stations, but it is also important in the steel indusry. Once again Alberta is the chief producing province (44%) followed by British Columbia (25%), Saskatchewan (18%), and Nova Scotia (ten percent). There is considerable international trade in coal: we export it from the western fields to Japan and import it to the large Ontario markets from the United States. This is a more profitable operation for everyone concerned than if Alberta were to send its coal to Ontario, because the overland transportation of coal is so expensive. Nevertheless, Ontario is making arrangements, in the interests of national self-sufficiency, to buy coal from Alberta, and to ship it by rail and lake freighter.

Hydroelectricity is Canada's second most important source of primary energy, accounting for 26% of total supplies. The requirements for hydroelectricity are:

(a) regular flow of water (hence the need for reservoirs)
(b) large amounts of water (another need for reservoirs)
(c) hilly land to contain reservoirs
(d) firm foundations for dams
(e) difference in height between reservoir and turbines.

These requirements are illustrated in Figure 14-8. They are best met in the province of Quebec, where there is plenty of regular precipitation coupled with the firm, hilly ground of the Canadian Shield. This is fortunate for Quebec since there are almost no other primary energy sources in the province.

At present, nuclear energy is the last and least of the primary energy sources. It accounts for only 0.7% of total supplies, and is almost all produced in Ontario, chiefly at the Pickering power

See Figure 11-11 for the locations of Quebec's major hydro-electric stations. The largest complex of stations is planned for the James Bay system, but work is also still progressing on the Manicouagan-Outardes system. Both systems, when completed, will be amongst the largest in the world. The largest single station in Quebec is at Beauharnois, on the St. Lawrence River near Montreal.

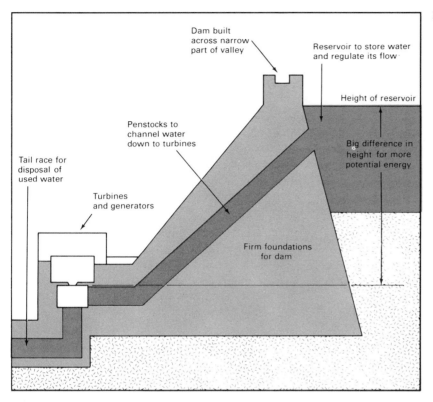

**Figure 14-8  Production of Hydroelectricity**

Dam built across narrow part of valley

Reservoir to store water and regulate its flow

Height of reservoir

Penstocks to channel water down to turbines

Big difference in height for more potential energy

Tail race for disposal of used water

Turbines and generators

Firm foundations for dam

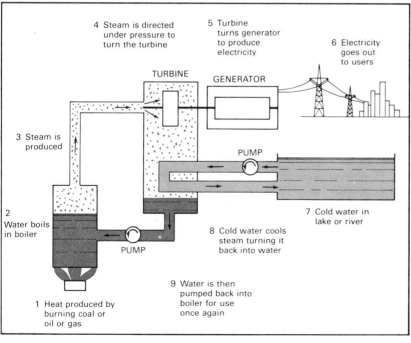

4 Steam is directed under pressure to turn the turbine

5 Turbine turns generator to produce electricity

6 Electricity goes out to users

TURBINE

GENERATOR

3 Steam is produced

PUMP

2 Water boils in boiler

PUMP

7 Cold water in lake or river

8 Cold water cools steam turning it back into water

9 Water is then pumped back into boiler for use once again

1 Heat produced by burning coal or oil or gas

**Figure 14-9  Greatly Simplified Operation of a Thermal Electricity Generating Station**

Hydroelectric stations are still being built, of course, but they are a long way from centres of population and until recently it was not possible to transport the electricity which they would have produced over the long distances which would have been necessary. It is only the recent improvements in transmission technology which have permitted the remote hydro sites to be developed.

Ontario Hydro has long pursued a policy of bringing its fuels in from as wide a variety of places as possible, and of using as wide a variety of fuels in the process as it can. The reasons for the great variety are primarily that Ontario is an energy deficient province, and it has never wished to become too reliant either upon one or a few suppliers or upon a limited range of fuels. The nature of the variety of fuels used in Ontario is shown in the variety of fuels used to provide power for Toronto, mentioned earlier. By contrast, Alberta and Quebec do not need to diversify their power production in quite the same way, because they are both energy adequate provinces; they do not have to rely upon some other place.

station east of Toronto and the Bruce power plants on the shores of Lake Huron.

Figure 14-9 shows that secondary energy may be generated as thermal electricity if we burn some of the oil, gas, and coal that we produce. In this way, thermal electricity has come to account for about 7.5% of Canada's total energy supplies. It is produced by using the heat from the combustion of oil, gas, or coal to boil water into steam, the steam then being directed under pressure on to the generators' turbines, thus making electricity (Figure 14-9). As this happens, however, the oil, gas, and coal are used up. Why is it done?

| | |
|---|---|
| Quebec | 45.0 |
| Ontario | 23.0 |
| British Columbia | 14.0 |
| Newfoundland | 6.3 |
| Manitoba | 5.3 |
| Alberta | 2.0 |
| New Brunswick | 1.9 |
| Saskatchewan | 1.8 |
| Nova Scotia | 0.5 |
| Northwest Territories | 0.1 |
| Yukon Territory | 0.1 |
| Prince Edward Island | — |
| **Total** | **100.0** |

**Figure 14-10   Canada's Hydroelectricity Generating Capacity  (%)**

As we have noted, oil, gas, and coal are all in one way or another awkward to handle. But there is also another reason for their conversion to thermal electricity. Electricity is *more useful;* it provides light and heat; it drives motors; it powers communications systems; it is more easily distributed; it is immediately at work at the click of a switch; it produces no waste at its point of use. Electricity is so useful indeed that Canada has *needed more of it than could be generated from hydro means alone;* so we convert some of the other primary fuels to electricity as well.

Altogether electricity of both primary (hydro and nuclear) and secondary (thermal) types accounts for almost 35% of Canada's energy supplies, thus ranking it second after oil in Canada's total energy picture.

Thermal power stations are located in every province and territory of Canada. Ontario has the largest thermal generating capacity (50% of Canada's total), but do not forget that this is the only major power source in which Ontario ranks first. Even for its thermal power production, Ontario has to import coal from Alberta and the U.S.A. and oil and natural gas from Alberta and Venezuela.

Generally Ontario is an energy deficient province in that it relies on other places for its primary fuels.

Alberta (13.0%) ranks second in thermal power output; it uses local oil and coal in its power stations. British Columbia (9.0%) is third and Quebec (6.0%) is fourth. Prince Edward Island (0.5%) is unique: thermal energy is the only type of commercial power that it produces; there is no coal, no oil, no gas, and no hydro.

You may have noticed that New Brunswick is the only province not so far mentioned; this is because New Brunswick has not ranked high in any of Canada's home produced fuels. It produces some hydro (1.9% of Canada's total) and some coal (2.8%), but no oil or gas. However, it imports a great deal of oil from Venezuela for its thermal stations (4.0% of Canada's thermal power). So do Nova Scotia (5.0%) and Newfoundland (3.0%). All the Atlantic provinces indeed rely to a large extent on imports for their power supply needs. Figure 14-11 summarizes the energy supply position of the provinces.

Mostly coal.

**Figure 14-11  Percentages of Canada's Energy Production, by Province and by Type of Energy**

| | Oil | Gas | Coal | Hydro | Nuclear | Secondary Thermal |
|---|---|---|---|---|---|---|
| | | | Primary | | | Secondary |
| Newfoundland | — | — | — | 6.3 | — | 3.0 |
| Prince Edward Island | — | — | — | — | — | 0.5 |
| Nova Scotia | — | — | 10.7 | 0.5 | — | 5.0 |
| New Brunswick | — | — | 2.8 | 1.9 | — | 4.0 |
| Quebec | — | — | — | 45.0 | 10.0 | 6.0 |
| Ontario | 0.2 | 0.7 | — | 23.0 | 90.0 | 50.0 |
| Manitoba | 1.1 | — | — | 5.3 | — | 3.0 |
| Saskatchewan | 18.0 | 2.8 | 17.9 | 1.8 | — | 6.0 |
| Alberta | 75.4 | 82.7 | 43.4 | 2.0 | — | 13.0 |
| British Columbia | 5.1 | 13.7 | 25.2 | 14.0 | — | 9.0 |
| Yukon Territory | — | — | — | 0.1 | — | 0.2 |
| Northwest Territories | 0.2 | 0.1 | — | 0.1 | — | 0.3 |
| **Canada Total:** | **100.0** | **100.0** | **100.0** | **100.0** | **100.0** | **100.0** |

- 5. Leduc #1 was going to be the last well drilled after 133 others had failed to find oil; if it had not struck oil, exploratory drilling would have closed down. In not more than a page, describe what you think the energy situation in Canada nowadays would have been like if Leduc #1 had not struck oil.

It nearly ceased *before* Leduc #1, because people were becoming disillusioned about the prospects of finding oil. The search was proving costly, and hope was diminishing; Leduc was planned as the last attempt.

- 6. Construct a divided percentage bar graph to illustrate the information in the primary fuels section of Figure 14-11 of this lesson. In what ways do you think these proportions might change in the future?

● 7. If you were the Premier of Prince Edward Island at a Provincial Energy Policy meeting, what would your policy be if Alberta wanted to raise the price of its oil? Why would you take this view?

● 8. If the price of oil on world markets increased greatly, how would Alberta probably react?

● 9. If the price of oil rises (whether from Alberta or abroad), what would probably happen to Canada's production of:
(a) coal; (b) natural gas; (c) hydroelectricity; and (d) nuclear electricity?
Which provinces would (i) benefit most, and (ii) suffer most?

## C: THE FUTURE SOURCES OF CANADA'S ENERGY

As we have seen, Canada's major oil and gas fields are located in Alberta, Saskatchewan, and northeastern British Columbia, the area known as the Southern Basin. This region is the most highly explored oil area in Canada. Exploratory drilling has been going on for a long time, back to before World War I. It did not cease when the tiny Turner Valley oil field was discovered in 1914; nor did it come to an end when the much more spectacular Leduc #1 well struck oil south of Edmonton in 1947. And it has still not stopped. Exploratory drilling is still going on in the Southern Basin (Figure 14-5) as oil companies try to find new oil fields. So far about 50 000 exploratory wells have been drilled across Alberta, Saskatchewan, and northeastern British Columbia. Not all of these wells have struck oil; indeed most have not. For example, before any oil was struck at all — even the tiny amounts in the Turner Valley field — as many as 2000 dry wells were drilled. Nevertheless, enough of them have succeeded over the years to make the Southern Basin a rich oil producing region. Altogether about 16 billion barrels (2.6 billion cubic metres) have been found. About six billion barrels (one billion cubic metres) of this have already been produced and used, leaving about ten billion barrels (1.6 billion cubic metres) still remaining as "proven reserve". If we divide this reserve by the amount we use each year, then we have enough left to last us about 15 to 16 years.

The figures for natural gas are very similar in significance: over two trillion cubic metres have been found; 0.5 trillion cubic metres have already been used; 1.5 trillion cubic metres still remain as proven reserve, giving a *life index* to the gas fields of about 23 or 24 years.

The business of sinking trial wells, to see whether or not oil actually exists, is called *wildcatting*. It is the only way to tell, despite all the advanced scientific equipment used to help in the search. On the average, about one wildcat in ten proves successful. Finding oil is a chancy and expensive business, and becoming more so.

World oil figures are usually quoted in *barrels* (bbl). One barrel contains 159 litres of oil; its weight varies, however, according to its density, which in turn varies from oil field to oil field. Some barrels of oil are therefore heavier than others.

We use more now than we used to.

A trillion is a million million.

That does not mean that in 15 to 16 years for oil and 23 to 24 years for gas that the producing fields will suddenly cease producing. It means that production will start to decline around 1980, and get lower and lower every year after that (Figure 14-12), tapering away very gradually until what is left is not worth pumping out any more.

Under these conditions, costs of production will inevitably rise as more and more effort is required to obtain smaller and smaller quantities.

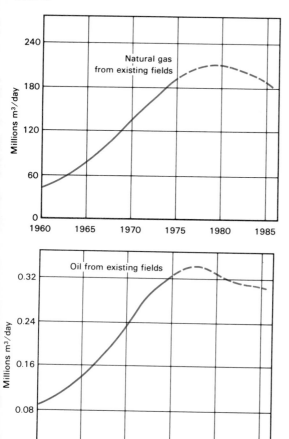

**Figure 14-12 Oil and Gas Production from Existing Fields Will Start to Decline Around 1980**

So what is to be done in the face of this "energy crisis"? There are several answers to the problem:

*Option #1.  Rely increasingly on imports from other countries.* For the first time since Leduc #1, Canada, in 1975, imported more oil than it exported. This could develop into a trend as Canada uses up its Southern Basin oil and gas. This option has the advantage of being cheaper than the other alternatives, but it has the disadvantage of putting us at the mercy of OPEC (the Organization of

OPEC consists of some of the major oil exporting countries in the Middle East, Africa, and the Caribbean. It tries to set prices for world oil, so that other countries have to buy oil at increasingly higher prices.

Petroleum Exporting Countries). Canada will likely pursue this option only if it also takes up the other options as well, otherwise we would become too dependent on other countries for our major energy supply. Do not forget that oil and gas together account for about 65% of all our energy supplies.

*Option #2. Find new sources of oil and gas inside Canada itself.* It is not very likely that big new finds will be made in the Southern Basin. There will probably be a few small ones, but not enough to affect the life index to any significant degree: at most, they may add a few years. Major new oil and gas finds will need to be made elsewhere if the problem is going to be solved in the near future. The oil companies know this, and they are therefore setting up exploratory drilling operations in the so-called *Frontier Areas* (Figure 14-13). There are four of these frontier areas that are very promising for the future: the Mackenzie Delta region, the Beaufort Sea, the

**Figure 14-13   Frontier Oil Areas**

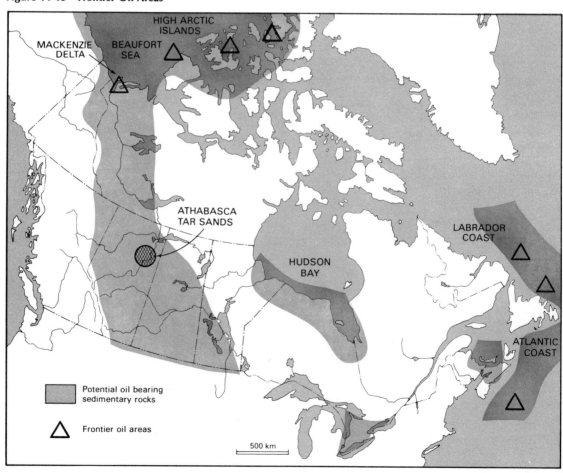

The amount of oil and gas required to make it worthwhile constructing pipelines into the centre of the continent is called the *threshhold* quantity. Activity in all frontier areas is currently focused on building up proven reserves to a threshhold quantity. The problem of pipelines then has to be solved, for pipelines cross territory used for other purposes. If a pipeline brings gas from the High Arctic to Toronto then it also has an effect on fish, birds, animals, terrain, native people's lifestyles, and land claims. The effects are not necessarily detrimental, although they may be. Great care is needed.

The development of an operating technology is quite different from the development of an experimental technology. Experiments can be very successful in a laboratory, but total failures in the field. An operating technology has all sorts of problems to solve that simply do not exist in a laboratory. What can you think of?

High Arctic Islands, and the east coastal seas off Labrador, Newfoundland, and Nova Scotia. Oil and gas have been found in all four areas, but work has only just started and there is undoubtedly much more oil and gas yet to be found. Federal Government figures show the potential supply of oil and gas to be about the equivalent of 190 billion barrels (30 billion cubic metres) of oil. The discoveries will indeed have to be huge, otherwise it will not be worth all the expense of constructing pipelines to supply the major users in the centre of the continent, such as Ontario.

*Option #3. Manufacture oil and gas from non-conventional sources.* It is possible to make oil and gas from tar and coal. The oil and gas produced artificially are called *synthetic* oil and gas, to distinguish them from regular, or *conventional*, oil and gas found in the ground. Canada is fortunate in having very large supplies of tar and coal. The chief tar deposits are the *Athabasca Tar Sands,* which cover about 30 000 km² in northeast Alberta, and which contain the equivalent of up to 800 billion barrels (128 billion cubic metres) of oil. However, only about 300 billion barrels (48 billion cubic metres) can be produced using existing technology. The other 500 billion barrels (80 billion cubic metres) will be recoverable when the technology is developed. There are two firms working on this problem: Great Canadian Oil Sands and Syncrude (*synthetic crude*). They will have spent many millions of dollars by the time an operating technology is developed. In addition to the Athabasca Tar Sands there are other very heavy oils in Alberta, such as at Cold

Rates of use will increase in the future, especially as we have to rely more and more upon coal as a replacement for increasingly scarce oil and gas (in certain uses).

Many people are scared of nuclear power. They think that the hazards of radiation are inescapable, and they are not reassured by the fact that nuclear technology has the best safety record of all power sources. They think also that the wastes, which will remain lethal for centuries, are incapable of being cared for, and they are not reassured by plans to bury the wastes deep in stable parts of the earth's crust.

The CANDU system uses heavy water as a coolant, whereas most of the other reactors in the world use either light (ordinary) water or gas. The Gentilly reactor in Quebec uses ordinary water as a coolant, but it is the only one in Canada to do so. The CANDU heavy water system is not particularly advanced technically, but it works well; its operating technology is good.

Lake 250 km northeast of Edmonton. These also need special treatment, and research is being carried out by Imperial Oil.

Canada's reserves of coal total about 120 billion tonnes, sufficient to last about 6000 years or more at present rates of use. The deposits contain the energy equivalent of over 400 billion barrels (64 billion cubic metres) of oil, and the experimental technology for converting the coal to oil and gas already exists. The problems are, however, cost and the development of a large scale commercial technology. It is most likely that Canada will not pursue the manufacture of oil and gas from coal, especially as there are already huge potential alternative supplies in the frontier areas and the tars and heavy oils. It is more likely that coal will be developed for the manufacture of thermal electricity.

*Option #4. Switching energy consumption away from oil and gas.* This means pushing the development of electricity, which is Canada's second power source at present. *Hydroelectricity* is unlikely to be developed much further in Canada because most of the best locations have already been used. As for the remaining sites there is growing resistance from Indians and Eskimos to the spread of hydro stations and their giant reservoirs into the northland. There is also growing resistance from conservationists who do not like to see wild rivers "tamed" by having dams put across them. On the other hand there is strong pressure to develop all available hydro sites because hydro is both everlasting and non-polluting. What do you think?

*Thermal electricity* from coal is a good prospect, because Canada has plenty of coal. The problem is transportation: most Canadian coal deposits are in Alberta but most electricity is needed in Ontario. Work is being carried out to try to find ways to make coal easier and cheaper to transport, including experiments in special trains and lake ships, and even in a pipeline. The pipeline would be a *slurry* pipeline, carrying powdered coal in a fluid such as water or oil. It is unlikely that thermal power will be developed in the future from oil and gas, because the oil and gas will not only be increasingly scarce unless Options #2 and #3 quickly succeed, but they will also be increasingly expensive.

*Nuclear electricity* is also a good prospect. It has the problem of potential danger from radioactive waste, but it is much cleaner than coal and also now much cheaper. Canada also has vast uranium reserves in Northern Ontario as well as one of the world's best operating technologies: the CANDU system. In order for nuclear power to become everlasting, however, there has to be much suc-

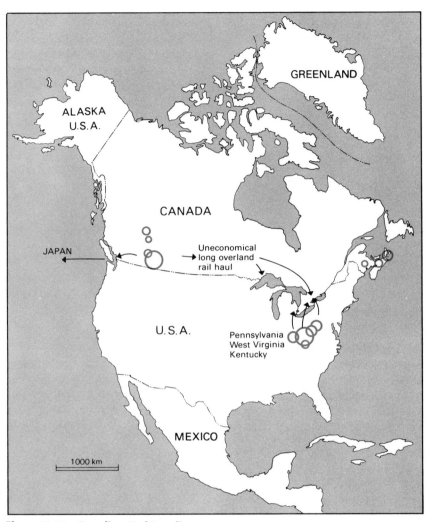

**Figure 14-15   Canadian Coal Supplies**

cessful research carried out on something called *nuclear fusion*. At present we split atoms (*fission*); this produces energy, but not as much as if we could cause atoms to combine (*fusion*). We need to cause four hydrogen atoms to combine to form one atom of helium. This is what the sun does all the time to produce energy. It is what we do in a hydrogen bomb. However, we cannot do it yet in a power station; we would blow it up.

Nuclear fusion is thought to be a good bet for commercial application sometime early in the next century, after the year 2000.

**Figure 14-16   Canada's Potential Recoverable Reserves of Fossil Fuels (in barrels of oil equivalent)**

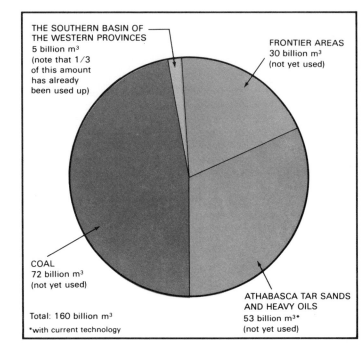

THE SOUTHERN BASIN OF THE WESTERN PROVINCES
5 billion m³
(note that 1/3 of this amount has already been used up)

FRONTIER AREAS
30 billion m³
(not yet used)

COAL
72 billion m³
(not yet used)

ATHABASCA TAR SANDS AND HEAVY OILS
53 billion m³*
(not yet used)

Total: 160 billion m³
*with current technology

# Canada Has Energy to Last 600 Years, Conference Told

By Patrick Fellows

Looking 30 years ahead, Canada could easily be self-sufficient in energy supplies, a chemicals conference was told yesterday.

In a paper prepared for delivery to the Canadian Manufacturers of Chemical Specialties Association, R. A. Burnside, solvents department manager of Esso Chemical Canada, said only Canada among the industrialized nations could in the long run supply its own energy needs.

That was the good news. Burnside was less certain about the prospects for the next 20 to 30 years.

We have the resources, he said, but unless certain economic and technological aspects of energy supply are recognized and appropriate market conditions and government policies allowed to develop, we could face tight supply.

Burnside said the energy contained in Canada's reserves of conventional oil and gas, in the vast Alberta tar sands and heavy oil deposits equals the energy in 550 billion barrels[1] of oil.

Coal reserves add the equivalent of about 450 billion barrels[2] of oil, for a total fossil fuel equivalent of about 1000 billion bar-

[1] 88 billion m³
[2] 72 billion m³

rels[3] (three times the reported oil reserves of the Middle East.)

Add uranium and hydro-electric sources, he said, and Canada has the equivalent of 600 years of supply

[3] 160 billion m³

at demand rates expected for 1990.

Furthermore, Burnside said, new technology will bring other new energy sources into production, such as tides, the breeder

reactor and even the sun itself.

In the nearer term, he said, "adequate" prices will be needed to bring additional reserves of conventional hydrocarbons into the Canadian supply system.

from the Toronto *Star*, October 23, 1973

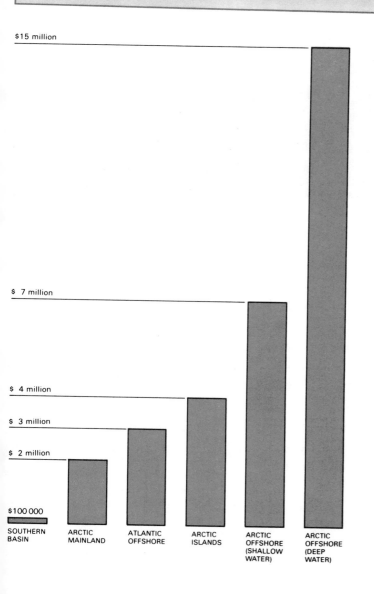

**Figure 14-17   Average Drilling Costs Per Well Across Canada**

**Figure 14-18** Drilling for oil in Alberta.

● 10. Using what you have read in this section can you define the term *life index*?

● 11. How do you think the costs of frontier exploration (Figure 14-13) will be paid for?

● 12. How do you think the costs of research and development in the Tar Sands and the heavy oil areas will be paid for?

● 13. What do you see as two of the problems of a *coal slurry* pipeline from Alberta to Ontario?

● 14. Give two reasons why oil and gas prices must keep on rising as time goes by, regardless of inflation.

● 15. In 1976 the Ontario Government told Ontario Hydro to cut back its investment plans. Do you think this was a wise decision?

● 16. What are your views *now* on Story A and Story B in the Introduction? Is there really an energy crisis? Use the information in Figures 14-12 and 14-13 to help you answer this question, as well as what you have learned in the rest of the chapter.

# CHAPTER 15

# TRANSPORTATION

## SPATIAL INTERACTION

## INTRODUCTION

The study of spatial interaction is the study of the ways in which one part of the world interacts with another. The key ways in which this interaction is carried out are by communication and transportation. Communication involves the transmission of ideas, images, and messages, while transportation involves the transmission of people and freight. The telephone system is a medium of communication; the railway system is a medium of transportation. In this chapter we will be concerned with the ways in which Canada's transportation systems help to bring one part of the country into interaction with another.

Communication has always been a problem across such vast distances as are found in the nations of North America. It is therefore no coincidence that the telephone was invented partly in Canada and partly in the United States. The theory and the first simple model of a telephone were developed in Brantford in 1874, but the first practical application was made in Boston in 1876. Subsequently, the first long distance telephone call was made between Brantford and Paris, Ontario. The inventor, Alexander Graham Bell, eventually became President of the National Geographic Society in Washington, D.C.

**Figure 15-1  As urban transit systems try to attract more passengers, the number of passenger cars and kilometres of surfaced urban roads continue to increase.**

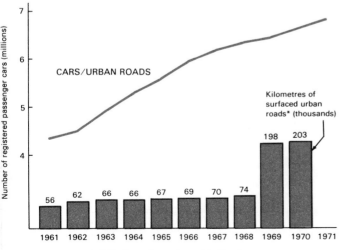

*Sudden increase in 1969 reflects takeovers by municipalities of some roads formerly under provincial jurisdiction.

309

**Figure 15-2  Despite big growth in population (up 82% since 1945), urbanization, and transit facilities, urban transit systems are carrying fewer passengers than they did 20 years ago.**

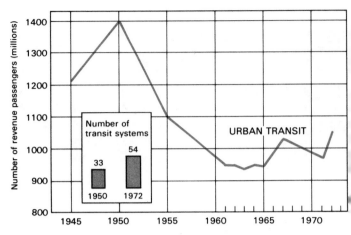

● 1. Examine Figures 15-1, 15-2, and 15-3. Each graph has a caption which indicates that something strange has been happening: for example, Figure 15-1 tells you that the number of passenger cars has been increasing during a time that transit systems have been trying to attract more passengers; Figure 15-2 tells you that transit systems are now carrying fewer people than they used to even though Canada's population has risen; Figure 15-3 tells you that air transportation has increased faster than population.

(a) Write not more than a page explaining each of these graphs and their apparent contradictions.

(b) Write as much as you like, and use any other information you like to support your ideas, on the topic: *During the*

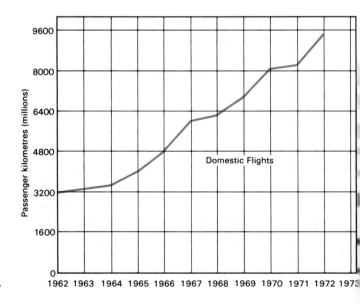

**Figure 15-3  Between 1962 and 1972, Canada's population increased by less than 20%. But passenger-kilometres flown were nearly three times what they were a decade ago.**

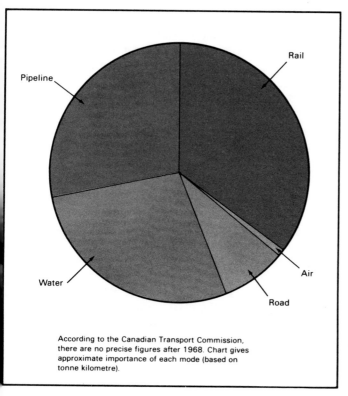

**Figure 15-4 Domestic Freight: Which Moves Most?**

According to the Canadian Transport Commission, there are no precise figures after 1968. Chart gives approximate importance of each mode (based on tonne kilometre).

*Last Few Years Canada Has Become a Richer and More Mobile Society.* You should refer to the graphs to help support your ideas.

- 2. Figure 15-4 shows the breakdown of carriers for freight: you will notice that rail, water, and pipeline account for the bulk of freight movements, at about a little under a third each. The remainder is carried mostly by road transportation, with a small amount left to air carriers. Clearly this breakdown has not always been the same thoughout Canada's development. In the early days water was vastly more important than anything else; there would not even have been pipelines and airplanes. Later, rail had its heyday, and it became the most important. In not more than about a page can you suggest *how* and *why* the breakdown will be different in the year 2000?

## A: THE ROLE OF TRANSPORTATION

For its population Canada has probably the best transportation network in the world. Twenty three million people have the use of two major transcontinental railways (Canadian Pacific and Canadian National), two major international airlines (Air Canada and CP Air),

Canadian National was established in the 1920s to consolidate the varied services provided by a number of separate railway companies, many of which were in some sort of financial trouble. It has grown to include under its corporate umbrella a great number of allied transportation and communications operations, such as Air Canada, founded in 1937 as Trans-Canada Airlines, as well as coastal and insular ferry services, bus lines, highway transportation, hotels, telecommunications, and resort management. Its expertise in these fields has become internationally famous, and CN consultants are often asked to help in the development of transportation and communications networks in newly developing countries.

Canada has 68 800 km of railway track and 711 600 km of highway, of which 92 500 km have an all-weather surface.

the world's longest highway (the Trans-Canada Highway), one of the world's major canal and inland waterway systems (the St. Lawrence Seaway and the Great Lakes), and some of the world's longest pipelines (such as the Interprovincial pipeline from Edmonton to Montreal).

Canada has such an impressive transportation system for a variety of reasons:

*Reason #1.    Canada is a big country.* Figure 1-11 in Chapter 1 shows you just how big Canada is in relation to some other countries. It is fairly obvious that a big country needs big transportation systems.

*Reason #2.    Canada's population is well scattered.* People live all along the southern fringes of Canada, though they are clustered into five distinct regions (Figure 15-5). Good transportation is necessary to link the population clusters with each other.

*Reason #3.    Canada's early exploration and development was by river.* You learned in Chapter 1 how Canada's rivers and lakes were of major importance to the early explorers and traders. From the very earliest days, the river and lake navigation routes have been used and developed; major cities lie next to them; important industries line their banks; loaded barges and ships ply their waters. The waterways have always been part of Canada's heritage.

**Figure 15-5    Canada's Main Population Clusters Now**

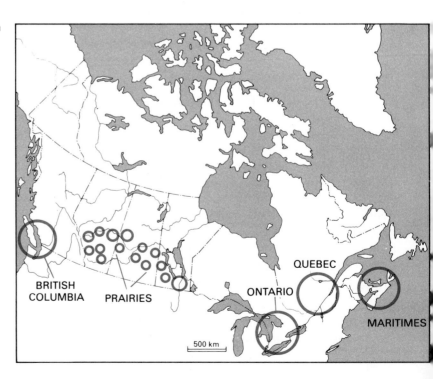

*Reason #4.    Canada became a nation with the help of the railways.* Figure 15-5 shows you the main clusters of Canada's population *now,* but it was not exactly like that when Canada became a nation in 1867. At that time, as you can see in Figure 15-6, the Prairies contained few people. Most people lived in the three eastern clusters, with some also in British Columbia. The railways were important to both the eastern and western groups. In the east the British thought it would be easier to set up a profitable railway to link the Maritimes with Quebec and Ontario *if* the different colonies were united into a single country; accordingly they were encour-

At the time of Confederation in 1867 there were about 3 500 000 people in all of Canada, so that even those places described as *populated* were still largely empty by today's standards.

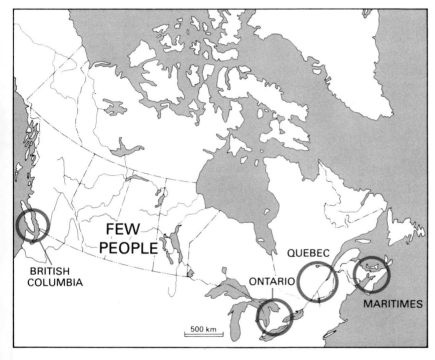

**Figure 15-6 Canada's Main Population Clusters 100 Years Ago**

aged to arrange Confederation and the creation of an independent Canada stretching from the Maritimes to Ontario. A few years later (in 1871) British Columbia joined Canada rather than the United States, on the promise that it would get a railway link across the continent to the eastern clusters. After the railway was eventually built to British Columbia, people began to use it to move into the Prairies; so the fifth population cluster began to develop. Canada was becoming a nation, thanks partly to the railway.

*Reason #5.    Canada needs good transportation to maintain itself as a nation.* Figure 15-7 shows some of the landscape barriers which exist between the five population clusters. In which direction do the physical barriers run? Do they encourage the Canadian clusters

The railway which was built through the Maritimes in the 1870s was called the Inter-Colonial Railway. It was built as far from the American border as economically possible, thus running along the east coast of New Brunswick rather than the St. John Valley, and thereby making Moncton an important railway junction town.

One of the most diffi-
cult stretches in the
construction of the
Canadian Pacific rail-
way was the Rockies
and the Selkirks in
eastern British
Columbia. There was
much dispute as to
which of the several
passes through the
Rockies should be
used, until eventually
the Kicking Horse Pass
was decided upon. By
contrast there was
little dispute as to
which pass through
the Selkirks should be
used, for there was
none known until
surveyor Rogers dis-
covered one in 1882.
The eventual crossing
of Rogers Pass meant
very steep grades, and
both these and the
equally steep grades
of Kicking Horse have
been replaced by
tunnels: the spiral
tunnels at Kicking
Horse, and a tunnel of
eight kilometres under
Rogers Pass.

to have contact with each other? Or do they more easily permit the separate clusters to have ready contact with people in the United States? If Canada wishes to remain as a unified single nation, the task becomes easier if there are good transportation links between the different population clusters. Good transportation may overcome the physical obstacles to unity.

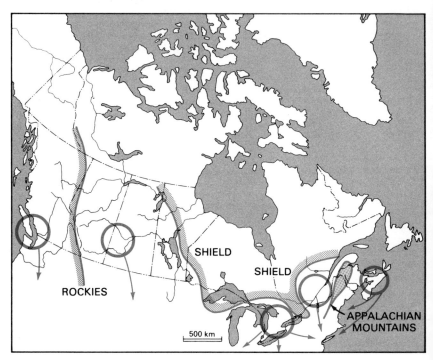

**Figure 15-7    Canada's Main Population Clusters are Divided from One Another by Topographic Barriers**

●  3.  You can see from Figures 15-5, 15-6, and 15-7 that Canada's main population clusters are across the south of the country. This is also where the chief transportation links are. Clearly the scarcity of people across the north is one reason for the lack of transportation there. How many other reasons can you think of?

## B: THE TRANSPORTATION OF PEOPLE

People are transported from place to place by a variety of means. Within cities the most popular means are buses and, if they exist, subways, although cars are also very important. Between cities the means change: if the cities are close together cars are the favoured form of transportation, but if the cities are far apart then air travel becomes important, while railways may also be used. People also

**Figure 15-8**  Waterways have always been part of Canada's heritage.

travel on ferry boats. Just about the only means of transportation that people do not use is the pipeline.

Let us look at these different forms of transportation one by one. The first important transportation medium was water. People arrived in Canada by water, and penetrated into the inland districts by water; they usually also settled next to water. The waterways were literally the social lifeblood of early Canada. Throughout the entire period from the early 1600s to about 1850 water was the dominant medium of transportation for people. There were only the muddiest of dirt roads; there were no railways and no airways. If people wanted to travel in reasonable comfort, they travelled by water. For decades the main point of entry into Canada was either Quebec City or Halifax, and the chief means of penetrating the

The construction and operation of urban subways requires a large concentration of people. The minimum, or *threshold,* number is probably about 2 000 000, but other factors such as the concentration of lines and times of movement are also important. Toronto's subway was first opened in 1954 when its population was about 1 500 000, whereas Montreal's subway was not opened until 1966, when its population was about 2 500 000.

One of the earliest ways of producing a road relatively free from mud was to lay a series of logs across it. Such a road was called a *corduroy road.*

**Figure 15-9**  Quebec City has long been a port of entry for immigrants.

interior was by way of the St. Lawrence River system and the Great Lakes. In the earliest days, the waterways of the entire continent were used by the voyageurs, who travelled widely in search of furs. Even after the fur traders had disappeared into history, and the first pioneer settlers were moving into the Great Lakes area, the waterways remained of great importance. The north shore of Lake Ontario is, for example, strung along with small harbours, which were originally landing points for early settlers. Toronto was just such a landing point when it was founded in 1793.

**Figure 15-10**   The docks of Halifax, an old port of immigration.

Water transportation has never been completely reliable. Even such a regular phenomenon as winter ice causes problems in fall and spring, when boats may be frozen out or frozen in. Unexpected phenomena such as storms and fogs are, however, much more hazardous. In the fall of 1975, for example, an iron laker called the *Edmund Fitzgerald* sank during a severe storm at the eastern end of Lake Superior.

For some small coastal communities the arrival of the annual ship is a time of great excitement.

However, from being the only fairly reliable means of transportation in the 1600s, 1700s, and early 1800s, water has declined in importance over the last 100 or more years. Today almost no one travels by water, except under very special circumstances. The first set of special circumstances exist wherever water is either the only means of transportation or by far the cheapest (provided the time of the journey is not excessive). For example, people travel to remote coastal settlements along both the Atlantic and Pacific coasts by water, simply because there is no reasonable alternative. They also travel between islands and between mainland and islands by water, simply because the alternative of air travel is much more expensive. Ferries linking the mainland of Canada to Prince Edward Island are far more popular than competing air services, while ferries to Newfoundland and Vancouver Island are also enormously popular. Ferries also connect north and south shores along the St. Lawrence downstream from Quebec City, as well as the Toronto Islands to mainland Toronto. In all these cases, people prefer to travel by water because journeys are fairly short, and competing air services are either missing or greatly expensive. The second set of special circumstances exists because of pleasure boating. Increasingly, people are turning to the water for recreation; it is slower than land transportation, but for many people the slow pace represents a rest as well as a return to the more leisurely pace of earlier days.

The monopoly on transportation held by the waterways was first broken by the railways. The first railways were built in Canada to act as links and replacements for the water transport systems; they were essentially subservient to the demands of the waterways. However, their advantages were soon recognized, and by the second half of the nineteenth century they had completely taken over the business of moving people. They were faster and much more reliable. Important railways were built to link the Maritimes with Quebec and Ontario, and to serve the increasingly populated and productive areas of the St. Lawrence Valley and the Great Lakes triangle of southern Ontario. The promise of a railway was even sufficient to bring British Columbia into Confederation. The eventual construction of a transcontinental rail line was a prodigious act of faith in a country of only about 4 000 000 people, especially as the line crossed almost uninhabited land for over half its original length. The results of the Canadian Pacific line of the 1880s were manifold: most obviously, British Columbia remained in Confederation; less obviously, but still of importance, Canada remained a separate country. The surveyors and builders of the first transcontinental line in Canada had deliberately run it across the dry southern prairie rather than through the more moist and more productive northern prairie for the simple reason that they wanted to seal the border against any possible extensions of U.S. land claims. They were successful in this, although there were complaints that the railway land was not always the most productive available. A further result of the railway was the eventual settling of the prairies by immigrants brought in from lands throughout Europe. They were brought in partly to secure Canada as a nation, to fill up the middle as it were, and partly to provide business for the new railway. Additionally the railway wanted to get some of its investment back, for it had almost gone bankrupt trying to build the line. It could get some of its money back by selling land to settlers. In every township opened up across the prairie, the railway company had rights to half the land, which it could sell as it wished.

Following the success of the Canadian Pacific, many railway companies came into existence, and rail lines were built feverishly in many areas that could barely support a rail facility. By the early

Technically, it is possible to link Prince Edward Island to the mainland by tunnel or bridge, but it is not done. Part of the reason lies in the cost, but more lies in the wishes of Prince Edward Islanders to remain isolated.

The first railway in Canada ran from the upper navigable part of the Richelieu River down to the St. Lawrence, by-passing the rapids. The year was 1836.

Much of the pride of early railway workers lay in their adherence to strict timetables; railway clocks and pocket watches were built to high standards of accuracy, and engineers drove their trains to equally high standards. It is no coincidence that the most famous railway builders of all time include the Canadian Sandford Fleming, who was also the inventor of the world's system of time zones.

Land grants were important to the early railways which were built into future pioneer lands: they provided a security against which they could borrow money to build the line. Once the line was built, the railway companies then had to attract settlers to create the potential for future land sales in order to be able to repay loans.

The distribution of track responsibility is approximately 52% to CN, 38% to CP, and 10% to the remainder, chiefly the Ontario Northland, the British Columbia Railway, the Algoma Central, and the Quebec North Shore and Labrador Railway.

During this same period the population increased from approximately 8 700 000 to approximately 21 500 000. In 1920, therefore, there were about 5.9 railway passenger journeys for each inhabitant of Canada. By 1970 the number had fallen to about 1.1 railway passenger journeys per inhabitant. This is a considerable loss of traffic to the railways.

years of the present century many railway companies were running into severe financial trouble; they were eventually saved by the actions of the federal government, which bought them up and amalgamated them into Canadian National Railways. A few independent railway companies still exist, mostly operating specialized services, but for the most part Canada's rail services are now operated on lines owned either by Canadian Pacific or by Canadian National.

Generally, passenger rail services have, over the years, proved to be uneconomical. There has been a fairly steady decline in the number of passengers carried, to the extent that the railways have persistently lost money on their passenger services and have required government subsidies to keep them going. In 1920, for example, the number of passengers carried was 51 300 000, but by 1970 the number had declined to 23 800 000. In the meantime, freight transportation had increased by more than 100%. Consequently, the railway companies were trying to get out of passenger services during the early 1970s, and in 1977 they succeeded in handing over such services to a new government operated passenger railway system called *VIA*. VIA actually runs all Canada's major passenger railway lines, leasing track from Canadian Pacific and Canadian National for the purpose.

There were two major causes of the loss of passenger traffic by the railways: first, the short distance traffic was lost to the car and the bus, and second, long distance traffic was lost to the airlines.

**Figure 15-11** The CN transcontinental line.

Cars and buses began to capture the short distance market during the early years of this century. They provided the convenience of door-to-door transportation and greater frequency, and in the case of cars, personal immediacy. Within a few years, railways had also begun to lose the long distance traffic to newly developing airlines, which offered the enormous advantage of great speed over long distances. In both cases, time was being saved.

Canada now has the second highest per capita car ownership of any country in the world, as well as an excellent network of sur-faced all-weather roads. It boasts the longest paved highway in the world, the Trans-Canada Highway, which runs, with breaks for water links, from St. John's in Newfoundland to Victoria on Van-couver Island. Despite the fact that the road is the longest paved highway in the world, most long distance passenger traffic does not travel by road, but by air. The distance which separates road passen-gers from air passengers is difficult to determine; generally, distances less than about 400 km are quicker by road, because of the time lost in airport transactions.

Air travel has grown consistently since the introduction of regular air routes. At one time, people would have to change aircraft in order to travel across the continent, because the piston-engined aircraft were incapable of making such long, non-stop journeys. The introduction of jets in the 1950s opened up new possibilities, enabling non-stop transcontinental flights. Jets also produced much greater reliability in service, as well as much safer flying conditions. Their most important asset, however, is providing scheduled services in densely populated areas, such as across southern Canada. In the north, smaller aircraft are much more useful, and Canadian flying owes a great deal to the activities of pioneer bush pilots throughout the north.

Air transportation is now the main method of long distance pas-senger movement, and the system is highly organized. At the trans-continental and international level stand the two "flag carriers", Canadian Pacific Airlines and Air Canada. In the second rank, act-ing as regional carriers, stand the five main "feeder" airlines, and below them the "third level" carriers, such as Air Gaspé and Nor-Ontair. At the bottom of the pyramid are the hundreds of local carriers, occasionally providing scheduled services, but more usually providing services upon demand.

A special problem connected with the movement of people is the transportation of commuters in cities. Buses and cars are the chief means, although subways are used in large cities such as Toronto and Montreal. The chief pattern of commuter movement within large cities is, broadly, *into* the downtown area in the morn-

The railways were in an impossible position: if they raised fares to attempt to cut their losses then they lost even more passengers, and finished even worse off; but if they left fares stable they still suffered losses, and they knew that fare reductions would make matters even worse, because no new passengers would be attracted to rail travel.

Some long distance freight was lost to trucks, but here we are concerned only with passengers.

It is difficult to say exactly how long the Trans-Canada Highway is, because in some parts of the country there are two or more different routes. For example, across Ontario there is the northern route through North Bay, Cochrane, Hearst, and Thunder Bay, and also the southern route through North Bay, Sudbury, Sault Ste. Marie, and Thunder Bay. Both routes ultimately link Ottawa and Winnipeg.

A *flag carrier* is an airline or other agency that has official government approval to carry the Canadian flag (or Canadian presence) into foreign parts.

ing and *out* to the suburbs in the evening. Certain problems are thereby created: road congestion and crowding of the public transit system are two of the most obvious; but the costs of roads and transit facilities is another, as is the cost of fuel, and the loss of farmland caused by lateral expansion of cities into surrounding countryside. There are no simple answers. If lateral expansion is restricted, then cities must build upwards, and some people are opposed to the construction of high rise buildings; on the other hand if low rise buildings are favoured, then cities must spread outwards, and people then become concerned about the loss of farmland. Additionally, they become worried about the ebb and flow of commuters into and out of the downtown area, and the resultant demands for expressways, parking spaces, and rapid transit systems. If these concerns are listened to, then the apparent solution becomes one of dispersing the central business activities throughout the metropolitan area rather than having them concentrated into a Central Business District; in such a case the links of the business world are to some extent destroyed and certain efficiencies and economies may be lost. As we have said, there are no simple answers.

This will not stop you from hearing simple answers, of course; some people always have simple answers to complex problems.

●  4.  Give five reasons why you think people want to move from place to place, requiring transportation to achieve their purpose.

●  5.  Suggest as many reasons as you can for the loss of passenger traffic by the railways during the last 50 years.

●  6.  In what ways do air services in the north differ from those in the south?

●  7.  Answer the following questions:
    (a) Why are airplanes important for travel in the north?
    (b) In what ways do airlines in the north *now* compare with railroads in the west *a hundred years ago*?
    (c) Why do you think things cost so much in the north? Can you suggest a second reason as well?
    (d) What are some of the problems in running an airline in the north?

## C: FREIGHT TRANSPORTATION

Figure 15-4 shows you that most freight is moved by rail, water, and pipeline, with some also by road and by air. Why are these modes of transportation chosen in this order? What factors influence a shipper in his decision in choosing a method of freight transportation?

The reasons are complex, and have to do with *distance, quantity,* and *type of product.* Generally, except for small quantities, it does not matter whether there is a road or a railway or a dock or a landing field at the destination or not: *if* the need is there, then people will build one. For example, if a mineral is discovered in a remote area and people want to get that mineral to an industrial area, then they will build a railway, pipeline, or whatever else is suitable.

Small quantities generally travel by road, especially over short distances; it really does not matter what the type of product is. Over longer distances small quantities still travel by road, but they may also travel by rail or air. The decision of which to use would be a very close one, and would be affected by such considerations as delivery schedules, availability of trucks, and so on.

Larger quantities hardly ever travel by road, whatever the distance. They are transported instead by rail, water, or pipe. It is a safe rule that if you can ship by water then you will do so because it is cheap. Ships are not cheap to operate, but they can carry so much at one time that the costs per tonne are quite low. It is for this reason that the St. Lawrence Seaway and the Great Lakes waterway are so important: they can carry ships which transport large quantities of products at *low unit cost* (low cost per tonne). This is ideal for transporting large quantities of wheat or iron ore, because then the products can be sold without costing too much. Over land, pipelines offer similar advantages. However, pipes work best if the product is a liquid or a gas, such as crude oil or natural gas. Solids are awkward to move by pipeline. Rail is the most versatile of the large bulk carriers. It can carry almost any type of product; it can even carry mixed loads. As a result, trains carry more freight than the other forms of transport do.

We can now have a closer look at how the different freight transportation methods operate. Let us look at them in historical sequence, as we did for passenger traffic.

Waterways have been important since the very earliest times, ever since the first days of the fur trade. At that time, the rivers and lakes of the interior complemented the seas of the exterior, so that internal trade fitted into external trade very well. The connection today is not quite so simple, because there are thousands of goods involved, as well as many different countries. As far as international trade is concerned, Canada has links to most countries in the world. The links are forged through shipping lines which operate into and out of the chief ports, namely Vancouver, Montreal, Halifax, and Saint John. Approximately 65% of the import trade consists of

The present pattern of roads, railways, air and water routes, and pipelines did not come into existence all at once. It was created a bit at a time, according to the needs which were seen to exist. As our needs change, so does the pattern of transportation links: some parts close down, other parts are extended or created.

You can see everything from apples to yachts being transported by road, in a variety of specialized trucks.

What factors can you think of that might affect the decision to transport goods by road or rail or air?

You can transport goods by water whenever speed is not an important consideration, provided a water route (river, canal, or lake) either exists or can be constructed.

Railways combine the advantages of speed and bulk carrying capacity; they lack the advantage of low unit cost.

In the early days, water transportation was the chief means of transportation. Roads were muddy or dusty, and potholed anyway; rail, pipe, and air did not exist. As a result, the fur trade flowed downstream and across the ocean to Europe, while the flow of manufactured items moved back across the oceans and then upstream into Canada. Water provided both the internal and the external means of transportation.

Containers are big boxes. They are made in a limited variety of sizes, so that they fit neatly onto the trailer of a semi-truck, as well as onto a railway flat car, and also into the hold of a ship. Containers can carry almost anything, and they have the advantage of being easy to handle by machinery — giant cranes and hoists — and easy to bond through customs. More and more of the world's trade is being handled in containers, and most of the world's major ports are equipping themselves rapidly with container handling facilities.

finished goods, while only about 40% of the export trade consists of similar products. This large volume of end product trade is largely handled in containers, and there are therefore large container handling facilities at all the major ports. Much of the remainder of imports and exports is composed of various types of raw materials, which lend themselves to bulk handling. International trade is permitted to enter the Great Lakes as well as the leading coastal ports by means of the St. Lawrence Seaway. The Seaway was

**Figure 15-12**    Part of the container dock at Halifax.

opened in 1959 as a joint venture by the United States and Canada; it runs from Montreal, which has access to the open ocean, all the way inland to Lake Superior, thus giving Thunder Bay and other lake ports access to the sea also (Figure 15-14). It is therefore not unusual to see ships from Japan and the U.S.S.R. docked in Great Lakes ports. But despite this, most Great Lakes shipping is still internal — that is, within the Great Lakes system itself; it never sets out to sea. It operates between one part of the system and another, such as between Port Cartier in Quebec and Chicago in Illinois, or between Cleveland in Ohio and Toronto in Ontario. Because it is trade between two countries, it is, of course, international, but it is also local.

Local waterways trade is of considerable importance. It is important both along the rivers and lakes of the interior and along the coasts of the country. The chief navigable rivers are the St. Lawrence and the Mackenzie: the St. Lawrence forms part of the Seaway system, and is heavily used for about eight months of the year, while the Mackenzie is the chief transportation route to the north, and sees considerable use for about four months of the year. The Mackenzie was a disappointment to its discoverers, because it flowed into the Arctic instead of the Pacific, but it is a boon to today's northern Canadians. It offers not only navigable water linking southern and northern Canada, but also an ameliorating effect upon the northern climate; without it the northwestern Arctic would be a forbidding territory indeed.

The ships which sail on the Great Lakes, never setting out to sea, are called *lakers*. They are usually built to be as large as the smallest locks in the Seaway system. Generally, this means that, in relation to sea going ships, they are long and relatively narrow. If they were put out to sea, the waves of the oceans would most likely cause them to break their backs and sink. Sea going ships can thus use the Great Lakes, but lakers cannot put out to sea.

**Figure 15-13** Part of the St. Lawrence Seaway. This is the St. Lambert lock at Montreal. The St. Lawrence River is on the right.

Ice is a closing hazard, although experiments are taking place to use air cushion vehicles (hovercraft) to break the ice and allow prolonged navigation.

Note that the Mackenzie carries relatively warm southern waters northwards, thus providing an ameliorating effect (ameliorating = making better) to the northwest Arctic.

Coastal trade is of incalculable importance to many otherwise isolated communities along the shores of Canada. The day of the ship's arrival is a major event in the life of such communities, for it may be months before a ship comes again. Often, supplies for the year are brought in. The community band and the village folk are usually in attendance as a welcoming party. For example, hundreds of small communities around the eastern and northeastern shores of Canada are served in this manner (see Figure 15-15).

Railways, coming later than early river and canal traffic, at first tended to compete with shipping for the traffic of the Great Lakes and St. Lawrence regions. They offered greater speed, but at a higher cost. Early competition, however, was eventually replaced with a complementary relationship, because as the railways were

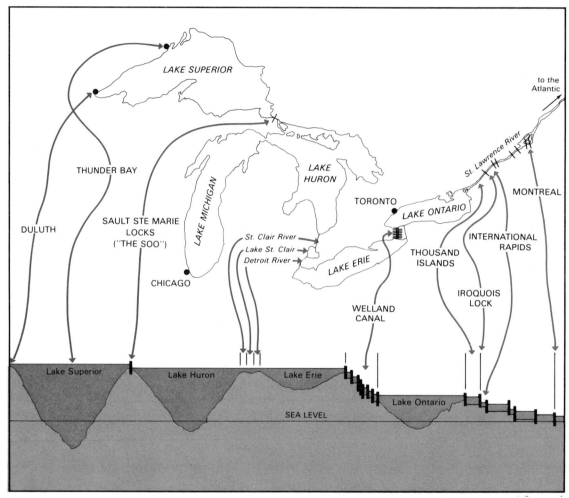

**Figure 15-14   The Great Lakes-St. Lawrence Seaway**

For goods in containers, both cheapness and speed are desirable. Montreal and Halifax therefore compete with each other to provide good container facilities. In 1977 a large CN container shipping subsidiary called CAST transferred its operations from Montreal to Halifax. Is this a sign of the future?

pushed into the interior, across the prairies, they generated entirely new traffic, and this traffic also used the St. Lawrence waterway. Both forms of transport therefore benefited, each from the other. In such a system, the transshipment points, where rail gave way to water, or vice versa, became important routeway control towns, such as Thunder Bay and Montreal. Today there is a degree of competition returning to the rail-water system: water might be cheaper, but rail is quicker, and accordingly there is a struggle between those ports such as Montreal which benefit from the cheapness of water transport and those ports such as Halifax which benefit from the speed of rail. There are advantages to be gained by both types of ports, because the needs of different types of freight are not identical. For example, wheat exports benefit from cheapness, while car imports benefit from speed.

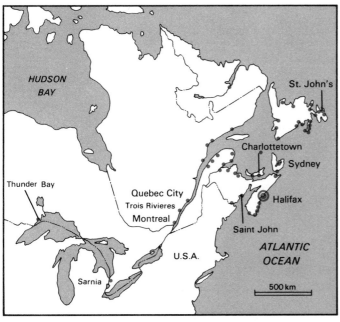

**Figure 15-15    Ports Served by Coastal Trade from Halifax**

Freight traffic on the railways has been very profitable for the railway companies, and they now indeed concentrate on that. Several innovations have been made for freight, such as unit trains, computer-controlled marshalling yards, non-stop loading and unloading facilities, and crewless trains.

The sort of competition that railways gave to waterways a hundred years ago has been paralleled in the last 70 to 80 years by competition to the railways from pipelines, trucks, and air traffic. Although the railways have undoubtedly lost traffic to all three competitors, they have nevertheless managed not only to survive but to prosper as far as freight traffic is concerned. This has been largely because of the rapidly growing total freight market, and also partly because railways offer certain advantages, such as cheapness compared with air transportation, speed compared with water transportation, bulk carrying capacity compared with trucks, and freight variety compared with pipelines.

Air freight has been a very rapidly growing sector of the air business, not as important as passengers, but growing in importance at a faster rate. The advantages of speed and areal penetration are sufficient to offset the high cost in many cases, and indeed for some areas air freight represents almost the only way to move goods in and out. Throughout the northland, for example, air freight is the only form of transportation possible away from the navigable rivers and seas.

Thunder Bay marked the closest point to navigable water for most of the prairies, and therefore developed naturally as the wheat trans-shipment port for most of the region. Montreal marked the closest point to ocean water (tidewater) for most of interior Canada, and therefore it developed naturally as a major ocean port. Montreal's development was aided also by the fact that it lay just downstream from the junction of the St. Lawrence River and the Ottawa River, therefore being in a good position to take traffic from both areas, as well as the areas that these valleys gave access to.

Since air exists everywhere over the earth, aircraft can theoretically fly anywhere. The limiting factor is the existence of landing and take-off facilities. However, for all remote areas it is almost always cheaper to build runways which stretch at most a few kilometres than it is to build roads and railways in and out. Thus all remote places rely on air transportation.

A unit train is one which stays together at all times. Normally a train is composed of cars which come together from various places: a few flat cars, a few box cars, all carrying a variety of freight, and a caboose; perhaps a few tank cars, and maybe a refrigerated car or two as well. A mixture. And broken up at destination — a flat car left off at one place, a couple of box cars left off at another, and so on. A unit train is quite different from this: it never gets broken up, it never gets assembled; it stays as a unit at all times. The cars are all the same type, the origin is the same place, and the destination is another single place; the load is all the same as well.

Pipelines serve almost an exactly opposite freight market to aircraft. They carry only bulk freight between set points, whereas aircraft carry a variety of small items between a multitude of points. Pipelines also do not carry a crew, and are free from crash hazards, whereas aircraft need an expensive crew, and are at hazard in operation. Pipelines are virtually independent of the weather, whereas aircraft are almost at the weather's mercy. And pipelines are cheap in operation, despite high initial costs, whereas aircraft are expensive in operation. The chief freight carried by pipeline is one or another of a variety of liquids or gases, such as crude oil, distillation products, water, natural gas, and liquid sulphur. The main pipeline in Canada are shown in Figure 15-17. Can you suggest reasons for the fact that some of Canada's pipelines pass through parts of the United States, instead of being located entirely within Canada?

Road freight lies somewhere between aircraft and pipelines. Trucks can penetrate most parts of the country, but their use throughout the northland is limited by the lack of roads. They have great versatility in load capacity, but they cannot carry bulk items in a continuous stream. They compete more with rail transportation than with air or pipeline, but the total market has grown at a sufficiently rapid pace for all to share in the increase; none has really lost traffic.

Rather than creating competition between the different forms of transportation, the major transportation companies, chiefly CN and

**Figure 15-16**  Laying a natural gas pipeline in Alberta.

CP, have fostered the development of what they call *intermodal* transport systems. This means that, by way of containers, goods can be carried for part of a journey by road, then possibly rail, then water, then road or rail again until the destination is reached. The idea is that the freight is carried by water in those areas where water transportation is preferable, and by rail where rail is appropriate, and by road where road is most suitable. The purpose is to achieve maximum efficiency in the use of facilities; the result is to produce lowest cost transportation between given points.

In all ways, for a country with such a relatively small population and such a huge territorial area, Canada has the world's best *system* of transportation, for moving people and freight.

● 8. Using the map and section in Figures 15-14 and 15-15 as a guide, write two imaginative accounts:
   (a) about the voyage of a grain ship from Thunder Bay to Montreal after the grain harvest.
   (b) about the voyage of an iron ore carrier from the St. Lawrence River up to Chicago in December.
   In both accounts try to visualize what the weather would be like, and how it would affect not only shipping conditions in the open water of the lakes but also the narrow water of the rivers and locks.

Throughout the northland, winter is the main time when trucks can penetrate into off-road areas, for then the ground and the waterways are frozen. In summer the ground is often marshy and trucks cannot go anywhere. You can read a fascinating account of northern trucking in *Denison's Ice Road* by Edith Iglauer; your library should have it.

A transportation system is not just roads, for that is a road system; nor just railways, for that is a rail system. It is everything together.

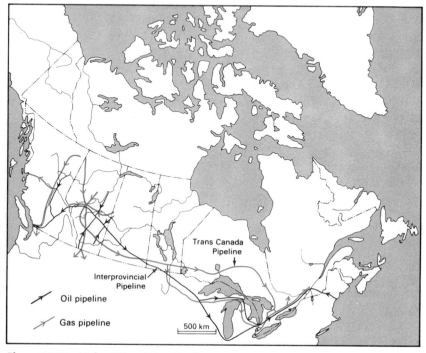

**Figure 15-17   Major Oil and Gas Pipelines**

# CHAPTER 16

# CANADA AS A WHOLE

## GLOBAL VIEW

### INTRODUCTION

In the north there are the native people, there are people who do not like crowds, and there are workers from the south who get paid extra for working in the north.

Nearly 24 000 000 people live in Canada. As we have seen in the preceding 15 chapters, most of these people live in the southern parts of the country, partly because the climate is not only more bearable but also less expensive to counteract, and partly for reasons of available food supplies, jobs, cheaper transportation possibilities, and closer proximity to trading opportunities. Can you suggest any other factors that help to influence most Canadians towards living in the southern parts of the country?

We have also examined the landscape of Canada, together with its climates, resources, and transportation systems. And we have seen how the different areas display their own individuality, whether through cultural distinction, as in Quebec, or any one of a number of other characteristics, such as the process of change persistently at work in the Arctic.

Out of this amazing mixture of people and places has come a nation of which most Canadians are extraordinarily proud. Is this pride justified?

- 1. What reasons can you suggest for Canadians feeling pride in being Canadian?

- 2 Can you suggest any things that might cause Canadians to feel less proud about being Canadian?

### A: CANADA'S ROLE IN THE WORLD

#### Canada As A Producer

Canada is very fortunate. For many products it ranks highly among world producers. In some cases it is the world's chief producer. You can see in Figure 16-1 how Canada ranks in the production of 20 important items listed by the United Nations in their *Statistical Yearbook*. The table shows all those products in which Canada ranks among the top five countries. It ranks first in five, second in another seven, and third in four more. This is an extraordinary number of high rankings. In many other products, Canada ranks just outside the top five — somewhere in the top ten. These products include wheat, petroleum, coal, steel, motor vehicles, television sets, and radios. It is because of the great number of high production rankings that Canadians are able to enjoy one of the highest standards of living in the world.

**Figure 16-1   Production Data**

| Barley (a) | | Oats (a) | | Natural Gasoline (a) | | Natural Gas (b) | | Uranium (c) | |
|---|---|---|---|---|---|---|---|---|---|
| 1. U.S.S.R. | 37 | U.S.S.R. | 14 | U.S.A. | 23 | U.S.A. | 650 000 | U.S.A. | 10 000 |
| 2. China | 19 | U.S.A. | 10 | Canada | 7 | U.S.S.R. | 220 000 | Canada | 4 000 |
| 3. Canada | 12 | Canada | 5 | Mexico | 2 | Canada | 82 000 | S. Africa | 3 000 |
| 4. France | 10 | Poland | 3 | Venezuela | 1 | Neth. | 60 000 | France | 1 000 |
| 5. U.K. | 9 | W. Germany | 3 | Kuwait | 0.5 | U.K. | 26 000 | Australia | 250 |

| Iron Ore (Fe content) (a) | | Copper Ore (Cu content) (a) | | Gold (d) | | Lead Ore (Pb content) (a) | | Molybdenum Ore (Mo content) (c) | |
|---|---|---|---|---|---|---|---|---|---|
| 1. U.S.S.R. | 113 | U.S.A. | 1.5 | S. Africa | 900 000 | U.S.A. | 0.6 | U.S.A. | 50 000 |
| 2. U.S.A. | 46 | U.S.S.R. | 1.0 | Canada | 65 000 | U.S.S.R. | 0.5 | Canada | 11 000 |
| 3. Australia | 39 | Chile | 0.7 | U.S.A. | 50 000 | Australia | 0.4 | U.S.S.R. | 8 000 |
| 4. Brazil | 28 | Zambia | 0.7 | Japan | 26 000 | Canada | 0.4 | Chile | 6 000 |
| 5. Canada | 25 | Canada | 0.7 | Australia | 23 000 | Mexico | 0.2 | China | 1 000 |

| Nickel Ore (Ni content) (c) | | Silver (c) | | Zinc Ore (Zn content) (a) | | Potash (a) | | Sulphur (a) | |
|---|---|---|---|---|---|---|---|---|---|
| 1. Canada | 250 000 | Canada | 1500 | Canada | 1.3 | U.S.S.R. | 5.5 | U.S.A. | 10 |
| 2. U.S.S.R. | 130 000 | Peru | 1250 | U.S.S.R. | 0.7 | Canada | 4.0 | Canada | 4 |
| 3. N.C. (f) | 100 000 | U.S.S.R. | 1250 | Australia | 0.5 | W. Germany | 3.0 | U.S.S.R. | 4 |
| 4. Cuba | 36 000 | Mexico | 1100 | U.S.A. | 0.4 | E. Germany | 2.5 | Poland | 3 |
| 5. Australia | 35 000 | U.S.A. | 1100 | Japan | 0.3 | U.S.A. | 2.5 | France | 2 |

| Asbestos (a) | | Wood Pulp (a) | | Newsprint (a) | | Aluminum (a) | | Hydro-electricity (e) | |
|---|---|---|---|---|---|---|---|---|---|
| 1. Canada | 1.6 | U.S.A. | 39 | Canada | 8 | U.S.A. | 3.7 | U.S.A. | 57 |
| 2. S. Africa | 0.3 | Canada | 17 | U.S.A. | 3 | U.S.S.R. | 1.3 | U.S.S.R. | 34 |
| 3. Italy | 0.1 | Sweden | 8 | Japan | 2 | Japan | 1.0 | Canada | 33 |
| 4. U.S.A. | 0.1 | U.S.S.R. | 7 | Finland | 1 | Canada | 1.0 | Japan | 20 |
| 5. Swaziland | 0.1 | Finland | 6 | U.S.S.R. | 1 | Norway | 0.6 | Italy | 15 |

(a) millions t
(b) millions m$^3$
(c) t
(d) kg (does not include U.S.S.R. data)
(e) capacity in millions Kw
(f) New Caledonia

Source: the U.N. *Statistical Yearbook*

Canada does not rank in the first five in wheat production, for example, although many people think that Canada is one of the world's top producers. Both India and China regularly grow more wheat than Canada, while the U.S.S.R. normally grows as much as five to six times more than Canada. Canada is a major producer, of course, but its reputation lies more in the volume of its exports than in the total quantity of its production.

● 3. Most of the items for which Canada is ranked in the first five are metals or other primary products, whereas manufactured items rank mainly outside the top five. Can you suggest a variety of explanations for this?

● 4. (a) In which items in Figure 16-1 is Canada's lead as #1 the greatest? You should calculate ratios to help you find the answer.

(b) The greater the lead any country in the top position has, the more it can be said to be in a *monopoly* position for that product. Which country has the greatest degree of monopoly for one of the products listed in Figure 16-1? Which is Canada's nearest monopoly product?

Despite the high ranking achieved by Canada for many products, there are some that Canada either does not produce at all or produces in only insignificant quantities. These include such varied commodities as coffee, tea, oranges, peanuts, rice, cotton, wool, silk, tin, manganese, and rock phosphates.

### Canada As A Trading Nation

As we have just seen, there are some goods that Canada does not produce at all, or that it produces only in such small quantities that they make virtually no difference to the amount still needed to be imported to satisfy Canada's demand for them. In order to obtain these goods, Canada must buy them from the countries that produce them and are willing to sell them. For example, coffee is bought from Brazil, Colombia, and some Central American countries; tea is bought from India, Sri Lanka, and China; oranges from the United States.

See if you can find out where peanuts, rice, cotton, wool, silk, tin, manganese, and rock phosphate come from.

In addition to buying commodities that we cannot produce ourselves, we also buy goods that provide us with greater choice. For example, importers bring cars into Canada from several other countries, as well as clothing, cameras, stereos, radios, television sets, calculators, and magazines. These are all things that many Canadians want in order to have a wider choice of items to buy. Sometimes it is felt that these imported items offer better value than similar goods made in Canada; it is also thought that the greater choice being made available gives the Canadian consumer a better deal.

Imports may be defined as *any* purchases which require the expenditure of foreign currency.

The chief problem for Canada is that all the imported goods must be paid for. In order to earn the necessary money, therefore, Canada must sell what it can to as many other countries as it can. Such sales are called *exports*. They are vital to Canada if the people are to obtain not only commodities which they cannot produce for themselves, but also those which give them greater choice.

Exports may be defined as *any* sales from which we earn foreign currency.

**Figure   16-2** Canada   produces more  than  it  needs  of  many commodities.

Fortunately for Canadians they are able to sell many items to other countries. As we saw in the first part of this section, Canada ranks very highly in a great number of production lists. Canada produces much more than it needs itself of a great number of commodities, and it is thus able to sell the surpluses to as many countries as are willing to buy them. The ability to sell abroad depends on many factors: price, availability of alternative sources of supply, quality, delivery schedules, and a host of other considerations. The operation of these factors produces a complex situation for Canada's exporters, and generally they must try very hard to export successfully. The international markets for many commodities are very competitive, and if Canada's prices are too high or its delivery schedules are upset, then the buyers from other countries merely increase their buying from other sellers. As we noted in question 4, Canada does not have a high degree of monopoly in any product, and so buyers can always buy elsewhere if they come to think that Canada is uncompetitive. Therefore, if Canada is to export successfully it must remain competitive in world markets. This is not an easy task, and many people accordingly work very hard at keeping Canada competitive. Such people include our Trade Commissioners and Embassy staff abroad, as well as special trade missions which go abroad periodically, and thousands of business people and sales representatives based in Canada.

They generally succeed at selling more Canadian goods to other countries than we buy as imports, thus producing what is called a *favourable balance of trade*. In 1976, for example, the balance of

Remember that if exports are not successful then we cannot afford to pay for our imports.

Canada has about 250 Trade Commissioners posted in about 60 different countries around the world. Their job is to promote trade between Canada and the other countries.

In the period 1960-76 every year except one had a favourable balance of trade. The exception was 1975.

A favourable balance of trade is often known as a *trade surplus*.

An unfavourable balance of trade may be called a *trade deficit*.

Canada's *international accounts* are the summary of its dealings as a country in relation with other countries.

If Canadian telecommunications engineers go to help another country set up a telecommunications system then the money they earn for their business consultancy work ranks as an invisible export for Canada. If Canadian holidaymakers take their vacations abroad, then the money they spend abroad represents an invisible import to Canada. If Canadians travel on an American airline then they pay money to the Americans, and this counts as an invisible import to Canada. If Americans ship goods through Vancouver, then the money that Vancouver earns for providing this service ranks as an invisible export for Canada. Can you think of some other examples?

trade was $1.13 billion in Canada's favour, derived from *export earnings* of $38.02 billion and *import expenditures* of $36.89 billion. This compares with an *unfavourable balance of trade* in 1975 of $640 000 000, derived from merchandise exports of $33.35 billion and merchandise imports of $33.99 billion.

The term *balance of trade* refers only to the balance achieved by merchandise trade, that is, goods shipped and received. Sometimes this trade in merchandise is called *visible trade,* because the goods can be seen. If a freighter unloads Japanese cars in Vancouver, the cars can be seen; they are *visible imports,* and money goes out of Canada in payment for them. Similarly, a shipment of wheat from Baie Comeau is a *visible export,* and money comes into Canada in payment for it.

It is fortunate for Canada that there is normally a surplus on visible trade, because there is usually a deficit on *in*visible trade. *Invisible trade* is the term used to describe the movement of money to pay for services instead of merchandise. Services may be bought and sold just as readily as goods, of course, and the payments for them naturally enter into Canada's international accounts. Some examples of services which enter international trade are business consultancy, travel planning, tourist hospitality, telecommunications, leasing, and the provision of money for borrowing. On some of these things Canada just about breaks even, but on others it pays out more than it earns. In other words, *invisible imports* (money paid out) normally exceed *invisible exports* (money earned), and there is therefore a persistent deficit on invisible trade.

The combination of the normal surplus on visible trade with the persistent deficit on invisible trade produces an approximate balance in what is called the *current account section of the balance of payments.* In some years the balance of current account is favourable to Canada, and in others it is unfavourable. Much depends on the fortunes of the visible component, for the invisible section tends to vary little from year to year. When the current account balance is favourable to Canada, the extra money which comes in may be put to Canada's *international reserves* to help pay for the unfavourable years which may occur in the future. It may also be loaned or invested abroad.

Movements of money for international loans and investments form part of what is called the *capital account section of the balance of payments.* Such money moves both ways; although usually more comes into Canada than goes out, thus giving Canada a fairly reliable surplus in its overall balance of payments.

Canada's trading links are worldwide in scope. There are very few countries that do not trade at all with it, although there are many that trade very little. Most of Canada's trade, however, is with a relatively small number of countries, as the graphs in Figure 16-3 show. The dominant position of the United States as both a market and a supplier is shown quite clearly, but you should realize that Canada acts in exactly the same manner and extent towards the United States — that is, each is by far the other's largest trading partner.

The *balance of payments* is the balance obtained by measuring the amount of foreign money coming into a country (for both visible and invisible exports) in relation to the amount of money going out (for both visible and invisible imports).

*Reserves* are like Canada's savings. They are composed of U.S. dollars, gold, sterling, yen, French and Swiss francs, Deutsche mark, lira, and a multitude of other currencies.

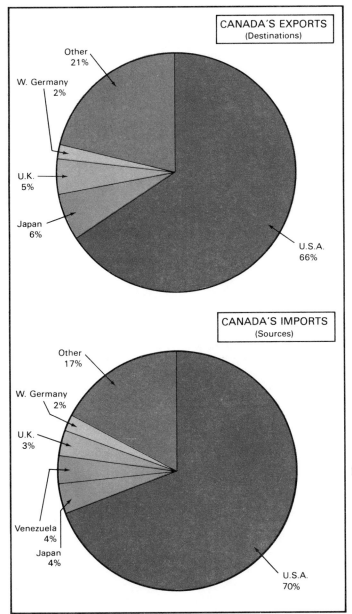

**CANADA'S EXPORTS** (Destinations)

Other 21%
W. Germany 2%
U.K. 5%
Japan 6%
U.S.A. 66%

**CANADA'S IMPORTS** (Sources)

Other 17%
W. Germany 2%
U.K. 3%
Venezuela 4%
Japan 4%
U.S.A. 70%

**Figure 16-3   Destinations and Sources of Canada's Merchandise Trade, 1976**

There is hardly any trade at all with North Korea, for example, and there are some other countries, such as Albania and Togo, that we export to but do not import from. Can you suggest why this might be so?

The concentration of the bulk of a country's trade on just a few major trading partners is not unusual. Many countries have this pattern.

Because the bulk of Canada's trade is with the United States it is misleading to show only seaports when investigating the main trade exit and entry points. Seaports are important, of course, but a great deal of Canada's foreign trade also flows through land frontier points, either by road and rail or by air. Figure 16-4 shows the main export and import points.

The chief classes of goods entering merchandise trade are shown in Figure 16-5. These are general classes and do not therefore show details; we should accordingly note that the largest single export item from Canada is cars, followed in order by newsprint, car parts, wheat, wood pulp, lumber, petroleum, and trucks. Among imported items, the largest is car parts, followed by cars, petroleum, trucks, motor engines, telecommunications equipment, tools and computers.

**Figure 16-4   Canada's Major Export and Import Points**

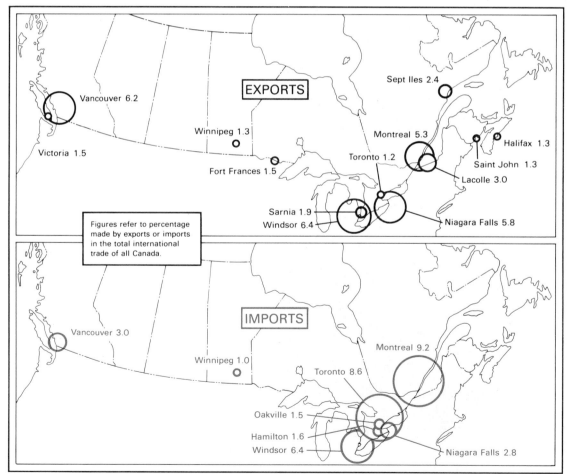

EXPORTS

Sept Iles 2.4

Vancouver 6.2

Winnipeg 1.3

Montreal 5.3

Halifax 1.3

Toronto 1.2

Victoria 1.5

Saint John 1.3

Fort Frances 1.5

Lacolle 3.0

Sarnia 1.9

Windsor 6.4

Niagara Falls 5.8

Figures refer to percentage made by exports or imports in the total international trade of all Canada.

IMPORTS

Vancouver 3.0

Montreal 9.2

Winnipeg 1.0

Toronto 8.6

Oakville 1.5

Hamilton 1.6

Windsor 6.4

Niagara Falls 2.8

**Figure 16-5  Canada's International Trade in Major Commodity Groups**

| | Merchandise Trade, in Dollars | |
| --- | --- | --- |
| | **Exports** | **Imports** |
| Live Animals | 67 341 000 | 39 305 000 |
| Food, Feed, Beverages, Tobacco | 2 035 341 000 | 1 117 523 000 |
| Crude Materials, inedible | 3 232 028 000 | 1 321 725 000 |
| Fabricated Materials, inedible | 5 784 812 000 | 3 140 164 000 |
| End Products, inedible | 6 170 736 000 | 9 820 719 000 |

Source: the *Canada Year Book*, 1976

Examples from these commodity groups include Holstein cattle to Italy, bacon to England, rye whisky to the United States, coal to Japan, plywood to the European Community, houses to the Middle East, and cars to the United States.

● 5. Define the following terms:
  balance of trade
  merchandise trade
  balance of payments on current account
  visible imports/exports
  invisible imports/exports
  reserves
  capital account

● 6. (a) Construct two percentage bar graphs, one for exports and one for imports, from the data in Figure 16-5.
  (b) Suggest explanations for the major differences in composition of both exports and imports.
  (c) Some of the detailed items exported and imported are similar to each other, for example, cars and petroleum. Why should similar items be both exported and imported?

● 7. One of the aspects of Canada's foreign trade that worries some Canadians is the large export of unprocessed (crude) materials. They assert that more processing should be done inside Canada before export occurs.
  (a) What would be necessary for this to happen?
  (b) What would some of the results possibly be?

## Canadian Aid

Canada is one of the richest countries in the world; its people live well by international standards, and they have the capacity to help other people less well off.

They give a great deal of aid to other countries, sometimes directly (which is called *bilateral aid)*, and sometimes by way of an international agency such as the Colombo Plan which disburses aid to many countries (which is called *multilateral aid*). Generally bilateral aid, or aid directly from Canada to a particular country, is more important than multilateral aid (Figure 16-6). It takes various forms, often being emergency supplies at times of famine or other disasters; but it may also be a planned mixture of cash, equipment, and instructors. The channels of direct aid are many and varied, ranging from the efforts of individual church ministers to official government bodies such as the Canadian International Development Agency (CIDA). CIDA, based in Ottawa, is responsible for all federal government aid. It therefore supplies multilateral aid as well as bilateral aid.

CIDA comes in for a lot of criticism from many people because they think it uses money wastefully. Other people think CIDA does a great job. Some of the things that CIDA has done in recent years include farming developments in the Sudan, earthquake relief in Guatemala, and health care in Haiti.

**Figure 16-6    Canadian Federal Government Allocations for Foreign Aid, in Millions of Dollars**

|                  | 1971  | 1972  | 1973  | 1974  | 1975  | 1976  |
|------------------|-------|-------|-------|-------|-------|-------|
| Bilateral Aid    | 286.9 | 283.3 | 329.3 | 367.7 | 498.5 | 525.7 |
| Multilateral Aid | 74.4  | 97.4  | 153.9 | 185.1 | 200.0 | 318.6 |
| Other            | 11.0  | 14.4  | 24.2  | 35.0  | 45.3  | 59.2  |
| **Total**        | **361.3** | **395.1** | **507.4** | **587.8** | **743.8** | **906.5** |

Source: *CIDA Review*, December 1976

One of the chief recipients of Canadian multilateral aid is the Colombo Plan. This was started as a Commonwealth project in 1950 to foster the development of countries in South and Southeast Asia. The member countries are shown in Figure 16-9. Canada supplies investment funds, trade loans, technical assistance, equipment, and student exchange facilities to the Plan, which distributes the aid to areas in need. The chief recipient of Canadian aid, both bilateral and multilateral, is India, as shown in Figure 16-7.

**Figure 16-7    The Chief Recipients of Canadian Foreign Aid**

| Country    | Dollars Received |
|------------|------------------|
| India      | $69 280 000      |
| Bangladesh | 58 270 000       |
| Pakistan   | 38 510 000       |
| Indonesia  | 21 640 000       |
| Tanzania   | 17 670 000       |
| Tunisia    | 13 060 000       |
| Nigeria    | 11 980 000       |
| Ghana      | 9 660 000        |
| Niger      | 8 400 000        |
| Kenya      | 6 190 000        |
| Sri Lanka  | 5 650 000        |
| Senegal    | 5 620 000        |
| Morocco    | 5 550 000        |
| Algeria    | 5 060 000        |

Source: *CIDA Review*, 1974

Other multilateral aid is disbursed through the World Bank and other United Nations agencies. In such ways, Canadian aid reaches many parts of the needy world.

**Figure 16-8** Indian women being aided in the construction of a dam as part of the Colombo Plan.

One of the major points about foreign aid used to be that the recipients had to use the cash or loans they received to buy from the donor country the products they needed. Such aid was called *tied aid*. Thus if Canada lent money to India for the development of a dairying industry, then India would have had to spend that money on buying Canadian dairy equipment, even if cheaper equipment was available elsewhere. Foreign aid used to be thus regarded by the donors as a means of increasing their own exports and the number of jobs they kept at home. The recipients used to object strongly, arguing that if the donors really wanted to help them they should let the recipients spend the money in the places where they could get the best bargains, and not necessarily solely with the donors. In 1975 Canada decided to go along with these arguments, and it untied its aid. Many other countries still give only tied aid.

- 8. (a) What are the possible arguments that a donor country could use for keeping its aid tied?
  (b) Should Canada have untied its aid? Why or why not?

The International Development Research Centre (IDRC) is an example of untied Canadian aid. It was established in 1970, and since then has committed many millions of dollars to the support of over 200 projects in Asia, Africa, and Latin America. The projects are usually small scale and rural in emphasis. For example, one project was to foster the growth of wood lots in Niger so that villagers would not have a day's walk to get wood; another project was to improve the preservation and packaging of the fish catch off the Ghana coast, so that fish could be sold into inland markets. At no time have the recipients of IDRC aid ever had to buy Canadian products merely because the source of aid was Canadian.

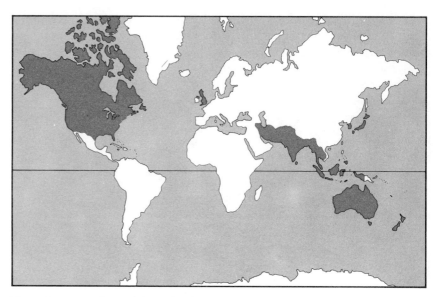

**Figure 16-9   Members of the Colombo Plan**

### Canada As A Peacekeeper

Lying as it does between the rival superpowers of the U.S.A. and the U.S.S.R., it would be unrealistic of Canada to try to develop any significant form of independent military strength. Instead, Canada has seen its role as being a member of a group, and in working towards continued peace rather than in provoking escalation and crisis.

To this end, Canada belongs to three significant organizations. The most local is the North American Air Defence Command (NORAD), in which Canada is allied with the United States in the defence of North America against air attack. The second alliance is regional, including all the countries of the North Atlantic Treaty Organization (NATO), as shown in Figure 16-10. On behalf of NATO, Canada keeps some of its armed forces in Europe, and permits European forces to train in Canada. The third grouping is the United Nations (UN). As one of its voluntary commitments to peace, Canada allows some of its armed forces to be used by the UN in helping to keep potential combatants apart in various parts of the world. Thus, Canadian troops are stationed in Cyprus, along the Suez Canal, in Kashmir, and between North and South Korea.

One of the most famous of NORAD's activities has been the construction and maintenance of the Distant Early Warning radar defence line (the so-called DEWline) across the Arctic from Alaska to Greenland. The DEWline maintains a 24 hour surveillance of the sky approaches from the U.S.S.R.

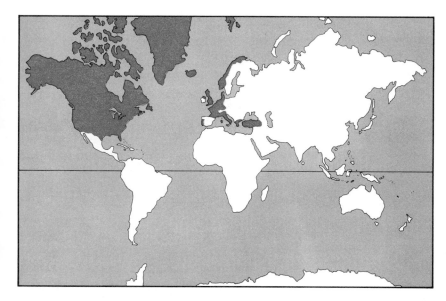

**Figure 16-10   Members of the North Atlantic Treaty Organization**

It was largely as a result of Lester Pearson's efforts in producing a fairly peaceful settlement to the Anglo-French invasion of the Suez Canal Zone in 1956 that he was eventually awarded the Nobel Prize for Peace.

### Canada As A Destination For Migrants

We examined the subject of migration in Chapter 5, so you should refer there for details. All we would say here is that few parts of the world have not felt the pull of Canada. Canada is an attraction to people from many parts of the world because it offers a potential lifestyle which is superior to that of most other places. It offers the opportunity for personal improvement and a higher standard of living.

- 9. Suggest as many things as you can that Canada has to offer potential immigrants.

## B: REGIONAL DISPARITIES

While it is true that Canada is one of the wealthiest nations in the world, it is not true that all parts of Canada share equally in this wealth. One of the fundamental policies of all federal governments has thus been to produce a greater degree of equality across the nation.

These long-standing efforts have consistently failed to improve the situation, although they may have prevented it from becoming worse. Fifty years ago, Ontario and British Columbia were at the top of the regional personal income scale, just as they are now. The Prairie region ranked next, more or less in line with the national average, as it does now. And within the prairies, Alberta came first, as it still does. Quebec was just below the national average, again, as it is now, while the Atlantic Provinces were at the bottom, as they are now. Fifty years ago the spread between the highest and lowest rankings was about 25% above the national average to about 25% below, and these figures also still hold true. So you can see that the gap has not narrowed; but neither has it widened.

Newfoundland has many of the characteristics of a lowest ranked region: its population is scattered through innumerable small fishing villages strung out around the coast; there is only one large town, St. John's, with a population in its metropolitan area of about 150 000; there is only one road across the island from east to west, and no road at all from north to south.

The persistence of regional disparities is largely a result of underlying geographical characteristics. The top ranked areas have advantages in resource availability, trading connections, and industrial potential that the other areas have in only lesser degree, while the bottom ranked areas have disadvantages of scattered populations, lack of metropolitan centres, and difficulties of transportation which the top ranked regions experience to a relatively small degree.

Federal government efforts to improve the situation or to prevent it from becoming worse take many forms. One of the most important is the transfer of money, by taxation, from the richest provinces to the poorest. In effect this means that Ottawa takes money, called *equalization transfers,* from Ontario, British Columbia, and Alberta, and distributes it to all the other provinces. The province receiving the most money in total is Quebec, but because it has the largest population among the receiving provinces it does not rank highly on a per capita basis. The distinction of ranking first on a per capita basis for receiving transferred tax money from Ottawa belongs to Prince Edward Island, as Figure 16-11 shows.

**Figure 16-11   Federal Equalization Transfer Receipts**

|  | Total $ | Per Capita $ |
| --- | --- | --- |
| Newfoundland | 110 000 000 | 210.69 |
| Prince Edward Island | 21 000 000 | 340.38 |
| Nova Scotia | 95 000 000 | 120.41 |
| New Brunswick | 94 000 000 | 148.13 |
| Quebec | 446 000 000 | 73.99 |
| Ontario | — | — |
| Manitoba | 50 000 000 | 50.59 |
| Saskatchewan | 55 000 000 | 59.38 |
| Alberta | — | — |
| British Columbia | — | — |

Source: *OECD Economic Survey of Canada,* December 1972

In addition to money transfers the federal government also acts to persuade industries to build factories in selected weaker regions. It does this through the Department of Regional Economic Expansion (DREE), which was established in 1969. The Department attempts to stimulate employment in the weaker regions by providing grants and tax incentives for private investment and by trying to create favourable frameworks for industrial growth in 23 selected *special areas.* The map in Figure 16-12 shows the locations of these special areas, as well as the broad regions covered by the grant and tax incentive plans. In Incentive Region A, comprising the Atlantic Provinces, the federal government grants up to 35% of the initial capital costs of opening a factory plus $7000 for each job created. In Incentive Region B the maximum is 25% of the capital costs plus $5000 for each new job. Incentive Region C, around Montreal and the lower Ottawa Valley, offers a grant of only ten percent of the capital cost plus $2000 for each job created.

The money paid to firms for the creation of new jobs in Incentive Regions is called the Regional Employment Premium.

● 10. Evidence supporting federal government action to combat regional disparity is slight; at best it has prevented the situation from deteriorating. What do you suggest the government should do? Why?

**Figure 16-12   Designated Regions and Special Areas**

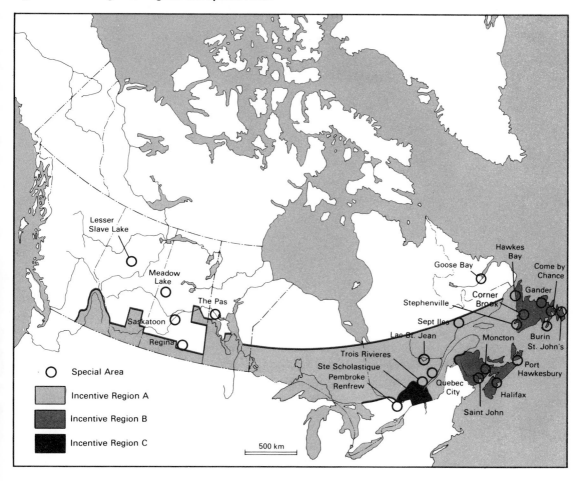

## C: CANADA IN RETROSPECT

We should, as our conclusion, look back to the first article in Chapter 1, entitled *Our Common Destiny . . .,* by Pierre Trudeau. We see that Trudeau noted the "vastness and natural beauty of this country"; we can look back at what we have studied and realize what he meant by that reference to vastness. We can also get an idea of Canada's natural beauty from the numerous photographs throughout this book. It is certainly a beauty of which we should all be proud.

What are some of the aspects of this Canadian vastness?

**Figure 16-13** The natural beauty of Canada.

Trudeau also noted the climate as a "stimulus for epic deeds". In the chapters on the Prairies, French Canada, and the Arctic we looked at some of the achievements and pride that people have produced in different parts of the country. The Canadian winter was analyzed in Chapter 2, and we should certainly realize that it was a daunting factor in the days of early colonization. The factor of distance that Trudeau mentioned as an additional stimulus for epic deeds was looked at in Chapter 15, and we should remember that the transcontinental rail and road links are not the only memorable achievements by Canadians in the conquest of distance: so also was *Anik,* the world's first domestic communications satellite.

In the article, Trudeau quotes the poet Rupert Brooke, who wrote of Canada that "the soul . . . seems to have indefinite room to expand." You have possibly experienced this feeling, that what you want to achieve you can, that your inner wishes are somehow capable of fulfilment. This is true in a number of ways. The obvious ways are to choose pioneering lifestyles in the north and west, to prospect for gold in the Yukon, to homestead the Peace River District, to trap in northern British Columbia; but there are other possibilities too. You could also realize your dreams in the cities and in the long established east; do you, for instance, want to build your own business?

In the chapter on French Canada we looked at the fur trading activities of the voyageurs, whose "courage and endurance" were thought by Trudeau to be almost unbelievable. But they are facts of Canada's development; carry them with you.

Trudeau also commented upon the Arctic and how little we really know of it. Chapter 12 should have opened your minds a little to what is really occurring there. The days of igloos and dog teams are long past, and might now be seen only in National Film Board productions such as the *Netsilik* or *Tuktu* series.

Further on in the article, Trudeau mentions the invention of marquis wheat and its impact on farming in the prairies. Chapter 9 examined the resources of the prairies; undoubtedly the imagination and inventiveness of the early inhabitants played a major role in creating the resources of the region.

Such imagination and inventiveness are not solely the possessions of the past, however. They are as alive today as they ever were, as Trudeau notes in his mention of oceanographic research, telecommunications development, snow vehicle construction, and STOL aircraft design.

Trudeau also comments on the limited nature of our "internal divisions". We have looked at the French Fact and the problem of regional disparities; we should be grateful that we are not riven by dissensions such as those which occasion shooting wars or revolution in some other countries.

As Trudeau said, our history is the narrative of "extraordinary efforts" and our reward is "happiness . . . absence of fear, in a landscape of breathtaking beauty." He asserted that we had developed a lifestyle which permitted us to be "more individual and less subject to uniformity than any peoples in the world." He went on to add that the essential character of Canada rested in its beauty and wildness, and that we would "no longer be Canadians" if we could not breathe the freshness of an Atlantic gale, or view the glory of a prairie sunset, or feel the silence of a northern lake.

Trudeau concluded by mentioning that we hail from many different lands, but that as Canadians we have a common destiny: "to perpetuate the character of this land and to share the benefits that result."

"Canada is not a country for the cold of heart."

● 11.  What does Canada mean to you?

● 12.  What would you hope Canada will be like in 50 years' time?

---

The first wheat grown in the prairies was called Red Fife, which had been developed in Ontario to grow in a shorter time than European wheats. It was a good wheat for the prairies, because it was also able to resist the occasional dry conditions, and it made a superior bread compared with the softer European wheat. However, Charles Saunders, a cereal expert working with the Canadian Department of Agriculture, developed in 1903 an even better wheat for the prairies. He called it Marquis wheat, and it was able to ripen eight days sooner than Red Fife. This meant that the crop was safer from frosts, and that the more northern parts of the prairies could also be brought into cultivation. The ten years which followed his discovery, from 1903 to 1913, saw more people move into the prairies than ever before — or since.

STOL = Short Take-Off and Landing airplanes. A regular jetliner may need as much as two to three kilometres for a runway, but a STOL plane may require only 200-300 m.

# APPENDIX A

| | |
|---|---|
| Dual highway .................................... | ═══ |
| Road, hard surface, all weather, more than 2 lanes . | ═══ |
| Road, hard surface, all weather, 2 lanes ............ | ═══ |
| Road, hard surface, all weather, less than 2 lanes .. | ─── |

*Red*

| | |
|---|---|
| Road, loose or stabilized surface, all weather, 2 lanes or more .................... | ═══ |
| Road, loose or stabilized surface, all weather, less than 2 lanes ................. | ─── |
| Road, loose surface, dry weather or unclassified streets ......................... | ─── |

*Orange*

| | |
|---|---|
| Cart track or winter road ......................... | ─ ─ ─ ─ ─ |
| Trail, cut line or portage ......................... | ............ |
| Road under construction ......................... | ═ ═ ═ ═ ═   *Orange or red* |
| Highway interchange with number; traffic circle ... | ◈ 42  ◇  *Red* |
| Highway route marker ........................... | ⑤  *Orange or red* |
| Built up area .................................... | *Red screen* |
| Railway, single track ............................. | ─┼─┼─ |
| Railway, multiple track ........................... | ─╫─╫─ |
| Railway, narrow gauge ............................ | ─┼─┼─ |
| Railway, abandoned .............................. | ─ ─ ─ |
| Railway station; stop; turntable .................. | ─▪─ ─ ─ ⟩─ |
| Bridge; footbridge ................................ | ⟩═⟨ |
| Bridge: swing, draw, lift .......................... | ⟩═⟨ |
| Tunnel .......................................... | ⟩= = =⟨ |
| Ferry ............................................ | |
| Ford ............................................ | |
| Navigation light ................................. | ☼ |
| Seaplane base; seaplane anchorage .............. | ⚓ ⚓ |
| House; barn; large building ...................... | ▪ ▪ ■ |
| Church; school .................................. | ╷ ╷ |
| Post office; telegraph office ..................... | P▪ T▪ |
| Elevator; greenhouse............................. | E▪ ▭ |
| Cemetery; historic site; historic battlefield ......... | [C] ⊕ ✕ |
| Tower, chimney, similar objects .................... | ⊙ |
| Well: water ...................................... | ● *Blue* |

| | |
|---|---|
| Well: oil, gas .................................... | ○ |
| Tank: oil, gasoline, water ........................ | ● |
| Pipeline: above ground, underground ............. | ─── |
| Telephone line .................................. | ┴┴┴┴┴┴ |
| Power transmission line ......................... | ⟍ |
| Mine ........................................... | ⚒ |
| Gravel or sand pit; quarry ....................... | ⬭ ⬭ |
| Dyke; fence .................................... | ⬝⬝⬝⬝ ×─×─× |
| Cutting; embankment ............................ | ⬛⬛⬛ ⬛⬛⬛ |
| International boundary with monument ........ | ▬ ▬ ▪ ▬ ▬ *Red screen* |
| Province, territory, or state boundary ............ | ▬ ▬ ▪ ▬ |
| County or district boundary ...................... | ▬ ▪ ▬ ▪ |
| Township, parish, borough boundary............. | ─ ─ ─ ─ |
| Township boundary, unsurveyed ................ | ▬ ▬ ▬ |
| Metropolitan area boundary ..................... | ─ ─ ─ ─ |
| City, municipality or parish (Québec) boundary..... | ─ ─ ─ ─ |
| Reserve, park, etc. boundary .................... | ▬▬▬▬ |
| Horizontal control point ......................... | △ |
| Bench mark with elevation ...................... | BM 1475 ↑ |
| Spot elevation: precise, non-precise ............. | ▪2520  ▪2247▪ *Brown* |
| Lake intermittent, slough ....................... | ⬭ |
| Flooded land, seasonally inundated land ........ | ⬭ ⬭ |
| Marsh or swamp ................................ | ⋯ ⋱ *Blue* |
| Dry river bed with channels ..................... | ⟿⟿ |
| Foreshore flats ................................ | ⬭ *Blue & B...* |
| Submerged reef ................................ | ⬭ |
| Rocks .......................................... | + + |
| Rocky ledge, rocky reef ......................... | ⬭ |
| Dams: small, large ............................. | ─┤├─ |
| Locks: small, large ............................. | «─ ╪ |
| Contours ...................................... | ≈≈≈ *Brown* |
| Cliff ........................................... | ≋≋≋ |
| Wooded area .................................... | ▨ *Green* |
| Orchard ....................................... | ▨ *Black & G...* |

# INDEX